The Challenge of Climate

BOOKS BY ROBERT SILVERBERG

SUNKEN HISTORY
EMPIRES IN THE DUST
GREAT ADVENTURES IN ARCHAEOLOGY
HOME OF THE RED MAN
LOST CITIES AND VANISHED CIVILIZATIONS
MAN BEFORE ADAM
THE MAN WHO FOUND NINEVEH
THE OLD ONES
THE WORLD OF CORAL
EARTHMEN AND STRANGERS (*editor*)
THE WORLD OF THE RAIN FOREST
VOYAGERS IN TIME (*editor*)
THE WORLD OF THE OCEAN DEPTHS
MEN AND MACHINES (*editor*)
THE CHALLENGE OF CLIMATE:
MAN AND HIS ENVIRONMENT
MOUND BUILDERS OF ANCIENT AMERICA
THE MORNING OF MANKIND

The Challenge of Climate:

MAN AND HIS ENVIRONMENT

BY ROBERT SILVERBERG

MEREDITH PRESS NEW YORK

First edition

LIBRARY OF CONGRESS
CATALOG CARD NUMBER: 69-19052

MANUFACTURED IN THE UNITED STATES
OF AMERICA FOR MEREDITH PRESS

Contents

1 THE PLAYTHING OF THE STORM GODS 1

2 THE MAKING OF CLIMATES 23

3 THE COMING OF THE ICE 42

4 MAN AND THE ICE 79

5 THE END OF THE ICE 112

6 FARMERS AND CITIES 131

7 IRRIGATORS AND NOMADS 198

8 THE LITTLE ICE AGE 232

9 CLIMATIC SHIFTS IN THE NEW WORLD 249

10 TOMORROW'S CLIMATE 285

BIBLIOGRAPHY 302

INDEX 309

MAN IS A CREATURE FIT FOR ANY CLIMATE, AND NECESSITY AND DETERMINATION SOON RECONCILE HIM TO ANYTHING.

—FERDINAND VON WRANGELL:
Narrative of an Expedition to the Polar Sea in the Years 1820–23

1

The Plaything of the Storm Gods

IN THE YEAR 1085 KING WILLIAM I OF ENGLAND SENT ROYAL commissioners through the land to take an inventory of the territory he and his Norman warriors had conquered nineteen years before. The result was the massive statistical compendium known as the Domesday Book, the first modern census report. According to the Domesday Book, there were thirty-eight vineyards in the England of William the Conqueror, aside from those belonging to the crown; the grapes grew as far north as Gloucester and York. The chronicler William of Malmesbury, writing about 1125, declares that the Gloucester region "exhibits a greater number of vineyards than any other county in England, yielding abundant crops and of superior quality: nor are the wines made here by any means harsh or ungrateful to the palate, for in point of sweetness they may almost bear comparison with the growths of France."

There has been no wine industry in England since the fifteenth century. Except in a few favored locations, grapes will not ripen in England's cool summers. Some of the vineyards of former times were located in regions that now suffer night frosts in late spring and even in summer.

In Armenia, the stone houses of a village can be seen twenty to thirty feet below the surface of the lake of Gyoljuk. They were built about A.D. 500, when the weather was dry and the level of the lake was far lower than it is today. Two thousand miles to the east, in the mountains of central Asia, ancient irrigation channels have been found in districts where there now is frost in midsummer, and where there is so much moisture that if agriculture were possible there at all, no irrigation would be needed. Farmers worked those fields in drier, warmer times.

A thousand years ago the Norsemen colonized Greenland. According to the sagas, there were three hundred farms along the big island's west coast, supporting ten thousand settlers and great flocks of sheep and cattle. By A.D. 1400 the climate had grown so harsh that few of these settlements remained, and those under the most terrible of circumstances. Pope Alexander VI lamented in 1492 that the freezing of the seas around Greenland had made it impossible for any priest or bishop to get there for eighty years. Ultimately Greenland had to be abandoned to the ice. In the southern part of the island there are old Norse graves, with tree roots twined among the bones, in soil that today is permanently frozen.

The archaeological record shows examples of great climatic changes in every part of the world; villages, cities, even whole cultures were overturned and destroyed by variations in the patterns of rainfall or the range of temperature. Only a century ago, most scientists believed that variations in climate were purely local and temporary matters, and that overall climatic patterns had never undergone any great shifts. We know today how false this belief is. We know of the great ice ages that gripped much of the planet again and again in past epochs; we know of the gradual retreat of ice, the return of the warmth, the changes in plant and animal life that such a return produced; we know of the fluctuations within each period, of cold snaps and warm spells lasting thousands of years.

We have found the remains of subtropical vegetation north of the Arctic Circle. We have found outcroppings of coal in Antarctica, telling of vanished forests. Fossil camels in Alaska and fossil elephants in New Jersey indicate other transformations of the environment. Abandoned roads and irrigation works in bleak deserts, traces of settlements where survival now would be a difficult matter, withdrawals from previously cultivated territory, all testify to these changes. Dramatic examples abound. The Sahara, five thousand years ago, had green and fertile districts. The Caspian Sea, in the time of Herodotus, stood at a level more than 150 feet higher than it does today. In Tudor England, courtiers amused themselves by sporting on the frozen Thames in winter; the Thames has not frozen over since 1814.

Climate changes, then, and its mutations have profound effects on man and his world. Much of the story of mankind is the story of the world's weather and how man copes with it, both on a day-by-day basis and when long-term patterns shift. It happens that the last million years—the period in which the human species appeared—has been a time of unusually turbulent climatic changes, after what was probably a much longer period without much variation in climate. An epoch of many millions of years in which most of the world had a mild subtropical climate gave way to a time of storm, chill, and upheaval which still continues, with minor intermissions.

The climatic fluctuations of that million-year period have had much to do with the shaping of human destinies. It may be, as some recent anthropologists have suggested, that the evolution of man out of less specialized primate forms was in part or wholly stimulated by certain changes in the climate of Africa, more than a million years ago. One school of geneticists, as we will see, has advanced the theory that not only man's physical form but even the development of the different races represents a response and adjustment to climatic conditions. If these ideas are correct, man has been shaped by climate in the most literal sense.

The evolution of human culture also appears to be climate-related. A naked ape has learned to use tools, to control fire, to fashion clothing, to build dwelling places; all these steps toward civilization can be linked to man's conflicts with weather patterns, man's desire to free himself from his slavery to the gods of the storm. The great transition from food gathering to food growing, which marks the beginning of modern civilization, has been suggested as a special response to changing climate in the Near East about ten thousand years ago. That theory is still open to doubt; but what can hardly be questioned is that much of man's technological progress since the birth of the great city-dwelling cultures of Egypt and Mesopotamia has been spurred by his relationship to his climate. Dams, irrigation, heating, cooling, the design of buildings, the shape of cities, and much more reflect man's concern with his environment and his gradual mastery of it.

This interplay of man and climate has produced the sociological theory of environmental determinism, which holds that human achievement is almost exclusively influenced by climate. This is obvious enough in the case of people living under extremes of climate: the Eskimos, the desert Bedouins, and the inhabitants of tropical rain forests must of necessity shape their culture to their surroundings. But the most outspoken of the environmental determinists, such as Ellsworth Huntington and S. F. Markham, go far beyond this simple truism. They argue that even in less extreme conditions, climate is the governing factor that determines progress.

According to their theories, the ideal climate is a temperate one, not so cold as to paralyze ingenuity nor so warm as to lull it into inactivity. The climate must present challenges—cold winters, warm summers, fluctuations of water supply—but these challenges must not be so great that dealing with them absorbs all available mental energy. Where man must extend himself to meet the challenges of his climate, he progresses; where he is defeated by his climate or is too happily coddled by it, he remains stationary. The most progressive regions of the globe—with "progressive" defined in terms of things like factory output—lie in temperate zones. Western civilization, with its dynamic expansionist momentum, has followed a northwest course out of Egypt and Mesopotamia into the Mediterranean region, then to western Europe and North America, and the determinists explain this by saying that there has been a shift of climate during thousands of years, moving the zone of most favorable environment away from the original cradles of civilization (now backward regions) and into areas formerly too cold for progress.

These concepts have a certain force, for no one can deny that modern technological civilization has evolved in temperate climates. But they have led to bitter controversy in recent years because of their racist implications. Ellsworth Huntington wrote in the early part of this century, when it was still possible to speak of underdeveloped peoples as inferior in some innate way, but to characterize them as sluggish and lazy, to maintain that cool-weather countries invariably prosper while warm-weather countries are doomed by their too-balmy climate to backwardness and poverty, is no longer acceptable. Still, the role of climate as a stimulating factor in the growth of society deserves careful analysis.

Not only climate, but *changes* of climate, are important to an understanding of history. Early man was the plaything of his environment. As Huntington wrote in 1922, "Previous to recorded history great climatic changes drove man this way and that, destroyed ancient types of culture, and either wiped whole races out of existence, or profoundly modified them, physically, mentally, and socially." Though man has attained immense control over his environment, he must still reckon with such unpredictable disasters as floods or hurricanes and such basic problems as long-term droughts or temperature shifts. The past is littered with instances where broad shifts in climate have overcome man's ability to cope with environmental changes. In the Indus Valley of India and Pakistan are the dead cities of an entire powerful civilization more than four thousand years old, whose downfall may have been due to climatic change beyond the powers of the city dwellers to handle.

The Indus people may have been the cause of their own troubles incidentally, for vast modifications in regional climates have been the doing of man himself, through cutting down of forests, diverting river flow, or otherwise tampering with the environment. But the essential fact is that climate does change, naturally or as a result of human interference, and that both primitive and civilized cultures have been and remain vulnerable to these changes.

Nor are changes in climate confined to the distant past. They continue to occur, although their nature becomes clear only over a number of years, and even a seemingly minor adjustment in climate is enough to trigger great transformations. The glacial eras may have been set off by a drop in mean temperatures of only five or ten degrees Fahrenheit, perhaps less. Rainfall fluctuations can be equally severe. It has been calculated that in Australia a rainfall of twenty inches a year makes it possible to keep six hundred sheep to the square mile, but a drop to thirteen inches a year reduces the number of sheep that can be supported to a hundred. A ten-inch annual rainfall will support only ten sheep per square mile, and so a sixtyfold reduction stems from a halving of the precipitation.

We may soon be able to turn the rain on and off by artificial means, to program the sort of climate we like, or even to abolish climate altogether by covering our cities and fields with artificial domes. But until then we must heed the moods of the climate, for it does not take a very great change in rainfall or temperature levels to create havoc even in our technologically advanced era. And changes of that sort are constantly under way. Rainfall patterns have been undergoing alteration for several generations; the tropics have been getting more rain than usual, the temperate zones less, and the trend appears to be accelerating. The grim "dust bowl" years of the 1930's are not yet forgotten on the Great Plains. In the 1960's we have had the spectacle of New York City and its surrounding regions in the grip of a prolonged drought which seemed to threaten the life of man's greatest metropolis. For New York, which normally gets some forty-five inches of rain a year, a drop to forty inches caused widespread difficulties, and a prolonged span of thirty-inch years might have led to catastrophe. Though the drought appeared to end in 1967, the possibility remains that some general and far-reaching change in the precipitation picture of the northeastern United States has come about, with grave consequences for the future of that densely populated region.

Not only have rain patterns been changing, but temperature levels have been on the move as well. Between 1890 and 1940, a sharp rise in temperature was observed in the temperate zones of the world, with the winters in particular becoming milder. The mean annual temperature at Philadelphia, for example, climbed from 52° F. in the middle of the nineteenth century to more than 56° F. by the 1930's. In Washington, D.C., there were 354 days of freezing temperatures during the spring months between 1872 and 1892; between 1913 and 1933 the total was only 237. Subzero readings were twice as frequent at Montreal in the 1880's as in the 1930's; the average temperature there in March rose by six degrees in that time, and average yearly snowfall fell from 130 inches to 80 inches.

The trend was the same in Europe, where the rise in mean winter temperature was about five degrees in less than a century. Iceland and Norway had their mildest winters in 750 years, and land was opened to cultivation that had been in the grip of sub-Arctic cold for centuries. The codfish catch of Greenland's west coast was 13,000 tons in 1946, compared with five tons in 1913, indicating a northward migration of ocean life into warming seas. Arctic ports remained open three to four weeks longer into the winter than formerly. In Siberia, the zone of permanently frozen ground retreated northward by several dozen yards per year. Glaciers also retreated; the Rhone Glacier in the Alps lost three miles of its length in the twentieth century, and several hundred smaller Alpine glaciers disappeared altogether. Between 1924 and 1944, the floating ice pack in the Russian sector of the Arctic shrank by nearly a million kilometers; the average thickness of the pack diminished from twelve feet to seven. Sea levels all over the world rose, partly because of the runoff from melting ice, partly because water expands as it warms. Though calculations of the rate of the rise vary, it has been placed at anywhere from four inches to two feet per century.

This striking period of increasing warmth caused much

speculation and some concern among meteorologists—perhaps all the more because it took place during the decades when meteorology as a science was undergoing great development. Was it possible that the explosive growth of mankind itself was changing the climate, setting in motion a cycle of warmth? A great deal of evidence, which we will consider in detail later, pointed to the possibility that man might be inducing a general rise in temperature as carbon dioxide from the machine age's new smokestacks poured into the air, altering the makeup of the atmosphere. A few alarmists spoke of a coming age of intolerable heat in which the polar icecaps would melt and thousands of miles of low-lying coastline would be drowned. It seemed quite clear that we were, however unintentionally, modifying our environment in the direction of warming.

But as the gloomy predictions reached a peak, about 1950, the climate indicators began to swing the other way. The trend seemed to have reversed itself, and it is slowly becoming apparent that fears of a worldwide tropicalization were premature. Temperatures have been swinging downward again; winters are colder, particularly in Europe. In 1962–63 England had its coldest winter since 1740, averaging 32° F. for three consecutive months in the lowlands. Snowfalls were more frequent, and depth of snow cover greater. It is not yet clear whether the post-1940 cooling constitutes a temporary setback in the warming trend that had been in force for several generations, or whether a new era of sustained cold is developing. However, the increase in the cold, like the increase of warmth that preceded it, has been attributed to the spread of industrialization: in this case the pollution of the atmosphere by dust, which screens the sun's rays and reduces the intensity of warming radiation that reaches the surface of our planet.

The hard truth is that the climate is never static and that we are only beginning to understand the reasons for its fluctuations. In a sense we are still playthings of the storm gods; we know a great deal, but not nearly enough. We have accumulated an astonishing amount of insight into the climates of the past, but we have very little knowledge of the probable climate of the year 1990. We can see the great bygone epochs of warmth and cold outlined with remarkable clarity; we know, thanks to remarkable scientific detective work, of ancient droughts and ancient deluges; we can explain in detail how climate has affected and altered other eras. But the future is nearly as murky as ever.

How do we learn about the climate of the past?

One obvious way is to consult historical records. Formal keeping of data on temperature and precipitation is something relatively new, hardly going back beyond the eighteenth century, but other documents tell us, by inference, of the climate. The Egyptians, five thousand years ago and more, kept careful records of the annual flood levels of the Nile, the river that was the source of their prosperity. From these hieroglyphic archives we can discover the likely rainfall in Ethiopia, where the Nile floods originate. Much later—in the second century A.D.—the Egyptian astronomer Ptolemy of Alexandria kept a systematic diary of local weather. Though he lacked thermometers and rain gauges, Ptolemy noted high winds, thunderstorms, rainy days, and such things, making it clear that Egypt's summers, rainless now, had a good deal of precipitation then; that thunderstorms, unknown there today, were frequent then in the hot season; and that the prevailing wind in the summer, now always from the north, sometimes blew from the south or the west eighteen centuries ago.

Medieval chronicles provide an invaluable source for European weather patterns. We have already cited William of Malmesbury's account of England's vanished twelfth-century vineyards. Unusual occurrences, such as ice on the Nile and the freezing-over of the Tiber one winter in the ninth century, went into the records kept by monks. Monastic annals tell of the output of farms in northern latitudes where cultivation now is impossible, and speak of ice-free navigation above the Arctic Circle in the eleventh and twelfth centuries. The recorded instances of the freezing-over of the Thames demonstrate the worsening of the English climate in late medieval times. No more than one or two freezes per century are recorded between A.D. 800 and A.D. 1500, but four freezes were noted in the sixteenth century, eight in the seventeenth, six in the eighteenth. Parish archives tell of cold weather possibly brought on by the presence of volcanic dust in the atmosphere, as in this Swedish record for 1601: "In that year the sun did not have its right natural shine or heat, but in a clear sky shone as though through smoke until 9 or 10 in the day and in mid-evening lost its shine again."

Actual statistics on the weather had to wait for the invention of measuring instruments. Galileo devised the first thermometer about 1600: a thin glass tube a foot and a half long, open at one end and blown into an egg-shaped bulb at the other. After warming the bulb in his hands, Galileo placed the open end in cool water. The air in the bulb contracted as the glass cooled, allowing water to rise in the tube. Later experimenters introduced the mercury-filled bulb now in use. Galileo's pupil Evangelista Torricelli invented the barometer, which measures atmospheric pressure, about 1643, using a glass tube and a basin of mercury. Several devices to measure relative humidity were introduced about the same time, and late in the seventeenth century Robert Hooke designed gauges for determining wind intensity and the amount of rainfall. (It was Hooke who in 1686 discovered fossil evidence that England had once had a tropical climate, and suggested a shift in the equator and poles to account for it.)

With these primitive instruments the first weather observations were made, though their reliability was limited, and such matters as agreeing on a standard temperature scale hampered proper statistical compilation. (The disagreements over temperature scale persist to our day, making it necessary to point out that all temperatures given in this book are in the Fahrenheit scale.) Knowledge of overall climatic patterns depended on obtaining information covering wide areas; thus simultaneous observations were needed. The earliest such observations of which we know were made between 1649 and 1651 in two French cities—Paris and Clermont-Ferrand—and in Stockholm, Sweden. But by the end of the seventeenth century, keeping of weather records was a chore of learned societies in many cities, and the hobby of many scientifically inclined men. Benjamin Franklin was an eager meteorologist; so were George

Washington, Thomas Jefferson, James Madison, and others of their time. (Jefferson noted that on July 4, 1776, the morning of the signing of the Declaration of Independence, the 6 A.M. temperature in Philadelphia was 68° F.) Police stations in France were given the responsibility for keeping accurate weather records in 1775; a German meteorological society organized the first large international network of observation points, stretching from Greenland to Moscow, in 1781; by the nineteenth century abundant statistical records were being compiled in many lands.

Thus, by direct or indirect means, we can assemble a convincing sequence of weather patterns covering the last thousand years or more. But what of earlier times, and lands where thermometers were long unknown? Man's preoccupation with the weather is ancient, of course, and weather adds up, day by day, into climate; but how can we know what those ancient and unrecorded climates were? The "oracle bones" of Shang Dynasty China, the oldest Chinese inscriptions that we have, indicate that forecasting the weather through divination was practiced in 1500 B.C., and we can be sure that the weather was a concern of the farmers of Jericho in 7500 B.C., of the cave-dwelling European huntsmen of 25,000 B.C., and of the migrating tribes of 100,000 B.C. But what sort of world did they inhabit?

Here we move from the province of the historian to that of the archaeologist—specifically, to those archaeologists whose specialty is paleoclimatology, the study of ancient climates. Using clues great and small, they have filled in the story of climate back through prehistoric times, and on into the unimaginable past, before all chroniclers, before the advent of man himself.

Geological studies have shown that through most of the world's history the weather has been considerably warmer, all over the globe, than it is now. Whether our planet was formed as a hot body pulled from the sun, or as an accumulation of cold cosmic dust, the general belief is that it reached a stable temperature quite early—perhaps within half a billion years of its formation. (The earth is considered to be about five billion years old.) Land masses appeared above the primordial sea;

rock eroded into soil; plant life evolved. Mild, genial temperatures seem to have prevailed over nearly the entire planet, however; polar icecaps were unknown, as were sharply differentiated zones of climate. During 90 percent of the past 500 million years, for example, the worldwide average temperature has been 72° F. Palm trees grew all over the United States; New York State was as warm as present-day Florida. (The global average temperature today is about 58° F.) The great climatologist C. E. P. Brooks has termed this universal warmth the "normal climate of geological time."

However, periodically the "normal climate" has been punctuated by harsh epochs of lower temperatures in which glaciers covered large areas of the planet, warm-weather species were driven into extinction, and a seemingly eternal winter persisted for thousands or even millions of years. The cause of these glacial periods is still the subject of vigorous scientific debate, and we will consider some of the current theories in a later chapter. What cannot be doubted is that the ice ages did occur—and with remarkably regular frequency, about 250 million years apart.

The evidence lies in the earth itself—in the fossil deposits, and inscribed on the rocks. Since the early nineteenth century, scientists have worked to establish a chronology of geological events based on the rock strata and their fossil contents. This work was hampered at first by the fundamentalist belief that the world had been created in 4004 B.C., but gradually the true age of the earth has been perceived, and a sequence of epochs determined. Five great geological eras have been marked off (*see* table): the Proterozoic or Archaeozoic ("era of most primitive life"), the Paleozoic ("era of ancient life"), the Mesozoic ("era of middle life"), and the Cenozoic ("era of recent life"). The Proterozoic was a time of sea life exclusively; the Paleozoic saw the appearance of amphibians and reptiles; the Mesozoic was the heyday of the dinosaurs; in the Cenozoic the warm-blooded birds and mammals emerged.

These eras have in turn been subdivided into periods, each representing some millions of years. The Paleozoic's periods—Cambrian, Devonian, Silurian, and so on—draw their names from particular places where the geological formations con-

TABLE OF GEOLOGICAL ERAS

ERA	PERIOD	APPROXIMATE LENGTH	TYPICAL ANIMAL LIFE
HOLOCENE or RECENT		Past 10,000 years	*Homo sapiens*
QUATERNARY	PLEISTOCENE	1,000,000 years +	Human and prehuman forms Large mammals
CENOZOIC (TERTIARY)	PLIOCENE	12,000,000 years	Manlike apes
	MIOCENE	15,000,000 years	First anthropoid apes
	OLIGOCENE	10,000,000 years	Monkeys. Small primates
	EOCENE	20,000,000 years	Early hoofed mammals
	PALEOCENE	12,000,000 years	Small mammals
MESOZOIC (SECONDARY)	CRETACEOUS	60,000,000 years	Dinosaurs. Marsupials
	JURASSIC	35,000,000 years	Dinosaurs. First birds
	TRIASSIC	45,000,000 years	Dinosaurs. Earliest mammals
PALEOZOIC (PRIMARY)	PERMIAN	30,000,000 years	First large reptiles
	PENNSYLVANIAN	20,000,000 years	Amphibians. First reptiles
	MISSISSIPPIAN	30,000,000 years	Amphibians
	DEVONIAN	60,000,000 years	Fish. First amphibians
	SILURIAN	35,000,000 years	First jawed fish. Invertebrates
	ORDOVICIAN	75,000,000 years	Invertebrates. First jawless fish
	CAMBRIAN	90,000,000 years	Invertebrates
PRE-CAMBRIAN (PROTEROZOIC, ARCHAEOZOIC)		2,000,000,000 years +	First living creatures

taining the "key" or "type" rocks and fossils of the period were first found. "Cambria," for example, is the Latin name for Wales, where Cambrian period deposits first were identified. The subdivisions of the Cenozoic, on the other hand, are not geographical in nature, but make time distinctions: They have meanings such as "most recent," "less recent," "early recent," and even "ancient recent." The period in which men evolved was the Pleistocene, which commenced between one and two million years ago; it is often set off in an era of its own called the Quaternary, a name which is a surviving vestige of an obsolete nineteenth-century division of the main eras into Primary, Secondary, Tertiary, and Quaternary. Finally, the last ten thousand years are sometimes further isolated as the Holocene or Recent period.

Each of these eras, with its attendant periods, stages, and smaller divisions, identifies itself to the geologist by characteristic rock formations and fossils. Fossils have become important indicating factors in determining ancient temperatures, for certain organisms have distinct preferences for specific climates. Coral reefs, for instance, cannot form in seas where the mean temperature drops below 70° F. Therefore the presence of fossil coral in an ancient deposit is an indicator of a warm climate. In the Silurian period of the Paleozoic, some 375 million years ago, reef-forming corals existed in Tennessee, Indiana, New York, much of western Europe, and even in northern Greenland. This shows that in Silurian times those regions were covered by warm seas. (One can also argue, of course, that in Silurian times corals were capable of forming reefs in cold water. But it is more reasonable to assume a change of climate than a fundamental change in an animal's living habits.)

The presence of warm-weather marine animals demonstrates the prevalence of Brooks's "normal climate of geological time" throughout most of the Proterozoic. But about a billion years ago a glacial period gripped much of the earth. The evidence is mainly geological. When a glacier, which is simply a slow-moving river of ice, travels, it carries with it a mass of debris. The stones and boulders borne by a glacier grind the glacier's signature into the area beneath its path. At the place where the glacier halts its advance, it dumps its load of debris to form what geologists call a terminal moraine. Two of the most conspicuous moraines in the United States are on Cape Cod and Long Island: irregular hummocks of rock, sand, and gravel, carried southward and dropped by the most recent of the glaciers.

The ice age of a billion years ago left its mark across a thousand-mile east-west strip of northern Ontario, and a 750-mile north-south line stretching up from Lake Huron. It consists of a tillite: a mixture of pebbles, boulders, and clay, consolidated into rock; and it rests on a scratched or polished surface of older rock. The boulders included in the tillite are not always local; some were transported from considerable distances. There are ways for tillites to be formed other than in glacial moraines, but the evidence is strong that these Canadian deposits represent an early ice age—not necessarily the earliest one, at that.

When the Proterozoic glaciers relented, the "normal climate of geological time" returned, as is indicated by the few known fossils of the pre-Cambrian era. But about a quarter of a billion years later there was another ice age, about which little is known; and there was still another 250 million years after that one, or about 500 million years ago. This glaciation occurred at one of the major turning points of geological time, the transition from the Proterozoic to the Paleozoic. Because it preceded the Cambrian, the first period of the Paleozoic, it is referred to as the infra-Cambrian or the Eo-Cambrian glaciation.

The first evidence of this glacial period was found in 1891 by the Norwegian geologist Hans Henrik Reusch: a tillite deposit atop a striated rock formation beside Varanger Fjord in northern Norway. Subsequent deposits found elsewhere in Scandinavia, Greenland, and the Arctic regions have been assigned to this time, as well as similar glacial deposits from southern Africa, Brazil, and Australia. (The wide distribution of the infra-Cambrian glacial remains has led to a startling but now well-supported hypothesis that the continents once were packed close together, so that all could be covered by a single ice sheet, and drifted apart later to take their present positions.)

The infra-Cambrian ice age was followed by a biological explosion: the sudden appearance of large, complex forms of animal life. The seas of the Proterozoic era were inhabited chiefly by algae, and by animal forms so primitive and ephemeral that scarcely any fossil evidence of them remains. The infra-Cambrian glaciation descended upon these organisms like a curtain; and when the infra-Cambrian ice was gone, an altogether different assortment of life forms appeared, an abrupt proliferation of sponges, mollusks, crustaceans, virtually all types of invertebrates. Whether this flamboyant evolutionary upheaval, which marks for us the opening of the Cambrian period of the Paleozoic era, was a direct result of the intense worldwide glaciation that preceded it is a puzzle for future scientists to solve. But the evidence uncovered so far tends at least toward the probability that there is some relationship between dramatic climatic change and the outpouring of new creatures.

Again the warm weather returned, and Paleozoic seas swarmed with life. The continents were low and mainly submerged beneath great inland seas much of the time; this was the epoch in which coral reefs covered the heart of North America. Though in the hundreds of millions of years of the Paleozoic there were long spans of cool weather, and geological convulsions in which continents rose from the sea, mountains were born, and groups of organisms wiped out, the trend was generally toward warmth. The climax of this long tropical idyll came in the Carboniferous ("carbon-bearing") period, some 300 million years ago, in which much of the world was a vast swamp thick with lush vegetation. From Spitzbergen and Greenland, far above the Arctic Circle, to the southern reaches of Africa and South America, a steamy, torrid jungle covered the earth. It was in this period—now usually subdivided into Mississippian (early) and Pennsylvanian (late) periods—that the great masses of organic matter accumulated in the dense, huge swamps which became, after eons of pressure, the vast coal beds of Europe and North America.

The existence of the Carboniferous marshes in regions now cold or arid argues for a generally dank, moist, superheated climate; and the fossil record of animal life supports this, for the dominant creatures of the Carboniferous were large amphibians and primitive reptiles. These are cold-blooded animals, which would become sluggish and helpless in cold or even cool weather. Small cold-blooded creatures today can survive unfavorable weather by going into hiding and suspending their life processes; but the big reptiles, such as alligators, large lizards, snakes, and tortoises, avoid cool climates almost entirely. It is impossible to imagine really large amphibians, such as those of the Carboniferous, thriving in anything but tropical conditions; and it would be evolutionarily unwarranted to imagine that they could have been warm-blooded and thus able to resist fluctuations in their weather.

Right on schedule, after the usual (and perplexing) quarter-billion-year gap, came another glacial interruption of the "normal climate." The Permian period marks the end of the Paleozoic; and the Permian glaciation of about 240 million years ago killed the lush forests, sent the big amphibians into limbo, and brought in a new epoch in which giant reptiles—the dinosaurs—dominated the postglacial world.

In this Permian glaciation mountains began once more to rise; precipitation fell as the temperatures dropped, so that enormous arid zones were created. Permian levels in Utah, for example, show sand dunes hundreds of feet thick covering a vast area. The three greatest salt deposits in the world—in Texas and New Mexico, in Germany, and in Russia—were laid down in the Permian, indicating the drying out of large inland seas. Apparently there were four or five sieges of glaciation in the Permian, separated by warmer interludes, and taking in altogether some ten million years. During these periods glaciers spread from points of high elevation until they covered areas of continental size. Interestingly, the Permian glaciation seems only to have directly affected the Southern Hemisphere. Traces of ancient moraines and glacier-scraped rock have been found in Permian levels across a widely separated zone: in Africa south of 20 degrees South, in Australia, India, Argentina. The distribution of the Permian glacial zones has also been used as an argument favoring the theory that the continents once were clustered compactly.

By mid-Permian time another cycle of warmth was beginning. But the giant insects with two-foot wingspreads, so characteristic of the Carboniferous jungles, were replaced by smaller types that had adapted to the cold; a hardier vegetation took hold; and the amphibians retreated in importance, yielding to the reptiles, which to some extent were better equipped to face the cooler (though not cold) climate of the postglacial world.

Then came the Mesozoic Era—some 140,000,000 years long—in which the climate gradually reverted to the old mildness. Once again warm, shallow seas covered the continents; marine life became abundant; vegetation flourished, though not as extravagantly as in the Carboniferous. Coral reefs grew in England and Germany; Mesozoic beds in Greenland have yielded fossil figs, breadfruit, cinnamon, and tree ferns. Reptiles evolved into forms of unparalleled bulk, the dinosaurs, which as cold-blooded animals could never have survived in anything but warm weather. Some of the largest of the dinosaurs inhabited Mongolia, Canada, Wyoming, Montana—hardly places of gentle climate today. A more rigorous climate toward the end of the Mesozoic, about 70,000,000 years ago, may have had something to do with the disappearance of the dinosaurs; but there was no general glaciation marking the boundary between the Mesozoic and the succeeding Cenozoic, only a slow, extremely gradual downward trend from tropical to temperate climate. A study of fossil plants and animals indicates that northwestern Europe had a mean temperature of about 72° F. at the beginning of the Cenozoic, of about 62° F. midway through the era, and of about 52° F. near its close. Comparative figures for the western United States along the Canadian border show a range of 77° F. at the start of the Cenozoic to 46° F. or less at the end of it. During the succession of periods this spans, from Eocene to Pliocene, most of the familiar birds and mammals of today were evolving; and among them, quite late in the day, came the primates out of which the human species ultimately developed.

The later Pliocene was marked by oscillating spasms of cold weather, heralding the return of the 250-million-year cycle of glacial epochs. The onset of the ice came on time, something less than two million years ago; the new glaciation put an end to the Pliocene and inaugurated the period we call the Pleistocene, a time of convulsive mountain building, stormy weather, and severe temperature declines. If we can accept certain recent findings to be discussed in the chapter on the ice ages, the transition from Pliocene to Pleistocene came with astonishing swiftness: within a span of five thousand years or less.

The Pleistocene is the epoch of man. At its beginning, certain protohuman creatures existed in Africa; by its conclusion (if we can properly speak of it as over) *Homo sapiens* held the center of the global stage. In the million or more years spanned by those two terminals, the world has been seized by glacial epochs on four occasions—or, looking upon it from the perspective of millions of years hence, the world has been gripped by a single ice age characterized by warmer intervals. We are living in one of those warmer intervals now, for the climate is far more favorable than it was some 25,000 years ago. But in terms of Brooks's "normal climate of geological time," we are still in the Pleistocene ice age. Our polar icecaps, the glaciers that cover the mountains of the Arctic, the severity of the winters even in temperate zones, all indicate conditions far more cruel than anything known in 90 percent of the earth's existence.

The fluctuations of the Pleistocene glaciation, and of the postglacial (or interglacial) time in which we live, are far better known to us than the fluctuations of the Proterozoic, infra-Cambrian, or Permian glaciations. Partly this is an obvious matter of more accessible records; the geological and biological evidence is at the surface, whereas much of the record of more ancient times has been destroyed in the upheavals of a billion years. Also, many of our techniques for interpreting the ancient climatic record are applicable only to the relatively recent past. There is also a psychological factor: that which is closest to us is more readily analyzed and classified. Whereas we talk of pre-Cambrian climates in terms of millions of years, we discuss more recent climatic fluctuations in units of hundreds of thousands of years, of thousands, and ultimately of decades.

Since the pattern of Pleistocene climate will be discussed in detail below, a brief outline of these fluctuations will suffice here. We know—from examination of moraines and from a study of the dominant flora and fauna—that the glaciers advanced and retreated many times in the past million-odd years. Each of the major glaciations brought world temperatures several degrees below the present average, caused large-scale migrations of animal life and changes in the distribution of flora, covered great areas with thick masses of ice, and pulled sea levels down by hundreds of feet as water was locked up in the ice sheets. Among the animals driven to and fro by the swings of the climate was man, and through much of the Pleistocene the story of the ice is the story of man's increasingly more successful struggle to cope with his environment.

Scientists disagree on the chronology of the Pleistocene. The first glaciation was thought for a long while to have begun between 600,000 and 1,000,000 years ago, but conflicting views based on recently developed analytical techniques have led on the one hand to the suggestion that the first great ice sheet began its advance only 300,000 years ago, and on the other that the glaciation started closer to 2,000,000 years ago. The latter chronology seems more widely accepted at the moment. According to the time scheme proposed in 1964 by David B. Ericson and Goesta Wollin of the Lamont Geological Observatory of Columbia University, based on examination of deep-sea sediments, the first advance of the ice came about 1,500,000 years ago and the period of climatic severity lasted some 125,000 years. Following an interval of mild interglacial weather covering 170,000 years, a second advance of the ice occurred about 1,205,000 years ago. This endured for 145,000 years, and was followed by a second interglacial lasting 640,000 years. The third onset of the ice came about 420,000 years ago, and the third interglacial 80,000 years later. The fourth and (so far) last encroachment of the glaciers began about 115,000 years ago, and the withdrawal of the ice, which is still going on, set in approximately 11,000 years before the present.

The succeeding postglacial period, during which man's first agricultural civilizations emerged and city-dwelling cultures evolved, is quite finely divided into climatic eras. Such ingenious techniques as pollen counts, varve analysis, carbon-14 dating, tree-ring counts, and others, which we will examine later, have provided a precise and detailed view of the shifting weather in this most critical phase of human prehistory and history. The area known in most detail is Europe, where the science of prehistory developed; and the Near East and North Africa have come in for study more recently, while the paleoclimatology of North America is now catching up with Old World scholarship.

Glaciers similar to those in Greenland and Antarctica today covered northern Europe some 25,000 years ago, reaching as far south as England, Germany, Poland, and northern France. The retreat of the glaciers was slow and not always continuous, but about 13,000 years ago the climate was warm enough to permit the growth of trees in England and Denmark. Man slowly moved northward into the new forests, abandoning the caves and tundras of France, where he had lived during the worst of the glacial years. At that time, there came an interruption in the retreat of the ice, lasting perhaps a thousand years. Then, 12,000 years ago, the glaciers began to withdraw again, pulling back so that the margin of the ice lay in central Sweden and south-central Finland about 11,000 years before the present (B.P.). Birch forests now grew in England, willow in Holland and Denmark. But now came the final relapse of the ice age, a brief but intense cold wave in which, within some 50 to 80 years, the new forests were killed and ice repossessed much of its former territory. The climate eased again about 8,000 B.P., with the final breakup of the European ice sheet and the pullback of the glaciers to the extreme Arctic. In the New World a similar pattern had been acted out at roughly the same time. An ice sheet that had covered North America as far south as the Ohio and Missouri rivers retreated, with many oscillations and changes of direction, until it covered only the Canadian northlands.

As the average temperature rose, the world's climate also grew more moist, leading to an epoch from 6000 to 4000 B.P. that is often called the "postglacial climatic optimum." Summer temperatures in Europe and North America were some five degrees warmer on the average than they are today; winters were somewhat warmer as well; the Arctic had much open water; in the Sahara and those parts of the Near East that are desert today, summer precipitation was high. Temperate plants and animals grew much farther north than they can grow today; subtropical organisms moved into what now are temperate provinces. Man himself expanded his dominion greatly. Then came a time of storms, setting in four or five thousand years ago, and a colder period, marked particularly by rainy, chilly summers, with the worst of the weather coming between 900 and 450 B.C. The Alps and the Rocky Mountains once more bore glaciers, and what had been grassy meadows turned into swampy bogs. The Arctic ice cover returned.

Both the geological record and the historical, which we can use for the first time, show that after A.D. 400 the climate gradually became warmer and drier, reaching a peak between 800 and 1000. In this storm-free era the first Viking voyages were made through seas previously (and at present) choked with ice. This was the time when vineyards flourished in England and the Norse colonies were planted on Iceland, Greenland, and quite likely North America. By A.D. 1200 climatic instability was setting in: floods and droughts, severe storms, icy winters. This led to the so-called "little ice age" of the sixteenth and seventeenth centuries, in which an increasingly harsh climate caused major disruptions in European life. Lastly, a warming trend began early in the nineteenth century, accelerated sharply between 1890 and 1940, and in the past few decades seems to have undergone a halt or a reversal.

From this outline it should be clear that climate, no less than weather, is fickle and inconstant. Warmth and cold, moisture and drought, storm and fair weather, follow rhythms of their own. Climate has many cycles: some last only a few years, some for generations or centuries, and one, apparently, the cycle of major glaciations, returns at intervals of a quarter billion years. Man's struggle to protect himself against the ordinary vagaries of weather—the cold snap, the dry spell, the devastating downpour—has been vastly complicated through the ages by these large-scale climatic swings. As we will see, the fate of civilizations has sometimes been decided by such swings; and, for all our vanity, it may yet be decided by them in the epochs to come as well.

2

The Making of Climates

CLIMATE IS SIMPLY WEATHER PLOTTED ON A LARGE GRAPH; and to understand why patterns of climate are subject to fluctuations, we should first examine the factors that govern the weather. These are, in particular, the sun; the movements of the earth along its orbit and on its axis of rotation; the atmosphere; and the geography of the earth's surface, its mountains and valleys, its oceans and lakes, its deserts and ice fields. The interplay of these four chief factors—sun, planet, atmosphere, geography—produces our weather in all its glorious complexity; and a major change in any one of those factors can create a long-term alteration in the weather (which is to say a change of climate) affecting perhaps a few counties or perhaps the entire world.

The weather dealt out to different regions of our planet at any given time varies spectacularly, of course. Along the coasts of Peru and in the deserts of Africa there are places where rain may not have fallen in thousands of years; but in Cherrapunji, India, the rainfall averages more than an inch every day—437 inches in 1952, 905 in 1861. Even Cherrapunji's rain is inconsistent; there are dry seasons lasting several months, and then seasons in which, according to one observer, "the rain comes down in drops the size of baseballs, blown by the fierce winds with rifle velocity." The Caribbean isle of Dominica rarely has a rainless day, and on its green, mist-swept slopes grow giant bamboos and lacy tree ferns; but the island of Antigua, a few minutes by airplane to the north, is so parched that it is best fitted for growing cactus. On the western slopes of the Cascades in the American Northwest, precipitation amounts to several hundred inches a year in some places, creating a temperate-zone rain forest in which moss-festooned trees grow to awesome size; on the eastern slopes of the same mountain range there may be no more than a dozen rainy days a year. There are good reasons for these wide variations in precipitation. So, too, for the ranges in temperature: the unbroken warmth of the tropics, the frightful cold of the Antarctic, the pendulum from ninety-degree summers to twenty-below-zero winters that afflicts the American Midwest.

The chief engineer of our climate is the sun, that awesome emitter of energy that is the source of all life on earth. Although the interior of the earth is molten-hot, this geothermal heat plays no role in climatic matters. Our entire energy income is the result of the continuing thermonuclear reaction taking place in the sun, 93 million miles away. This immense ball of gas, 865,000 miles in diameter and having the mass of 330,000 earths, is a cosmic furnace in which hydrogen is converted to helium by a fusion process. Intense heat is a by-product of this process. At the core of the sun, temperatures may reach 30 million degrees; at the surface the heat is "only" about 6,000° to 10,000° F. Every second the sun consumes 4 million tons of its own mass in this energy-producing reaction; but it has been doing this for at least five billion years, and has enough fuel to keep it up for a good many billion years more.

Energy pours outward from the sun at the speed of light. Only one two-billionth of its output reaches the earth, but even that represents more energy every minute than all of humanity consumes in all forms every year. The solar energy arrives as electromagnetic waves of three kinds: the short, high-frequency waves of ultraviolet, the long waves of infrared radiation, and, in between, the waves of what we call the visible spectrum, those that react with the structure of our optic system and permit us to see. Some 35 to 40 percent of the earth's energy income is reflected right back to space by the tops of clouds, by ice fields, and by the surface of the ocean. The reflectivity of a surface is known as its *albedo,* and has much to do with the quantity of solar energy that is available to it. The albedo of an ice field is about nine times as great as the albedo of a field of dark soil; thus a high-albedo region such as ice-covered Greenland will bounce much of the solar energy it receives uselessly back toward its source. This illustrates one basic feature of climatology: extreme conditions tend to reinforce themselves by their own nature. An ice-covered region, which is already cold, will tend to get still colder because of its energy-reflecting albedo.

Another 15 to 20 percent of the incoming sunlight is intercepted and absorbed by our atmosphere. The remaining 40 percent or so of the solar energy gets through to the surface of the earth; some of this is absorbed by the ocean, some is bounced back and forth between land and sky, some is taken up by solid matter. Our dependence on the sun's radiation is absolute. If the sun's output were to increase by 9 percent, the earth's global mean temperature would rise to a tropical 72° F. If it were to drop by the same percentage, the world's average temperature would fall to about 40° F., as in the coldest of the glacial periods. If the sun were to go out altogether, the oceans would freeze in a few weeks, and the temperature of the earth's surface would drop toward absolute zero through loss of heat to space.

The amount of insolation, as incoming solar radiation is termed by meteorologists, varies greatly from place to place. This variation is governed by the earth's two motions—its 24-hour spin on its own axis and its 365¼-day revolution around the sun—and by its tilted position in its orbit. As the planet turns each day, of course, it presents now one side to the sun, now the other; the side away from the sun gets no insolation and cools through the night, usually reaching its lowest temperature just before sunrise. On the side facing the sun, insolation varies with latitude. At the equator the sun's rays strike from directly overhead, and are the most intense; the mean temperature is high. Where the rays must travel at a slant, losing energy by passing through more of the atmosphere and undergoing absorption, reflection, and scattering, temperatures are lower. The greatest degree of slant is found at the poles. Since, in addition, energy arriving at the equator is concentrated in the smallest possible area, and energy arriving at an oblique angle is spread over a wider area, the poles receive the least insolation per square foot of any region on earth.

Since the earth's orbit around the sun is elliptical, not circular, its distance from the sun is different at different times of the year; but this is not a factor in climate at all, as can be seen from the fact that the earth is closer to the sun in January than it is in July. What is of importance is the tilt of the earth's axis. This tilt of 23½ degrees further modifies the angle at which the sun's rays arrive. As the earth travels around the sun, it presents its northern hemisphere toward the sun from March to September, so that by June 21 sunlight is at a maximum everywhere north of the equator, and summer arrives, while the southern hemisphere is experiencing its shortest day of the year, and enters into winter. The cycle reverses itself from September to March, bringing winter to the north and summer to the south on December 22. Again, because the sun's rays fall more obliquely as they approach the poles, the climatic effects are governed by latitude. Along the equator the intake of solar energy is much the same all year around, and there is little variation in the relative lengths of day and night in winter or in summer. But with greater distance from the equator, the length of day and the amount of insolation both are much greater in summer than in winter. The ultimate effects are most obvious at the extremes of the earth: in Alaska, the insolation in January is less than 10 percent of that in July, and at the poles the sun does not rise at all during winter, producing "nights" and "days" lasting six months apiece.

Climate depends not only on the vagaries of solar energy, but on the influence of the atmosphere and oceans, which serve to transport and redistribute heat. Earth's atmosphere is a blanket of gases, made up mostly of nitrogen (about 78%), oxygen (almost 21%), argon (0.9%), and carbon dioxide (0.03%), with traces of several other elements, and such extraneous materials as dust and water vapor. Though it has a depth of more than a hundred miles, all but 1 percent of the atmosphere lies in a belt nineteen miles thick about the earth. Gravitational attraction holds the atmosphere in place and ensures that it will be at its most dense close to the earth; about 50 percent of the atmosphere's molecules are contained in the first eighteen thousand feet above our planet's surface. This great volume of gases has substantial weight; and the weight, or air pressure, of the atmosphere increases with density, so that it is heaviest at sea level. There the atmosphere exerts a pressure of 14.7 pounds on every square inch of our bodies. We do not feel it because the atmosphere within our bodies pushes outward with an exactly equalizing force; but if we go even a short distance upward to a region where the external atmospheric pressure is lower, the effect registers most clearly upon such sensitive membranes as the eardrums.

The atmosphere shields us from the full impact of the solar radiation. Without it, earth would have daytime temperatures as high as 180° F. at the equator; at night this heat would rapidly flee, causing the equatorial temperature to drop to 220° F. below zero. The atmosphere protects us by day by absorbing and reflecting much of the incoming energy; by night its retained heat keeps us warm until the sun again rises. Another heat-retaining property of the atmosphere has been termed the "greenhouse effect," for the glass of greenhouses admits solar energy but prevents the escape of the long-wave infrared radiation by which heat is dissipated outward.* Certain components of the atmosphere—mainly carbon dioxide, water vapor, and ozone—have the same property of admitting heat and blocking the escape of infrared radiation. Instead of bleeding off into space, the trapped heat remains in the atmosphere and warms the planet below.

Through the atmosphere move turbulent currents of wind—rivers of air that rule our day-by-day weather. The wind may carry rain, snow, bitter cold, clammy humidity. It is the great

* The atmosphere is transparent in both directions to the shorter infrared rays.

redistributor of heat, blurring and transforming the pattern established by the essential fact that the equator receives more solar energy than the poles.

As Aristotle pointed out in his *Meteorologica* over 2,300 years ago, the winds derive their energy from the heating of the air by the sun. Warm air is less dense, and thus lighter, than cool air. At the equator, great masses of air are constantly being heated and begin to rise; the same concept can be expressed by saying that the pressure of the air mass decreases as it is heated, and the atmospheric molecules move outward and upward—away from the ground, and away from the equator.

Thus the steady and high insolation of the equator eternally sends masses of warm, low-pressure air drifting into the sky and off toward the north and south. This air has to be replaced, and so cooler air is drawn in, creating a cycle in which dense high-pressure air flows toward the equator, is heated, and rises to flow outward again. But the expansion of an air mass constitutes work, and can only be carried out through the expenditure of energy—in this case, heat energy. As the equatorial air masses rise, they lose energy, grow cooler, become more dense, and begin to sink, dropping to the ground far to the north or south and replacing the air that has begun its journey toward the equator. In this way the cycle of atmospheric circulation is perpetuated; it takes about twelve days, on the average, for the air to make the complete north-south journey, pole to equator and back. These shifting masses of air produce changes of weather in the regions over which they pass. A warm low-pressure mass of tropical air may pile up over one district for a few days, only to have an equator-bound high-pressure mass of cold air slip beneath it, push it skyward, and bring cooler temperatures.

If there were no more to the system than this, the atmospheric circulation would be a simple matter of north-south flow, and the winds, which are generated by differences in air pressure, would never change their direction. The atmosphere has a natural tendency to equalize pressures everywhere: high-pressure air rushes toward an area of low pressure to balance things. Thus the winds would blow unendingly from the poles toward the equator, with warmer air above drifting in the opposite direction, as the atmosphere performed its work of transferring heat from the world's middle to its ends. But many other factors interfere with the simplicity of the system—notably the Coriolis "force," more properly the Coriolis effect, which in essence deflects the air patterns from their basic north-south movements.

This effect is named for its discoverer, the nineteenth-century French mathematician G. G. de Coriolis, who made the first thorough analysis of the tendency of objects in motion to drift to one side. If you stand on a turning merry-go-round and attempt to throw a baseball at a post mounted aboard the merry-go-round, the ball will drift maddeningly away from its target, as though nudged by some invisible force. If the merry-go-round is moving counterclockwise at a rate of one complete turn every ten seconds, and you throw your ball at a speed of twenty feet per second toward a post fifteen feet away from you, the ball will seem to curve to the right and miss the post by six feet or so.

Actually the ball does not curve at all; no true force is acting on it to push it out of the straight line in which you aimed it. The problem is that you have failed to compensate for the movement of the merry-go-round during the time the ball is in flight. When the ball lands, the post is no longer where it was when you took aim.

The earth is like a giant merry-go-round, turning constantly from west to east, and the complete rotation that it makes every twenty-four hours introduces a Coriolis effect for bodies in motion on its surface. The effect is smallest near the equator and greatest at the poles, since the earth's circumference diminishes steadily from equator to pole. All points on the earth go around the axis in one day, and therefore a point on the equator, covering a greater distance than a point in a high latitude, must travel at a faster rate than other points. Objects moving northward from the equator on an intended straight path would end up to the east of their planned destinations; objects heading southward to the equator would fall behind in their journey and land west of their intended targets. In other words, the Coriolis effect causes all moving objects in the Northern Hemisphere to wander to the right of their direction of travel, and in the Southern Hemisphere to the left.

An artilleryman who fires a shell at 2,500 feet per second at a target 20 miles away will miss by more than 200 feet unless he calculates for Coriolis drift and aims his gun accordingly. A supersonic jet plane going at 1,800 miles an hour, starting from the North Pole and headed for New York, would actually land in Denver if its pilot did not compensate for the Coriolis effect produced by the turning of the earth as the plane flies.

The winds are not immune to Coriolis drift. In both hemispheres, air traveling away from the equator is deflected eastward, and air traveling toward the equator is deflected westward. Since the Coriolis effect is stronger as distance from the equator increases, there is hardly any deflection at all near the equator, but in higher latitudes the winds are twisted until they blow at right angles to their original pressure-induced direction. This creates several belts of wind traveling around the planet in east-west paths.

The dominant climatic zones of the world, therefore, are formed by the north-south movement created by heating of equatorial air, and by the east-west deflection of the Coriolis force. At the equator the only movement of the air is vertical as it continually warms and rises. There is little wind there, and so a band of calms exists for hundreds of miles on both sides of the line. In sailing-ship days, captains quickly learned to avoid this windless band, which they called the "doldrums."

The rising air divides, some heading north and some south. About 30 degrees from the equator in both hemispheres it loses velocity and tends to pile up in another belt of calms, which early mariners nicknamed the "horse latitudes," supposedly because sailors on ships carrying horses from Europe to America shoved the horses overboard when the ships were becalmed in those latitudes and water supplies began to run low.

Two streams of air do manage to escape from the pile-up in the horse latitudes; and since the Coriolis effect is strong here, they emerge turned sharply from their original poleward path.

One flow of air twists about and heads diagonally back to the equator; in the Northern Hemisphere it is traveling south, in the Southern Hemisphere it is traveling north, and in either case the Coriolis effect deflects it to the west. This produces the "trade winds," blowing always from the northeast above the line and the southeast below it; these are the winds that sped Columbus across the South Atlantic and carried Magellan across the Pacific. The other flow continues diagonally toward the poles, and is deflected in both hemispheres toward the east. These winds are the "westerlies," so named because under the archaic system of nomenclature we use, winds are designated by the direction from which they come, not the way they are going.

In both the northern and southern hemispheres the westerlies are broad, turbulent wind systems moving between the 40th and 50th parallels. These winds give the "roaring forties" of sailing men their stormy reputation, and provide the world's temperate zones with their changeable weather—for in the latitudes where the westerlies blow, warm air constantly collides with cold along definite boundaries known as fronts, with vivid results.

At any time, the westerlies are carrying warm moist air up from the horse latitudes, while cold air is steadily pushing down from the poles. Either sort of air mass may play the "aggressor's" role, and in either case the outcome will be stormy. Suppose a mass of warm, muggy tropical air has settled over a city; for several days the weather will be steamy and humid, with low-lying clouds. Now a mass of cold air—a cold front—moves in from the north. The cold air, being denser and heavier, will slide under the warm-air mass, shoehorning it away from ground level and forcing it into the upper atmosphere. As it rises, the warm air cools, releasing the moisture it holds; a sudden violent thunderstorm is the result. Or a region may be covered for a while by a mass of cold polar air, bringing a succession of cloudless, snappy days. Up from the tropics comes an advancing mass of warm air—a warm front—which slowly slides over the dome of cold air. Fog, drizzle, rain, or light snow mark the boundary of the two masses; the rain grows heavier, the air fills with clouds, the cold air gradually retreats; after hours or even days of steady rain the sun breaks through the clouds, but now it is the warm air that holds possession of the territory.

The clash of fronts is the reason why the westerlies are studded with the interesting irregularities known to readers of weather maps as "highs" and "lows." These are eddies and whirlpools of air formed when conflicting air masses meet in the regions ruled by the westerlies; along the fronts huge strands of warm and cool air curl around each other until trapped pockets are wholly severed from their surrounding air masses, and become the nuclei of giant whirls that the earth's rotation sends spinning off as islands of turbulence through the atmosphere.

Meteorologists term these traveling disturbances cyclones and anticyclones. A cyclone, or low, is a detached mass of warm air that has been set spinning around a central area of low pressure. Since air tends to rush from regions of high pressure to regions of low pressure, a cyclone sucks air toward its center, creating high winds. The Coriolis effect causes cyclones to whirl in a counterclockwise direction in the Northern Hemisphere, and clockwise in the Southern Hemisphere. Anticyclones are opposite in all respects: They are high-pressure systems, great masses of cold dry air with the zone of highest pressure at the core. Turning clockwise above the equator, counterclockwise below, they drift through the band of the westerlies bringing spells of fair weather—sunny, cool, and cloudless.

Cyclones and anticyclones may be 500 to 1,000 miles across, blanketing thousands of square miles at a time, and moving at speeds of 20 or 30 miles an hour. In their progression across the sky they bring continual shifts of weather. Cyclones, loaded with water vapor from the oceanic evaporation in the tropics, bring rain or snow, often in great quantities. (The violent storms known as hurricanes in the Atlantic and typhoons in the Pacific are specialized cyclonic formations originating in the tropics, however, and should not be confused with the less spectacular traveling cyclones that constantly move through the temperate zones. Nor are "twisters" or tornadoes to be thought of as cyclones.) When the barometric pressure begins to drop, indicating the approach of a cyclone, high winds and strong rain are likely. The coming of an anticyclone, on the other hand, means clear skies and falling temperatures. Those blessed interludes of low humidity and crisp autumnal weather that sometimes interrupt a sticky summer are the work of anticyclones; so, too, are the cold waves that grip us in winter for long spells of sunny days but severe temperatures.

The alternating dance of cyclones and anticyclones across the land is crucial in determining rainfall patterns. Rain is the release of water vapor from the atmosphere; every year some 95,000 cubic miles of water circulate between the earth and the sky, going up in evaporation to become vapor (80,000 cubic miles of it from the ocean, the rest from lakes, rivers, moist ground, and vegetation) and coming down as rain, snow, sleet, hail, or one of the other forms of precipitation. The global precipitation average is 40 inches a year; but the distribution is extremely unequal, with some areas getting an inch or less a year, and some receiving 400 inches or more.

Air that is warm has a greater capacity to retain water vapor than cool air. At the equator, the sun's heat induces heavy evaporation of the oceans, and also rapidly warms the air that is constantly arriving from cooler zones. The result is a steady upwelling of warm, moisture-laden air. The sun lifts billions of tons of water from the equatorial oceans; but most of this falls back immediately as the air that carries it cools and releases its burden of vapor. So the equatorial regions are zones of heavy rainfall, and the East Indies, the Congo and Amazon valleys, and other tropical regions get the 150-plus inches of rain each year that produces lush rain forests.

The air that moves away from the equator toward the horse latitudes still carries a good deal of water vapor. But the expenditure of energy involved in rising and making the journey from the equator shows up as a loss of heat: The air cools and grows heavier, and begins to sink toward the ground. Though it has become cooler, this air does not bring rain, for as it sinks it becomes compressed, and the heat generated by compression warms it again. A high-pressure system of descending air, therefore, yields no rain. In the horse latitudes evaporation invariably outpaces precipitation; hence most of the world's great deserts lie in the twin belts of perpetual high-pressure systems 30 degrees north and south of the equator. In this globe-girdling arid strip are the Sahara and Kalahari deserts of Africa, the Great Victoria Desert of Australia, the Arabian Desert, and the Sonora Desert of Mexico.

Still farther from the equator, in the regions where the westerlies blow, we have the zones of the traveling cyclones and anticyclones. Which kind of system goes where, and for how long, has a good deal to do with the sort of climate a temperate-zone locality will have. The lifetime of cyclones is usually shorter than that of anticyclones. A cyclone, being a mass of warm, moist, upward-flowing air, is born over water, and must remain close to water to sustain itself. As it travels it churns, releases its moisture, gives up its warmth, and equalizes with the surrounding air; unless it draws new moisture from an ocean, lake, or river, it will die within a few days through loss of the heat energy that lifted it from the surface in the first place. Sometimes a low may loiter and loaf, or even move back on its track, bedeviling one area for many days if it can find a steady supply of water vapor on which to feed; but more often the fate of the cyclone is to let go of its moisture and to draw in so much cold high-pressure air that it is squeezed to death by the anticyclone that catches up with it. Cyclones, then, do not thrive over great land masses; the interiors of the continents are usually dry as a result, except where penetrated by an arm of the sea, such as the Mediterranean, or where bodies of water of the magnitude of the Great Lakes provide sources of evaporation. Precipitation in inland regions is especially low in winter, when anticyclones thrive—for anticyclones, being masses of cold air that are not easily displaced, may settle for long visits, chilling and drying half a continent at a time. When the weather forecaster sees no prospect of an end to a cold wave, he means that he sees little chance that a prevailing high will move along.

Eventually the high does move along—in the temperate

zones, at least. But the migratory habits of highs and lows contribute to the climatic tendency of self-reinforcement: dry places get drier, because cyclones cannot sustain themselves there, and cold places get colder, because anticyclones do sustain themselves there. The polar regions, like the horse latitudes, are zones of perpetual high-pressure systems, and Antarctica in particular can be classed among the world's deserts, receiving only the most scanty precipitation. (The thick ice fields of Antarctica are explained by the fact that such snow as does fall does not melt, and accumulates over the millennia.)

It can be seen from this that a long-term change in the pattern of the westerlies can produce dramatic and far-reaching changes in rainfall patterns. If high-pressure systems begin, for some reason, to nudge aside lows that previously brought regular rain to a region, drought will develop; and as lakes and rivers grow dry, the drought reinforces itself by denying the atmosphere evaporated water that could return as rain.

The relative distribution of land and water affects not only the great planetary wind systems, but also local winds and breezes. They are generated out of the difference in temperatures between land and sea, which in turn arises out of water's great capacity to absorb and hold heat. The ocean serves as a kind of global thermostat because of its high specific heat—its ability to receive or lose large quantities of heat without great changes in its temperature. It takes much more heat to raise the temperature of one pound of water by one degree than it does to raise the same quantity of iron or stone by the same amount, for example. So the sea soaks up solar energy all day long without growing appreciably warmer; and at night, when the source of energy is no longer available, it gives off the stored heat of the day without growing appreciably cooler. Meanwhile the adjoining land, subject to the same alternation of day and night, rapidly warms and cools, creating a contrast between land and sea temperature.

Since the temperature of the sea hardly varies around the clock, the temperature of the air above it also remains fairly constant. But on land, going through its day-night cycle, the atmosphere is alternately heated and cooled by the changes in the temperature below. During the day the air above the land is warmed and rises, pulling cool air in from the sea to replace it. At night cool air rushes out from the land into the low-pressure region above the sea. So breezes blow from sea to land by day, from land to sea at night. These highly predictable winds are charming companions at seaside resorts, but such local phenomena as Italy's *ponente* and Hawaii's *kapalilua* have little effect on global climate. However, the same principle governs a wind system that has immense impact on the lives of millions of people—the Asian monsoon.

"Monsoon" is a word derived from the Arabic *mausim*, "season," and refers to a wind that blows according to a definite seasonal pattern. There are many monsoonlike winds throughout the world, but the best-known one is the South Asia monsoon, caused by the thrust of the subcontinent of India into the Indian Ocean. During the summer, the sun's rays carry great warmth both to land and sea, but only the land registers a significant change in temperature. For six months of the year the land grows hotter, heating the air above it and thereby forming a region of low pressure. Into the opening sweep moisture-laden winds off the sea, which dump hundreds of inches of rain in some parts of India. This is the southwest monsoon. In winter the system abruptly and emphatically reverses; the land quickly gives up its stored summer heat, and the winds of the northeast monsoon begin to blow from land to sea, inaugurating the long dry season. In ancient times mariners needed no compass to find their way from Arabia to India; they merely had to know the time of year, for all traffic was one way for half the year, and the other way the rest of the time, riding with the steady monsoons. Any change in the timing of the monsoons holds great dangers for India's teeming population. Nearly 80 percent of India's rainfall comes in the four months from June through September; but if the onset of the monsoon-carried rains is late, the rice fields wither and famine threatens. At Delhi, for example, the average date of monsoon arrival is July 2; but during the fifty-year period from 1901 to 1950, the actual burst of the monsoon ranged from June 17 to July 20, with ominous consequences in the years of greatest delay.

The ocean thermostat modifies land climate in other ways—particularly by acting as a stabilizer for coastal regions. Water's warmth-retaining properties smooth the peaks and fill the valleys of climatic fluctuations for areas near seacoasts or large inland bodies of water, so that those regions enjoy cooler summers and warmer winters than regions far from water. San Francisco, with its "oceanic" climate, has temperatures in the fifties and sixties all year round, while landlocked North Dakota, experiences a temperature range of more than a hundred degrees between frigid January and torrid July. The prevailing westerly winds counteract the ocean's influence to some extent, by carrying continental-weather air to the eastern coasts of the continents. In temperate zones, therefore, east coasts are exposed to air that has traveled across land, west coasts to air that has traveled over sea, and so temperature fluctuations both in winter and in summer are greater in New York or Boston than they are in San Francisco or Seattle.

The ocean's currents—those distinct and permanent rivers of water within water—have an important role in determining land climate. Many factors are involved in the shaping of currents, such as differences in the temperature and salinity of the sea, the location of large land masses, and the action of the tides, but the main influence is the direction of the prevailing winds. The trade winds, which always blow from the east on a diagonal toward the equator, produce the swift and strong westward-flowing North and South Equatorial Currents; when these reach the eastern seaboards of the continents they divide into two streams, one heading south and the other north, and as they enter higher latitudes they come under the influence of the westerlies, which drive them back across the ocean to complete the circuit. Apart from this main oceanic circulation, the placement of land masses creates a number of lesser streams traveling at tangents, and these carry water that profoundly modifies the climate of the coasts they touch.

The Gulf Stream is the main warm current of the North Atlantic. The two equatorial currents deliver water to the

Caribbean, from which it flows through the Yucatan Channel between Mexico and Cuba; blocked by the mass of water already in the Gulf of Mexico, it turns north past Cuba and the tip of Florida and, as the Gulf Stream, travels up the eastern coast of North America. It spreads the tropical warmth it carries up past New England, where it catches the westerlies and crosses the Atlantic to the western coast of Europe. At the place where it turns east the Gulf Stream meets two cold currents carrying water from the Arctic—the Labrador Current and the East Greenland Current—which lower its temperature by ten or fifteen degrees and creates banks of fog off Newfoundland where warm and cold waters collide. Nevertheless, the Gulf Stream retains enough heat to bring significant warmth to Norway and western Europe. The most densely populated regions of western Europe lie in the same latitudes as the icebound, nearly uninhabited wastelands of Labrador and southern Greenland—a testimony to the beneficial effect of the Gulf Stream and the adverse work of the two cold currents.

In the Pacific the Peru or Humboldt Current pulls Antarctic water up the western coast of South America with chilling results, while farther to the west the Kuroshio Current serves as a somewhat weaker version of the Atlantic's Gulf Stream. The Kuroshio comes up from the equator past the Philippines and Taiwan, travels northeastward along the western coast of Japan, and crosses the Pacific to become the Japan Current, which brings warmth and moisture to southern Alaska and the coasts of British Columbia, Washington, and Oregon. There it clashes with the Aleutian or Subarctic Current, coming from the Arctic, and produces fog of a density comparable to that of the Newfoundland fog banks. The Aleutian continues down the west coast of North America as the California Current, bearing cold water familiar to anyone who has tried to swim at a California beach.

Clearly any change in the pattern of ocean currents would be reflected in transformation of coastal climates. A southward deflection of the Gulf Stream would bring harsh winters to Norway and Great Britain, while if there were no Gulf Stream at all—as would happen if the Isthmus of Panama were submerged, so that the warm equatorial current continued from Atlantic to Pacific instead of being deflected to the north—London and Paris and Amsterdam would lie in the grip of an ice age. Such drastic events as the sinking of the Isthmus of Panama are not the only ways in which shifts of currents could happen. Changes in wind patterns would affect currents; if the trade winds or westerlies were to blow in slightly different latitudes, the Gulf Stream might not find its way to Europe. This might come about during a general decrease in global temperatures, and would result in a further decrease in the temperature of the Northern Hemisphere—another example of the troublesome self-reinforcing mechanisms so common in climatic matters.

The last of the important factors governing climate is the topography of the land masses—the presence of mountain ranges or lowland basins, which introduce local variations into the planetary patterns created by the sun, the winds, and the oceans. Mountains form barriers or conduits for wind-driven air masses. The Maritime Alps provide an ideal windbreak for the French Riviera, screening it from chilly northern winds. In North America, though, the Rockies and the Appalachians comprise the edges of a vast wind tunnel that conveys Arctic air across the heart of the continent; the downrush of polar air, meeting the warm, moist air from the Gulf of Mexico, spawns the storms and blizzards to which the Midwest is prone.

Mountains deflect not only wind but precipitation. Where lofty mountain ranges lie athwart prevailing wind belts, moisture-laden air is compelled to rise, thus growing cool and dropping its moisture on the windward slope; descending over the leeward slope it warms again and induces evaporation from the land, so that the same wind brings lush vegetation to one side of a mountain range and stark desert to the other. The deserts that lie on the eastern slopes of the Sierra Nevada are the product of this effect: the westerlies sweep in heavy with Pacific moisture, but leave it all on the thickly timbered western slope, giving us Death Valley on the far side of the mountains. The Sierra Nevadas are relatively young mountains; their rise during the Pleistocene must have brought catastrophic climatic change to the formerly well-watered inland regions of Nevada. The Cascades in the Northwest show the same rainfall distribution: heavy on the windward side, skimpy to the leeward. In South America, the trade winds crossing the Amazon Basin from east to west bring moisture to the tropical rain forests on the eastern slopes of the Andes, but the coastal strip on the far side of the mountains is one of the world's most arid regions. And in Asia, where a low-lying central basin is hemmed in to the south by the Himalayas and to the west and southeast by lesser but still mighty mountain chains, the interior of the continent is the largest area of desert wasteland in the world.

The factors that govern climate, then, are intricately interrelated. The temperature range and precipitation level of any region are governed by the intensity and duration of the sunlight it gets, the nature of the prevailing wind patterns, the influence of nearby oceanic currents, the local topography, and many other forces in delicate balance. Climatic effects tend to be consistent over long periods: Boston need not expect a snowy July, nor Bombay a rainy January. But climates have changed drastically over spans of hundreds of years, and even more drastically when viewed from a larger perspective. What are the causes of major climatic change?

They are still poorly understood. We know effects better than causes; we know what makes weather, but are still seeking real knowledge of the circumstances that bring about climatic upheavals. These are some of the suggestions put forth to explain changes of climate:

Changes in the intensity of sunlight reaching the earth.
Shifts in ocean currents.
Changes in the extent and distribution of land masses.
Shifts in prevailing winds.
Growth or decline in polar icecaps.
Changes in the moisture content of the atmosphere.

Even these are only secondary causes. What brings changes in ocean currents, for instance? Changes in the moisture content of the atmosphere? One factor, we can see, disturbs the other, bringing about a "domino effect" of global reshuffling of climate: If the wind belts change course, the ocean currents will be affected, polar icecaps may wax or wane, solar energy will be reflected more or less actively than before, air masses will bring highs or lows to other regions, land areas will be warmer or cooler than before, and further changes in wind patterns will be induced. But can we get at the prime cause that sets such a cycle of transformations into motion? Let us begin by looking at the most drastic period of climatic change in the last million years: the ice ages.

3

The Coming of the Ice

IT WAS ONCE CONSIDERED SUBVERSIVE TO ASSERT THAT climates could change at all. Until the early nineteenth century most people, educated and otherwise, accepted the belief that the world was about six thousand years old, that it had been created in a single act, and that nothing—neither the climate nor the species of animals and plants—had altered since Adam and Eve dwelled in Eden. The most celebrated exponent of this belief was Archbishop James Ussher of Armagh, in Ireland, who in 1650 added up all the significant dates in the Bible and placed the date of Creation at 4004 B.C.

The discovery of the fossilized remains of vast and unknown creatures helped to undermine the Ussher chronology. At first the fossils were dismissed as "models of God's rejected works" or "outlines of future creations," but gradually it became apparent that they must be relics of animals now extinct. The idea of extinction itself was a troublesome one—had God permitted some of His creatures to vanish from the Earth?—but as late as the eighteenth century the fossils could be explained away with an acceptable biblical dogma. They were the bones of the victims of Noah's flood, which had taken place in 2349 B.C., by the Ussher chronology. The strange species whose bones had come to light had simply failed to get aboard the Ark.

Toward the end of the eighteenth century a few daring scientists openly challenged the simplistic view of a six-thousand-year-old planet. The French naturalist Buffon (1707–1788) offered a rationalist approach: "Ages ago," he wrote, "the Earth was a dislodged fragment of the sun, which gradually congealed in the chill of space. It was not until this splinter of the sun had cooled to a certain extent that life began upon it." By laboratory experiments—heating two metal spheres and noting how long it took for them to cool—Buffon calculated that the Earth was 74,832 years old, and that it had cooled sufficiently to support life exactly 40,062 years ago. Within a generation of Buffon's death this figure had been greatly expanded, and the first geologists were beginning to analyze the rock strata that told of millions of years of slow, steady change.

One problem was the debris scattered over much of Europe—the boulders and rubble that seemed to have been strewn by a giant hand. This first came under examination in Switzerland at the end of the eighteenth century. The Swiss, living under the shadow of the Alps, were wearily familiar with the process by which in cold winters the Alpine glaciers pushed icy tongues out into their fields and villages, shoving loads of rock and rubble that remained after the glaciers had returned to their customary levels. It seemed clear to Swiss geologists that these erratic boulders lying somewhat north of the Alps were the moraines of glaciers that had descended through the foothills of the Alps and far below their present limits in some spectacularly severe winter. The presence of scraped, polished, and grooved bedrock—the characteristic result of the passage of glaciers—seemed to confirm this belief.

But boulders and moraines could be found far from the Alps, in regions where no one had ever seen a glacier: in northern Germany, in Scandinavia, in the British Isles. To argue that this debris had been carried that far by glaciers was to say that in the past Europe's climate had been fundamentally different from that of the eighteenth century—and advocating such an idea was dangerous in some quarters. Once again, Noah's flood was invoked as an explanation: In the time of the Deluge Europe had been submerged, and what looked like glacial drift had actually been spread across the continent by surging waves and currents.

However, that could not account for the scraped and grooved bedrock, which could have been produced only by the grinding of some unimaginably heavy force over the face of the land. A few troublemakers clung to the glacial theory despite its implication of a climatic change unmentioned in Scripture. In 1821 a Swiss civil engineer, Ignaz Venetz, read a paper before the Helvetic Society of Lucerne in which he suggested that much of Europe had once been in the grip of greatly expanded Alpine glaciation. Three years later Jens Esmark, a Norwegian geologist, offered the theory that Norway's mountains had once been covered by glaciers, and that these streams of ice had carved the fjords. A German professor of forestry named Bernhardi extended these ideas in a paper published in 1832, visualizing for the first time a colossal ice sheet extending from the North Pole to the Alps on one side and to central Asia on the other. Little attention was paid to any of these hypotheses, however.

In the summer of 1836 a young Swiss zoologist, Louis Agassiz, joined Ignaz Venetz's friend Jean de Charpentier on a field trip through the Rhone Valley, saw the evidence of moraines and glacial polishing, and was converted. The following year he spoke on the concept of an "ice age" to the Helvetic Society, independently restating Bernhardi's notion of a continental glaciation. In 1840 he published a book on the subject, and emerged as the most vigorous advocate of the ice-age theory, concluding that "great sheets of ice, resembling those now existing in Greenland, once covered all the countries in which unstratified gravel [boulder drift] is found." Agassiz came to the United States in 1846, joined the Harvard faculty two years later, and almost immediately took a position in the front rank of American science. Though he was active in many fields—notably marine research—he continued his glacial investigations, and, touring New England and the Great Lakes region, he came upon geological proof that North America, too, had had its ice age. Agassiz's enthusiasm brought many scientists to accept the theory, but as late as 1899 it remained a matter for controversy and was still considered both a religious and a geological heresy by some.

The weight of evidence eventually became overwhelming. Moraines, polished rock, and deposits of the remains of cold-weather plants and animals conclusively demonstrated that drastic and prolonged temperature drops had indeed occurred. But the picture of a single devastating ice age faded as techniques for analyzing the evidence were refined. In many places, two or more layers of glacial deposits were separated by strata of warm-weather deposits, and it became clear that there had been a series of glaciations interrupted by lengthy periods of mild weather. Elaborate sequences of glacial advance and retreat could be read from the fossil record. The first of these sequences was worked out in the Alps, where four ice ages were identified and given the names of Alpine valleys: in order of decreasing age, Günz, Mindel, Riss, Würm. In North America, a parallel sequence of glaciations was found: Nebraskan, Kansan, Illinoian, and Wisconsian. Other sequences followed for northern Europe, the Himalayas, the British Isles, and other glaciated regions. Later it was found that minor modifications had to be made in the system: the Würm glaciation had had two distinct phases separated by a warm spell, and the Wisconsian had had an earlier substage termed by some geologists the Iowan. Though the debate over terminology still goes on, the broad concept of four major ice advances remains intact. However, by the 1920's it had developed that all four ice ages were merely phases of a single phenomenon, the Pleistocene glaciation, and that there had been other glaciations at remote periods in the world's history.

Two major puzzles have confronted geologists since the glacial theory itself ceased to be controversial: how long ago did the various glacial periods occur, and what was their cause? A relation between the timing and the causation of the ice ages was sought, for if the glaciations could be shown to be cyclical, some light might be cast on their origin.

Dating events on the geological time scale was at first a matter of analogy and guesswork. In 1785 the Scottish geologist James Hutton postulated his Law of Uniformitarianism, which made the assumption that geological processes have operated at about the same rate all during time. By measuring the speed of geological change today, one can form some idea of the length of time needed to shape the present world. That is, by measuring the rate at which rivers carry soil to the ocean and build up a layer of sediment, it should be possible to determine how long it took to form mountains made up of solidified sediments, and so on. The application of such methods served to show that the earth must be many millions of years old; but actual determination of elapsed time could not be calculated directly until the development of ways of computing the breakdown of radioactive elements in the earth's surface. By analyzing the proportions of these elements in rock samples, scientists were able to work out approximate timetables for the various geological eras and periods.

So it was seen that terrestrial history has been punctuated by relatively brief ice ages occurring at widely spaced intervals and with striking regularity, coming about 250 million years apart. The Pleistocene glaciation, generally agreed to have begun less than two million years ago, was preceded by one in the Permian period, about 240 million years ago, by another just prior to the Cambrian period, about 500 million years ago, and by others that occurred 750 million and a billion years ago—and possibly farther on into the dawn of the world. There is no serious disagreement over the dating of these ice ages, since an error even as great as ten or twenty million years would not alter the basic cyclical pattern. But when we turn to the dating of the phases of the Pleistocene glaciation we find a wide range of opinion. The radioactive time indicators—uranium, thorium, rubidium, and others—used to calculate dates in geological history are of no value here, for their rate of decay is so slow that elapsed spans of less than a million years cannot be measured. Only recently have radioactive elements with swifter rates of decay been employed to yield information about relatively short-range events of the past.

The first estimates of the length of the Pleistocene glaciation were made by Walter Penck and Eduard Brückner, who in 1909 devised the Günz-Mindel-Riss-Würm Alpine sequence by studying the gravel deposits in an area northeast of Lake Constance on the Swiss-German border. They did not try to date each of the glaciations, but by measuring the rates of erosion of this gravel and the depth of soil deposits on land surfaces they arrived at figures for the interglacial periods and for the Pleistocene glaciation as a whole. They placed the onset of Günz at 600,000 years ago and the end of Würm at between 16,000 and 24,000 years ago. They suggested lengths of 60,000 years, 240,000 years, and 60,000 years for the Günz-Mindel, Mindel-Riss, and Riss-Würm interglacial periods, from which it was possible to construct a tentative scheme for the length of each of the ice ages making up the Pleistocene glaciation. Their sedimentation-rate estimates, though admittedly tentative, won wide favor and remained standard figures for many years.

The Serbian physicist Milutin Milankovitch approached the problem from a different direction, compiling, over twenty years' time beginning in the 1920's, a series of calculations of the amount of solar radiation that must have reached various latitudes of the earth's surface at various times. Working from Milankovitch's figures on solar cycles, Frederick E. Zeuner of the University of London offered in 1951 a revision of the Penck-Brückner estimates, still within the framework of 600,000 years for the entire glacial period. Zeuner put the beginning of Mindel at about 500,000 years ago, with two peaks, 476,000 and 435,000 years ago; the Mindel-Riss interglacial, he said, lasted 190,000 years; the Riss-Würm interglacial lasted 60,000 years, and the final or Würm glacial period reached three peaks, 115,000, 72,000 and 22,000 years ago, after which the ice retreated.

About the time Zeuner published these figures, the birth of the atomic age presented scientists with a variety of new radioactive clocks, so that for the first time an attempt could be made at absolute dating of the Pleistocene. Unfortunately, the results have been contradictory. One of the new techniques involved measurement of the decay of carbon 14, a radioactive isotope with a half-life of about 5,700 years. All living things absorb carbon 14 at a steady rate; when they die, the intake of carbon 14 halts, and the accumulated supply begins to break down. In the late 1940's Dr. Willard F. Libby of the University of Chicago discovered a method for determining the carbon-14 content of organic substances, through which the time elapsed since the moment of death can be found. Since all the carbon 14 in any specimen decays totally in about 70,000 years, the method cannot be used beyond that point; but carbon-14 dating has given us reliable information about the last of the ice ages. Radiocarbon dates from Wisconsin have shown that glaciers overwhelmed and crushed a forest less than 11,400 years ago and that the ice did not retreat there until about 8,000 years ago. At the other end of the scale, a carbon-14 date from Europe of about 65,000 years helped place the time of the onset of the Würm glaciation at about 70,000 years ago.

While Libby was perfecting radiocarbon dating, his University of Chicago colleague, Dr. Harold C. Urey, was at work on a way of determining ancient temperatures through analysis of radioactive isotopes of oxygen. Urey's work began in 1946 with the casual observation that as water evaporates, the three isotopes of oxygen (oxygen 16, 17, and 18) do not go off at the same rate; the lightest of the three, oxygen 16, is carried off first. He began to experiment with the oxygen-isotope ratios of various water samples, and at the suggestion of a Swiss crystallographer started to study the proportions of oxygen isotopes in calcium carbonate deposits from the ocean floor. These carbonates had been formed from the limy shells of tiny organisms, mostly of the group known as foraminifera, that fall in an endless rain through the levels of the sea as their owners die. Urey found that the amount of each oxygen isotope that these small creatures absorb while alive depended in part on the temperature of the water at the time their shells were formed. "I suddenly found myself with a geologic thermometer in my hands," Urey declared.

In fact more than four years of hard work remained before Urey had his thermometer; but by 1951 the technical problems were largely solved and the analysis of deep-sea sediments could begin. Oceanographers made available to Urey's laboratory a sampling of the material obtained using a "piston corer," an explosive device which shoots a collecting tube deep into the ocean floor and can bring up a cylindrical core of sediment more than sixty feet long. The Swedish Deep-Sea Expedition of 1947–48 had collected more than three hundred such cores from the Atlantic and Pacific; the Lamont Geological Observatory of Columbia University had gathered over a thousand. One of these cores, taken from the eastern equatorial Pacific at a depth of more than 13,000 feet, was believed to contain an essentially continuous sedimentary section covering the past million years. Others were found to come from extremely ancient layers of the ocean floor, many millions of years old.

Urey, succeeded in 1952 in this work by the Italian-born geologist Cesare Emiliani, carried out an analysis of the isotope ratios in the shells of bottom-dwelling species of foraminifera carefully removed from the deep-sea cores. "Our analysis showed," Emiliani wrote, "that 32 million years ago the bottom temperature of the Pacific was about 51° Fahrenheit; by 22 million years ago it had fallen to about 44 degrees; a million years ago the temperature was close to its present level—three degrees above freezing. During the last half million years the temperature has oscillated around an average somewhat colder than that of today."

Cores taken from points several thousand miles apart indicated that temperature cycles were consistent from ocean to ocean. The next step was to date them. Radiocarbon analysis of the shells showed, according to Emiliani, that "the most recent low point in ocean surface temperature . . . came about 18,000 years ago, which coincides with the peak of the last ice age glaciers in North America. The low points in the earlier cycles cannot be dated by the radiocarbon method, because they occurred too long ago, but by extrapolation and by comparing our cores with others dated by different methods we have worked out a tentative time scale for the full depth of our cores. We then correlated the temperature oscillations shown by the cores with the advances and retreats of the ice sheets on the continents. This correlation is certain for the last 100,000 years, but is less certain for older times. . . . If this dating scheme is correct, the first great ice sheet began its advance only 300,000 years ago, rather than 500,000 or more years ago, as geologists have hitherto estimated."

Emiliani's sequence cut the standard Penck-Brückner estimates sharply. He placed the Günz and Nebraskan glaciations from 300,000 to 265,000 B.P. (before present), Mindel-Kansan from 200,000 to 175,000, Riss-Illinoian from 125,000 to 100,000, and Würm-Wisconsian from 70,000 to 10,000. These calculations were supported by the findings of Rhodes W. Fairbridge of Columbia University, who in 1960 offered a dating system based on studies of sea-level fluctuations and correlated with the Milankovitch solar-energy figures. Fairbridge placed the peak of the Günz-Nebraskan glaciation at about 320,000 B.P.

These calculations have been challenged most strongly by two scientists using the same approach as Emiliani: analysis of deep-sea sediments. They are David B. Ericson and Goesta Wollin of the Lamont Geological Observatory, who in 1964 offered a radical revision of the accepted Pleistocene time scale. Using some of the same cores studied by Emiliani, along with others—26 in all—they formed a mosaic of overlapping sections taken from different depths and localities in the Atlantic. "We have no quarrel with the ages in years assigned by Emiliani to the various zones in [his] core," they wrote. "It is his correlation of the zones with the climatic events of the Pleistocene that we do not accept. We believe that the record in this core goes back from the present to a time no earlier than the beginning of the third ice age, the Illinoian or Riss." The Ericson-Wollin time scale, which has been given in detail in the first chapter, places the beginning of the Günz-Nebraskan glaciation at 1,500,000 B.P., and the final withdrawal of the Würm-Wisconsian at 11,000 B.P. Their investigations rest on new methods of radioactive dating involving the change in the ratio between an element known as protactinium and a thorium isotope called ionium, as well as on such ingenious observations as the discovery that one species of foraminifera, *Globigerina pachyderma,* grows shells that coil in different directions according to the water temperature. In the polar and subarctic regions, *pachyderma's* shell coils to the left; farther to the south a rightward-coiling variety takes over. The boundary between the two varieties was quite sharply drawn along the line dividing water colder than 45° from water warmer than 45° F. By extending this observation to extinct species of foraminifera, Ericson and Wollin were able to identify temperature zones in their deep-sea cores by determining whether the hardy left-coiling races or the warmth-loving right-coiling races were dominant in ancient times.

The work of other researchers thus far seems to confirm the Ericson-Wollin theory that the Pleistocene ice age began well over a million years ago, but the matter cannot yet be considered settled. There is little debate, however, about the broad details of how the glacial periods affected Europe and North America. The Mesozoic, the era of the dinosaurs, came to its end with most of the world enjoying tropical warmth. The new era of the Cenozoic, which opened about 70 million years ago, commenced with some general lowering of temperatures, but much of the decline was recovered during the Paleocene, the Cenozoic's first period, although there was never a full return to Mesozoic levels. Even so, through the succeeding Eocene and Oligocene periods the Dakotas had palm trees and alligators, while Alaska, Greenland, Spitzbergen, and northern Siberia had temperate-zone forests of elm, beech, and giant redwood. Not only was the climate warmer and milder, but the weather was less changeable; millions of years of erosion had reduced all mountain ranges to little more than rolling hills, which tended to ensure a uniform pattern of rainfall everywhere.

Later in the Cenozoic, during the Miocene and Pliocene periods, a slight cooling became evident; areas which had been subtropical became temperate, and borderline tropical areas shifted toward the subtropical. Still there were no polar ice-caps, no glaciers, no severe winters. Toward the end of the Pliocene a mighty stirring began in the earth's crust; a process of folding and heaving got under way, thrusting upward the ranges that would become the Alps, the Rockies, the Himalayas. The climax came something over a million years ago with a quick and catastrophic fall in temperature that marks the end of the Pliocene and the start of the turbulent, frosty era we call the Pleistocene.

Though most changes on the geologic time scale come about gradually, encompassing almost inconceivable spans, the shift from Pliocene to Pleistocene conditions seems to have taken place with startling speed: in five thousand years or less, according to Ericson and Wollin. Their chief evidence comes from seven sediment cores taken from the Atlantic which show the swift replacement of one group of foraminifera with others. The discoasters, a microscopic group of organisms with star-staped limy shells, vanish entirely from the cores at the Pliocene-Pleistocene boundary after having existed all through the 75 million years of the Cenozoic. Several other foraminiferans also disappear, to be replaced by similar species adapted for cold: left-coiling instead of right-coiling, larger and heavier shells, and so forth. This sweeping change among the tiny creatures of the sea, according to Wollin and Ericson, "records a climatic event of a different order from the climatic fluctuations which seem to have occurred repeatedly during late Pliocene time. This is why we believe that the boundary marks the beginning of the first ice age of the Pleistocene." And the change in shells, they say, "takes place within a thickness of sediment of no more than ten to fifteen centimeters. From the nature of the sediment at the boundary, we estimate that this thickness represents a time interval of no more than about 5,000 years. Since vertical mixing of the microfossils by mud-eating burrowers must have caused an increase in the apparent thickness of the transition zone, the real time interval represented by this zone was probably somewhat shorter."

This dramatic fall in temperature did not at once bring continental glaciations. A period of thousands or even hundreds of thousands of years elapsed while the new climate of cold winters and cool summers was helping to build up accumulations of snow. Summer melt failed to equal winter snowfall, so that each year there was a net gain in accumulated ice and snow; glaciers formed on the world's new mountains first, since temperatures are lower in high altitudes. (Africa's great volcano, 19,340-foot-high Kilimanjaro, wears a permanent snowcap today though it is within 3 degrees of the equator.) Eventually the glaciers began to flow down over the land, and the ice age proper began.

In Europe the main ice sheet spread out of Scandinavia, sprawling asymmetrically far to the east to touch a Siberian ice sheet. It reached as far south as 48°N., beyond Berlin; in the west it crossed the North Sea to merge with another glacier covering the British Isles. The huge Scandinavian glacier at its greatest extent was a dazzling white blanket more than 10,000 feet thick, covering over two million square miles. The British ice sheet was much smaller and shallower, but still engulfed a large area. Europe's other mountain systems spawned glaciers of their own: the Pyrenees, the Apennines, the Carpathians, and particularly the Alps. The Alpine glaciers penetrated into the Po Valley of Italy, and covered 11,000 square miles, in some places to a depth of 15,000 feet. At the peak of the Pleistocene glaciations all of Europe north of the Mediterranean region lay under these incredible sheets of ice.

The mountains of northern Asia produced glaciers that may have covered up to 1,600,000 square miles of Siberia; but because the snow precipitation was relatively light, they never reached a thickness of more than 2,300 feet, leaving some areas uncovered. The Caucasus, the Pamirs, the Hindu Kush, all repeatedly sent glaciers down in an obliterating cover of ice. Much the same happened in North America: the Laurentide ice sheet of the east, originating in the mountains of upper Quebec and Labrador, encompassed nearly five million square miles, touching the Greenland icecap on one side and the glaciers of the Rockies on the other. In the west, the Cordilleran ice sheet engulfed British Columbia and surrounding regions. All of Canada lay under this double burden of ice, and the United States was covered as far south as the valleys of the Ohio and Missouri rivers. Only the highest mountain peaks stood out above the plateaus of ice, more than a mile thick, that transformed the temperate zone into a wasteland of polar bleakness.

The Pleistocene glaciation was almost entirely confined to

the Northern Hemisphere, just as the Permian glaciation, 240 million years before, had been almost wholly a phenomenon of the Southern Hemisphere. Many explanations have been offered to solve the riddle of the Permian ice age—such as the concepts of shifting continents or wandering poles—but a glance at a globe will show why in the world's present geographical distribution a glacial period must fall more severely on the north than on the south. There is scarcely any land below the equator south of the 30th parallel. While billions of tons of ice crushed Europe and North America, the Southern Hemisphere's oceans must have filled with ice, but there were few places where continuous glaciers could form. The Andes and the mountains of New Zealand and Australia experienced some glaciation; and the Antarctic, which remains in its own ice age today, was hardly more genial then. The rest of the hemisphere escaped the worst of the cold.

Which is not to say that the world's middle felt no effects of climatic change. The presence of the ice sheets caused a shift in the belt of the westerlies, which carry the cyclonic storms, of some 15° to the south in the Northern Hemisphere and to the north in the Southern Hemisphere. During the glacial epochs, such regions as Africa, Asia Minor, the Mediterranean, central Asia and northern China, southern South America, and the southwestern United States experienced "pluvial" periods of greatly increased rainfall. A sequence of pluvials and interpluvials almost exactly corresponding to the glacials and interglacials of higher latitudes has been determined. During these prolonged rainy spells lakes and rivers grew, basins now dry filled with water, and deserts bloomed. Nevada contained more water than Minnesota does today; a vanished pluvial lake we call Lake Lahontan covered the northwestern part of the state. California's Death Valley had a pluvial lake more than a hundred miles long. The biggest of the American pluvial lakes was Bonneville, of which only the shrunken remnant we call Great Salt Lake remains. In the wettest periods Lake Bonneville was nearly a thousand feet deep where Great Salt Lake is only 30 feet; it reached into Nevada and Idaho and almost to Arizona, and left bizarre sand dunes and shoreline cliffs high in the mountain country of the West to mark the ancient level of its beaches. In the Old World, the Dead Sea was 200 miles long and rose 1,500 feet above its present level; there were lakes in the Sahara; rainfall was heavy in the Kalahari Desert.

At least four times in a million years the ice griped the north and the rains came to the south; and four times the climate softened. Each major shift brought upheavals in animal and plant life as warm-weather and cold-weather forms alternately took possession of the land. And, as we will see, among the creatures driven to and fro in the climatic oscillations of the Pleistocene was that newly evolved primate we call man.

What brought on the ice ages?

Scientists have been wrestling with this problem—the most fundamental puzzle of climatology—almost as long as the existence of the glaciations has been known. They have produced an amazing range of theories, some highly fanciful, others bolstered with lengthy and sober documentation, and none generally accepted by any substantial faction of science today. All these theories fall into three main groups:

"Astronomical" theories ascribing climatic shifts to changes in the Earth's position relative to the sun.

"Geological" theories pointing to such causes as migrations of continents and poles, uplifting of mountains, or changes in the content of the earth's atmosphere.

"Solar" theories connecting fluctuations of climate with variations in the sun's output of energy.

Jens Esmark of Norway was one of the first to propose a theory of glaciation. In the 1820's Esmark offered an astronomical theory based on the fact that the earth's orbit around the sun is elliptical rather than circular. Suppose, Esmark said, that at a certain time in the past the eccentricity of the earth's orbit was much greater than it is today, so that in its orbital swings the earth was extremely distant from the sun for thousands of years, greatly reducing the intensity of solar radiation reaching it. An ice age would result. Actually, the laws of celestial mechanics would have to be repealed before the earth could assume any such orbit as Esmark postulated; but there are indeed some much less drastic fluctuations in the eccentricity of the earth's orbit, and several theories of glaciation have been built on this fact. The nineteenth-century Scottish climatologist James Croll began from the legitimate observation that the earth's orbit goes through a cycle of increasing and decreasing eccentricity covering some 91,800 years. When the orbit is at its greatest degree of elongation, one hemisphere will tend to have its winters each year at an appreciably greater distance from the sun than the other hemisphere, and should receive appreciably less solar radiation. At present the Northern Hemisphere is in winter at perihelion—the minimum distance from the sun—and so has warmer winters and cooler summers than the Southern Hemisphere, which gets its winters at aphelion—maximum distance from the sun. But in 13,000 years this arrangement will be reversed.

Croll and his most important successor, the English astronomer Sir Robert Ball, worked from this and from the phenomenon known as the precession of the equinoxes, a wobbling of the earth on its axis through a 21,000-year cycle. This precession, which can be compared to the swaying of a spinning top, alters the tilt of the earth so that the relative lengths of summer and winter change minutely each year. Just now the Northern Hemisphere's summer is about seven days longer than its winter, but a time will come when the seasons are equal in length and then when winter is longer. At the extremes of the cycle one season may be as much as a month longer than the other. Croll and Ball suggested that a combination of the orbital eccentricity and the precession effect would occur every 25,000 years—giving one hemisphere a short summer and a long, extremely severe winter. A series of such winters would permit snow to accumulate until glaciers formed; the retreat of the glaciers would come when the unfavorable combination of orbital factors changed.

One important objection to this beautiful and ingenious

theory is that orbital variations do not seem to play much of a role in governing temperature: on Mars, what appears to be a polar icecap is largest on the hemisphere with its winter in perihelion. An even greater difficulty, as Ball himself saw, is that the Croll-Ball hypothesis would produce glaciation in only one hemisphere at a time, whereas ice ages have worldwide temperature-lowering effects. For a time the followers of this theory argued that there was no proof that the ice ages had in fact affected both hemispheres simultaneously. But it became clear that they had, at least during the Pleistocene; and the presence of icecaps both in Greenland and the Antarctic today seems to provide the final blow to the concept. Early in the twentieth century a Czech meteorologist, R. Spitaler, attempted to get around this by supposing that during the long severe winter of the hemisphere in aphelion, the ocean would grow so cold that it would chill the entire planet. But the Spitaler theory had too many flaws to win acceptance.

The next to tackle the astronomical approach was Milutin Milankovitch of Yugoslavia, who devoted many years to compiling a correlation of three astronomical cycles: the precession of the equinoxes (21,000 years), the variation in the eccentricity of the earth's orbit (91,800 years), and the changes in the angle between the earth's axis and the plane of the earth's orbit (40,000 years). Milankovitch, without the benefit of electronic computers which could have done the job in a few hours, laboriously plotted these cycles so that it became possible to determine the amount of heat received at a given latitude at any time in the past. The three fluctuations in the earth's position would bring about long periods of cool summers and mild winters, alternating with periods of hot summers and cold winters. Unlike Croll and Ball, Milankovitch thought it was the cool-summer mild-winter combination, rather than the cold-winter-hot-summer one, that brought ice ages. A prolonged period of cool summers which failed to melt much of the winter snow would allow ice to cover a much larger area than it does now. He calculated that the periods of coolest summers would come at intervals of about 40,000 years. Cesare Emiliani, some thirty years later, showed through the analysis of fossils in deep-sea cores that the low points in ocean temperatures did indeed occur at 40,000-year intervals. But, Emiliani added, "The main difficulty with the Milankovitch theory is that it fails to explain why the Ice Epoch developed only recently—within the last million years—after 200 million years during which the earth had no ice ages."

Emiliani invoked geographical as well as astronomical changes to deal with the discrepancy. Analysis of deep-sea cores laid down in the latter part of the Cretaceous period of the Mesozoic showed that about 85 million years ago world temperatures had reached a high point. "At that time," he wrote, "shallow seas occupied vast areas which are now land, and there were only a few low chains of mountains. Towards the end of the Cretaceous Period a large part of the Pacific bottom southwest of the Hawaiian Islands began to sink, and similar founderings may have occurred elsewhere in the Pacific. Simultaneously there opened a great epoch of mountain building which ultimately produced the Rockies, Andes, Alps, and Himalayas. These processes put millions of square miles of previously immersed land above water. Since dry land absorbs less solar radiation than water does, the world climate became steadily colder. Perhaps two million years ago permanent caps of snow and ice began to form in Antarctica and Greenland. This highly reflective ground cover absorbed still less of the sun's rays. Some 300,000 years ago the climate had become so cold that one of Milankovitch's cool-summer cycles could have extended the northern ice south to northeastern North America and Scandinavia—both regions of heavy snowfall. Back-radiation of solar energy was still further increased, and the first great wave of ice was under way." The spread of continental glaciers in the Northern Hemisphere must have influenced the entire planet's climate.

But during this period, Emiliani's oxygen-isotope studies showed, the surface temperature of the oceans dropped sharply, which set in motion a reversal of the glacier-forming trend: "Cooler oceans mean less evaporation, drier air, and less snowfall. Eventually winter snowfall decreased to a point where the summer shrinking of the glaciers was greater than their winter growth. A period of hot summers accelerated this process and pushed back the ice sheets until only those of Antarctica and Greenland remained." Since the mountain chains that encouraged the birth of the Pleistocene glaciers still exist, Emiliani suggests that in the next cool-summer cycle, about ten thousand years from now, the glaciers will return and bury the Northern Hemisphere once again. "Indeed," he declares, "we can expect periodic glaciations to continue until the earth's great mountain chains have been weathered down to hills."

There is little doubt that at the beginning of the Pleistocene the earth did undergo an upheaval in its crust, with the continents generally rising and with the world's present major mountain chains coming into being. Just as surely, elevated continents and high mountains foster cold winters and heavy snowfalls. Mountains obstruct the circulation of winds, encouraging precipitation by forcing air masses to rise and grow cool; higher elevations bring about snowfalls where rain might have fallen in lower-lying regions. The mountains provide catchment areas to collect snow and start glaciers. The presence of large semipermanent fields of snow increases the reflecting of solar energy, pushing prevailing temperatures down so that the snowfields expand still further. If these conditions persist, the cold wave becomes self-sustaining and can lead to an ice age.

Some geographers and climatologists were sufficiently impressed by these circumstances to maintain that the rise of mountains is a sufficient explanation for the onset of glacial epochs, without any need for the elaborate astronomical variations proposed by some authorities. The leading exponent of this school was C. E. P. Brooks of Great Britain, who set forth his ideas in a series of books published between 1922 and 1949. Brooks believed that a "revolution" in the earth's crust had occurred every 250 million years or so in which, over periods of 50 million years or more, colossal mountain chains were thrust up from formerly flat terrain. In each of these periodic convulsive "revolutions" the general elevating of the continents causes a drop in temperatures. The greatly increased temperature differential between the equatorial zone and the higher latitudes sends masses of moist air toward the poles. Cyclonic storms sweep over the land; where warm fronts clash with cold, precipitation increases; snow begins to accumulate, and eventually a point is reached at which the growth of ice fields triggers the self-propelled decline of climate into a glacial period.

Though Brooks worked this theory out in great detail and with scrupulous care, it left many questions unanswered, and toward the end of his life he began to doubt it himself. It did not account, for instance, for the fact that there had been crustal revolutions and periods of mountain building in which no glaciation had resulted. Nor did it explain the periodic advances and retreats of the glaciers within an ice age. Brooks had proposed that ice ages ended when erosion and land subsidence did away with the mountain ranges and restored the world to its usual flat topography; but it was plainly absurd, as he recognized, to think that mountains had popped up and down four times within the last million years alone, as the theory required to account for the Pleistocene glaciations. The birth of mountain ranges is a process lasting millions of years; the onset and decline of ice ages happens much more swiftly, and the evidence of the Ericson-Wollin deep-sea cores shows that the Pleistocene temperature drop came with astonishing abruptness. The current view is that a period of mountain building is a necessary factor in the spread of continental ice sheets, but that some other factors must also be involved.

One frequent suggestion is that volcanic eruptions associated with the epochs of mountain building altered the composition of the atmosphere sufficiently to cause a temperature decline. Volcanoes hurl dust and ash into the air when they erupt, sometimes in tremendous volume. The celebrated volcanic explosion of the Indonesian island of Krakatoa, on August 26 and 27, 1883, threw 13 cubic miles of debris aloft. Clouds of ash ascended to a height of 50 miles and blotted out the sun over a wide area. At a distance of 130 miles from

Krakatoa the darkness lasted for 22 hours; 50 miles away no sunlight penetrated for 57 hours. A few days after the eruption a fallout of fine white ash began to cover the decks of ships in the Indian Ocean, 2,000 miles away. Most of the ash, though, remained in the atmosphere, drifting eastward; it reached Arizona by October 19, the eastern United States eleven days later. The immense dust cloud produced unusual greenish-yellow sunsets and rosy twilights, and threw weird blue and purple halos around the sun and moon. By the end of November these phenomenal displays were being viewed in Europe, and as late as August of 1884, a full year after the eruption, the atmospheric effects could still be detected.

Krakatoa had one other significant effect: The month the dust cloud reached France, instruments at the Montpellier Observatory recorded a drop in solar radiation to 20 percent below normal. The solar energy received at Montpellier remained 10 percent below normal for the next three years, until the dust cloud was completely dissipated.

The eruption of Mount Hekla, an Icelandic volcano, in 1783 had also produced colored sunsets and strange hazes over much of the world; and the winter that followed was one of the most severe on record. Benjamin Franklin suggested in 1784 that the harsh cold might have resulted from screening of the sun's rays by the volcanic debris. The Krakatoa eruption seemed to confirm this shrewd guess; and the eruptions of Mont Pelée in the West Indies in 1902 and Mount Katmai, Alaska, ten years later, produced more evidence. The Katmai eruption cut solar radiation in Algeria, thousands of miles away, by 20 percent.

The American meteorologist W. J. Humphreys, investigating these phenomena, concluded in 1920 that volcanic ash in the upper atmosphere could well bring cooler temperatures by intercepting sunlight; the dust blanket, while shutting out some of the solar radiation, would not hold in the longer heat waves radiated back from the ground, thus compounding the effect. Since the density of the cloud varied from place to place, temperature differentials around the world would be increased, accelerating air circulation currents and producing cold, stormy winters and cool, cloudy summers. A series of immense volcanic eruptions, Humphreys supposed, could fill the air with so much debris that an ice age might be triggered. This theory was reinforced subsequently by the discovery that dust particles serve as nuclei on which water vapor can condense; this is the principle on which "rain-makers" work when they scatter particles of silver iodide in the atmosphere to induce precipitation. A pall of volcanic ash, it was claimed, would act to increase precipitation, and thus build up the accumulations of snow that lead to ice ages.

However, the science of meteorology was still in its infancy when Krakatoa blew its top, and the records of worldwide temperature change were scanty and uninformative. The advocates of the volcanic-ash theory had to fall back on negative proof: Since 1912 there has been no major volcanic explosion in the Northern Hemisphere, and in that time generally warming temperatures have been observed. Opponents of the theory pointed out that although there were many active volcanoes during the Pleistocene, there were just as many, and even more, during epochs of no glaciation. Nor did deep-sea cores reveal deposits of volcanic ash thick enough to indicate the likelihood of a climate-changing quantity of atmospheric debris. W. J. Humphreys had calculated that the amount of ash required to cut solar radiation by 20 percent, if discharged by volcanoes each year for 100,000 years, would yield a layer of dust just one fiftieth of an inch thick—hardly enough to detect in a deep-sea core. But he did not anticipate the extremely minute analysis of such cores carried out by scientists like Ericson and Wollin, who wrote, "Evidence from the cores of deep-sea sediment is entirely negative. Most cores from the Atlantic Ocean contain no evidence of explosive vulcanism in the form of windblown particles of volcanic glass or ash. Cores from the neighborhoods of volcanic islands and from parts of the Pacific . . . contain thin layers of volcanic ash as well as scattered particles of volcanic glass. But these are so distributed through the sequence of faunal zones as to leave no doubt that explosive vulcanism was as frequent during the interglacials as during the glacial ages, a circumstance which leaves the theory without support."

Another atmospheric change to which the ice ages have been attributed is a hypothetical decrease in the level of carbon dioxide. CO_2, as the British physicist John Tyndall first showed in 1861, has a definite effect on temperature: it is transparent to the short-wave radiation that carries the sun's energy to the earth, but is opaque to the long-wave radiation by which the earth returns heat to space. A rise in carbon dioxide levels would tend to trap heat in the atmosphere; a drop would release more heat to the void.

Normally the amount of CO_2 in the atmosphere is constant; it is given off in the respiration of living things and in volcanic activity that releases gases from the earth's interior, and it is consumed in the weathering of rock and the photosynthesis of plants. The ocean serves as a stabilizer in this system: when atmospheric CO_2 levels rise, the ocean absorbs the excess, and when they drop, the ocean releases enough from its great reservoir of the gas to restore equilibrium.

What factors could disturb the balance of this system? The American physicist Gilbert N. Plass suggested several in 1959: "The rate of volcanic activity could slow down as the rate of rock weathering increased, or an especially flourishing mantle of vegetation could take up huge quantities of carbon dioxide and form new coal beds and other organic deposits in marshy areas. After a geologically short time, the adjustment of the atmosphere-ocean equilibrium to the leaner supply of carbon dioxide could bring the atmospheric concentration down to .015 percent, half its present value. Calculations show that a 50-percent decrease in the amount of carbon dioxide in the air will lower the temperature of the earth 6.9°F." This, Plass said, would cause glaciers to spread over the land; and as the ice sheets took up water, the oceans would shrink. "At the height of glacial periods," he wrote, "ice sheets contain 5 to 10 percent of the oceans' waters. The glaciers contain little carbon dioxide, however, because ice can hold very small amounts of carbonates compared to the same volume of sea water. The shrunken oceans thus accumulate an excess of carbon dioxide which they must release to the atmosphere in order to return to equilibrium. And so the cycle draws to a close: as carbon dioxide returns to the atmosphere, the Earth's temperature rises and the ice melts away." The complete cycle, Plass estimated, would take about 50,000 years.

By this theory, the lushness of the tropical Carboniferous period induced the Permian ice age, by locking away billions of tons of carbon dioxide each year until the atmospheric supply was depleted. The same thing must have occurred in the swampy Mesozoic and in the warm early years of the Cenozoic. When the Pleistocene mountains were born, Plass said, they were subjected to intense weathering action, which is partly a chemical process in which carbon dioxide is withdrawn from the atmosphere. This increased drain on the atmospheric CO_2 supply touched off the glaciations. Only one point remains unexplained, but this renders the theory unacceptable to most geologists: since the carbon dioxide in the atmosphere is in equilibrium with that in the oceans, how can any increase in vegetation or rock weathering reduce the overall supply of atmospheric CO_2? Anything lost by the atmosphere would immediately be replaced from the oceans; and the theory will not stand unless it can demonstrate a major decline in the entire atmosphere-ocean system's CO_2 level. So far no evidence for such a decline has come forth.

Most ice-age theorists today have turned away from volcanic and carbon-dioxide explanations toward an idea so obvious that it was long condemned: the hypothesis that ice ages are brought on by fluctuations in the sun's energy output. This has been a persistent and tempting concept for more than a century. What could be more logical, after all, than to explain the cooling of the earth by a decline in the sun's radiation of heat? That the sun undergoes fluctuations of some sort that affect our weather has long been known; sunspots, which grow and wane in regular cycles of about eleven years, are associated with periods of electrical disturbances in the atmosphere and with cool, rainy weather. At the point in the cycle at which sunspots are at a maximum, the earth's average temperature drops by several degrees, the storm-bearing westerlies move closer to the equator, and precipitation rises greatly. In the early years of this century the American astronomer A. E. Douglass examined meteorological records going back to 1830 and found the eleven-year sunspot cycle to have been consistent in that time; then he began analyzing the growth rings of trees, which would be wider in wet years than in dry ones, and pushed his sunspot chronology far into the past. Taking cores from sequoia trees and from the wood in thousand-year-old Pueblo ruins, Douglass confirmed the pattern of cyclic variations of rainfall, evidently keyed to the sunspot fluctuations. He even found the eleven-year cycle in slabs of petrified wood 50 million years old. There was evidence of larger cycles, too—the whole sunspot pattern seemed to repeat itself about every 275 years.

If sunspots, with their influence over the frequency and path of cyclonic storms, occur in such regular cycles, is there a possibility of even greater solar fluctuations, coming at intervals of many thousands of years, and capable of triggering ice ages? So it was declared. But C. E. P. Brooks spoke for the majority of responsible scientists when he wrote in 1922, "We can at once dismiss fluctuations in the radiation emitted by the sun as a cause of *great* changes of climate. It is true that many small fluctuations are traceable directly to this cause, such as the eleven-year periodicity of temperature and rainfall; but these fluctuations are, and must be, greater at the Equator than at the poles, while the fall of temperature during the glacial period reached its maximum near the poles and was least at the Equator. Moreover, there is not the slightest direct evidence in support of such a theory, and it can only be admitted when all other hypotheses have failed."

The simplicity of the solar-fluctuation idea, though, made it perennially attractive, and the flaws in other ice-age theories continued to lead scientists back to it. Measurements made by the Smithsonian Institution from 1918 onward showed that the intensity of solar radiation could fluctuate from its average value by as much as 3 percent over a third of a century; and in 1947 Richard Foster Flint, professor of geology at Yale

University, gave new respectability to the solar-fluctuation concept by combining it with Brooks's mountain-building theory. The energy output of the sun, he proposed, may vary by as much as 10 percent in either direction from its present level. If one such downside fluctuation coincided with a period of general mountain-building, as may have happened at the outset of the Pleistocene, widespread glaciation would occur. The newly formed mountains would serve as points of origin for the glaciers that would accumulate. Further fluctuations in the sun's heat within a glacial period would account for the retreats and advances of the ice within the large pattern of the glaciation.

The possible causes of such solar fluctuations have undergone study by the Estonian-born Ernst J. Öpik, an astronomer at Northern Ireland's Armagh Observatory. "If the sun's heat were to drop only 13 per cent," Öpik wrote in 1958, "the whole earth would soon be covered with a mile-thick mantle of ice. Contrariwise, if the sun's radiation were 30 per cent hotter than it is, life on the earth would be destroyed by a heat wave." Far less sweeping changes would have profound effects: a drop in solar output of less than 10 percent would bring a cold wave equal to the worst of the Pleistocene, and an increase of about the same size would give the entire planet a tropical climate. But what might produce such shifts?

The sun uses hydrogen as its fuel, converting it into helium and giving off heat in a fusion reaction. "By and large," Öpik wrote, "we should expect the sun to keep its rate of radiation more or less constant. If it radiates energy away faster than it is being generated in the core, the sun will contract, raise its internal temperature, and so restore the energy balance; if its surface loses energy too slowly, the sun will expand and again reach a balance of energy production and outgo. So the sun usually maintains an equilibrium and a nonfluctuating output of sunshine, which accounts for the long warm periods on the earth."

But the sun contains other elements—magnesium, carbon, iron, silicon, oxygen, neon, nitrogen—which Öpik groups for the sake of simplicity as "metals." They serve, he says, to interfere with the sun's ability to transmit energy, acting "like smoke in air." He describes the process this way:

> Within the hot core the nuclear burning of hydrogen stirs and mixes the gas like water in a boiling kettle. The hydrogen in this cauldron does not mix with the inactive hydrogen outside the core. But as the fuel burns and is converted to helium, hydrogen slowly diffuses into the core from the surrounding mantle. It leaves behind the "metals," which are heavier and diffuse more slowly. The concentration of "metals" around the core therefore rises. This tends to block the radiation of heat outward from the core. As a result, at a certain stage convection currents develop in the immediate surroundings around the core. The currents bring more hydrogen into the core and it grows in size. More hydrogen means more fuel. The enlarged core produces more heat than can be transported to the sun's surface. Consequently the sun expands. In doing so it spends energy to overcome the contracting force of gravitation. The net effect is to reduce the amount of energy that can be radiated away by the sun in the form of heat and light. Thus when production of heat in its core increases to 10 per cent above normal, the sun actually becomes 10 per cent dimmer. On the earth, 93 million miles away, an ice age begins.
>
> Meanwhile in the expanded sun a reverse process sets in. The expansion lowers the temperature of the core and diminishes its production of energy. The core shrinks, the sun brightens, and within a few million years everything is normal again. The ice age now ends. It will not be repeated for hundreds of millions of years, because hydrogen diffuses into the core of the sun so slowly that it takes this long to build up again the "metal barrier" around the core that starts the disturbance.

Öpik admits that his theory rests on the as yet unconfirmed assumption that the "metals" in the sun amount to at least 3 percent of the solar mass. He also points out that it does not satisfactorily explain the short-term fluctuations within an ice age. "My own guess," he wrote, "is that they may represent a kind of 'flickering' of the disturbance in the sun—like a candle flame blown by the wind. They may be connected with the irregular mixing of matter in and around the core of the sun during the disturbance, or with allied events at the sun's surface." His calculations also show a steady decline in the quantity of hydrogen in the sun's core, which on a long-term basis has resulted in a continuing trend toward a hotter climate on earth. He suggests that prior to three billion years ago our world must have been in the grip of a permanent ice age; but as the sun grew hotter some of the glaciers melted, until about a billion and a half years ago the average world temperature during solar warm spells was about what it is today —58°F. "In the current era of the sun's and earth's history, beginning about 500 million years ago," he adds, "the average global temperature has been about 72°, aside from the brief ice-age interludes. When our ice age ends a few million years from now, it will return to that level. Thereafter the sun will resume its warming trend, raising the earth temperature at the rate of one degree per 100 million years at first and accelerating the warmup as time goes on. A billion years or so from now the average temperature will be 100 degrees—too hot for human life as we know it. . . . Some 82 million years later, if our timetable is correct, the output of heat by the sun will be more than three times what it is now, and the average temperature on the earth will be above the boiling point of water."

One group of scientists believes that ice ages are triggered by an increase, not a drop, in the sun's output of energy. This paradoxical theory was first proposed by the British geophysicist Sir George Simpson in 1934. A general cooling, he argued, would lower the moisture content of the air and slow the atmospheric circulation, reducing the storms and precipitations needed for heavy snowfalls. Even the cooler summers of such an epoch would be able to dispose of the light accumulated snowfalls of the cold winters. Furthermore, the freezing of the Arctic seas during a cold period would impose additional limits on the amount of atmospheric moisture and snowfall in northern latitudes.

A rise in the sun's radiation, though, would stimulate evaporation at the equator and send moisture-laden air heading toward the poles. Increased cloudiness and heavier precipitation would follow. In low latitudes a pluvial age would result, but closer to the poles even a fairly substantial rise in average temperatures would not be sufficient to keep the precipitation from taking the form of snow. From year to year there would be a net accumulation of snow, the warm summers failing to melt all the winter's heavy falls, until glaciers were created. The glaciers themselves would help to accentuate the general coldness by reflecting solar energy back to space.

Eventually, Simpson said, the continued increase in the sun's warmth would bring so much heat even to the high latitudes that rain would fall instead of snow. The glaciers would melt and a warm, wet interglacial period would begin. Then, as the sun's emission dropped back toward its normal level, rain would change to snow and the ice age once more would prevail. Finally, when the sun's heat had fallen below a certain level, evaporation would decrease, precipitation would fall off, and the glaciers would starve as light winter snowfall failed to replace summer melt. Now a cold, dry interglacial age would begin, completing the cycle. Two such cycles could account for the four Pleistocene ice ages.

If this was in fact the case, archaeological examination should indicate that the middle Pleistocene interglacial was cooler and drier than the other two. Evidence found thus far on land has not revealed any marked dissimilarities among the interglacials. But David Ericson and Goesta Wollin, supporters of the Simpson theory, point out that "evidence from the continents is really not very complete, particularly as regards the earlier phases of the Pleistocene. On the other hand, the core record strongly suggests that the middle . . . interglacial was distinctly different from the other two. Not only was it much longer, but apparently the climate of the equatorial Atlantic on the average was much less warm than during the other two interglacials." Also, the distinction between right-coiling and left-coiling races of foraminifera, so clear-cut at other times, seems to have broken down in the second interglacial. "Was this a consequence of poorly defined [atmospheric] circulation, and that in turn a consequence of decreased energy from the sun?" Ericson and Wollin ask. "We think that this is a very reasonable interpretation."

Their deep-sea cores provide other problems. Ocean-bottom sediments from the Atlantic show that during the ice ages dominant foraminifera were those adapted to cold water. What does this do to Simpson's hypothesis that warmer seas, causing higher evaporation and precipitation, characterized the glacial periods? Simpson's reply is that the Atlantic was cooled by enormous masses of ice drifting down from the north past Greenland. But a similar cooling of the Pacific did not occur because the narrowness of the Bering Strait prevented much outflow of Arctic ice; and so there was plenty of evaporation from the Pacific during the ice ages. Examination of Pacific cores seems to confirm this—somewhat to the surprise of the scientists studying them. "Until the evidence for two distinctly different kinds of interglacial climates had emerged from our complete record of the Pleistocene," wrote Ericson and Wollin, "we were repelled by the paradoxical appeal to more heat from the sun to explain the spread of continental glaciers. On the other hand, it is scarcely conceivable that glaciers could spread without increase in precipitation. But to expect a decrease in radiant energy from the sun to generate increased precipitation is worse than paradoxical; it is weak reasoning."

The connection of the Arctic and Atlantic Oceans is the basis for an ingenious and much-discussed theory of glaciation offered in 1956 by two New York geophysicists, Maurice Ewing of the Lamont Geological Observatory and William L. Donn of Brooklyn College. The Arctic Ocean, Ewing and Donn pointed out, is basically a landlocked sea, connected with the world's other oceans only by narrow, shallow channels flanking Greenland and by an even narrower, almost inconsequential waterway at the Bering Strait. During a time of generally mild climate, warm water from the Atlantic flows into the Arctic Ocean through the openings near Greenland, preventing it from freezing over. Evaporation is high in such an ice-free Arctic Ocean; moist air rising from its surface brings heavy precipitation in the form of snowfall to the surrounding land. Glaciers build up in high latitudes, growing so large that they begin to flow south. The presence of these great masses of ice brings about a worldwide lowering of temperatures and an ice age results.

But as the Arctic glaciers grow, they lock up so much water

that sea levels fall throughout the world. At some point, say Ewing and Donn, a self-regulating measure brings the ice age to an end: the sea levels get so low that the channels linking the Atlantic and Arctic turns into land bridges, making impossible further interchange of water between the two oceans. Deprived of the warmer flow from the Atlantic, the Arctic freezes, cutting off evaporation and thus ending the precipitation supply for the glaciers. As snowfall diminishes, summer melting takes charge, and the glaciers start to shrink. This returns water to the oceans; sea levels rise; ultimately the glaciers are virtually gone, but the Atlantic and Arctic are linked again, so that the entire evaporation-precipitation-glaciation cycle can begin anew. According to Ewing and Donn, the warming trend that has prevailed generally for the past ten thousand years is heading us inexorably into another ice age. The Arctic Ocean is at present frozen over, receiving little water from the Atlantic; but as the polar regions thaw out, evaporation will begin to rise in the north, snowfalls will grow heavier, and glaciers will once more descend upon the temperate lands.

The Ewing-Donn theory of an alternately open and frozen Arctic Ocean neatly explains the rhythmic sequence of glacials and interglacials that marked the Pleistocene; but it fails to deal with those periods of 250 million years or so in which no ice ages occurred. There is no reason why the Ewing-Donn cycle, as originally presented, should not continue indefinitely, producing an unbroken series of freezes and thaws every few hundred thousand years throughout all of time. Therefore they suggested that during the lengthy warm periods the earth actually occupied a different position relative to its axis—with the middle of the Pacific located at the North Pole, and the South Pole in the Atlantic near Africa. If that were so, ocean currents would easily mix warm equatorial water with that of the polar regions; the world's climate would be uniformly mild, and no glaciations would begin. The present ice age started, they said, when the poles migrated to their modern positions, making the landlocked Arctic Ocean a focus of chill that could set in motion the alternation of glacial and interglacial periods. Presumably this swing of the poles has occurred every quarter of a billion years to bring on the ice ages, with the world dipping back to the other polar arrangement for most of the intervening eons.

The idea of wandering poles is one of the oldest and most radical of the theories of ice-age causation. Conservative scientists have tended to regard it coolly; commenting on the Ewing-Donn suggestions, D. A. Livingstone of Duke University called polar migration "difficult to accept in the face of fossil evidence" that indicates the poles have held their present positions for at least 70 million years. And at a conference on climatic change held in 1954, John Wolbach of Harvard dismissed the concept "because such a change could be produced only by the action of enormous forces exterior to the earth." Scientists have been saying much the same thing for more than a hundred years. Sir George Darwin, son of the evolutionist, calculated that if an ocean bed 15,000 feet deep rose to become a continent the size of Africa 1,100 feet above sea level, and on the other side of the world an equal area became depressed, the effect would be a shift of the poles by about two degrees; if the earth's crust were plastic, the shift would be greater. To which James Croll replied in 1886, "There probably never was an upheaval of such magnitude in the history of our earth. And to produce a deflection of 3° 17′—a deflection that would hardly sensibly affect climate—no less than one-tenth of the entire surface of the earth would require to be elevated to the height of 10,000 feet. A continent ten times the size of Europe elevated two miles would do little more than bring London to the latitude of Edinburgh, or Edinburgh to the latitude of London. He must be a sanguine geologist indeed who can expect to account for the glaciation of this country, or for the former absence of ice around the poles, by this means. We know perfectly well that since the glacial epoch there have been no changes in the physical geography of the earth sufficient to deflect the pole half a dozen miles, far less half a dozen degrees."

Ewing and Donn avoided such objections by supporting a variant of the wandering-poles theory, in which the earth's position relative to its axis is thought to have been stable while the crust itself has slid around, carrying different geographical areas into polar positions at different times. They feel that such a crustal slippage at the start of the Pleistocene created the Arctic's enclosed basin of cold water, the thermostat by which the succession of ice ages has been turned on and off.

The theory of sliding continents also has a venerable history. Sixteenth-century explorers quickly noticed the startling similarities of contour in the eastern coast of South America and the western coast of Africa: the continents apparently fit together like two pieces of a jigsaw puzzle. Later, biologists puzzled over evolutionary problems inherent in the presence of ostriches in Africa and related birds, the rheas, in South America. How could these large flightless creatures have migrated from one continent to the other? In the late nineteenth century geographers began to push the continents about in various ways to solve the riddle. About 1900 the Austrian geologist Eduard Suess offered a picture of the world in Cambrian times that lumped the entire southern hemisphere into one immense continent that he called "Gondwanaland," after Gondwana, a key geological province in India. Gondwanaland, according to Suess, had stretched across half the globe from South America to Africa, and over the Indian Ocean as far east as Australia and New Zealand, with the lower half of India included. North of this supercontinent lay a long, narrow body of water, the Tethys Sea, above which were the land masses that would become North America and Eurasia. There was no Atlantic; the Pacific covered the region from the future New Zealand eastward to the future South America. Later, said Suess, contractions of the Earth's skin pulled Gondwanaland apart: "The collapse of the world is what we are witnessing," he wrote.

Suess's contraction theory was supplanted in 1912 by the continental-drift hypothesis of the German meteorologist Alfred Wegener. He, too, sought to explain the way South America and Africa fit together, the similar fit of Madagascar into Africa's eastern coast, and the affinities of geological formations and living and fossil animals in widely separated continents. Wegener supposed that the earth is composed of three layers of material that can be distinguished by their weight. The large, heavy core is made up mostly of nickel and iron, a material he called *nife*, from "nickel" and "*ferrum*," the Latin word for iron. Surrounding the nife core is a fairly thick shell made up of what Wegener termed *sima,* from "silicon" and "magnesium." Floating atop the sima lies a relatively thin mass of what he termed *sial,* from "silicon" and "aluminum." The sial layer does not make up a complete shell, but covers only about 25 percent of the earth's surface.

Originally, said Wegener, there was but a single block of sima, constituting all the globe's land in one giant continent. This great mass broke up under the action of forces generated by the rotation of the earth; the lower half became world-spanning Gondwanaland, and two chunks of sial to the north became the ancestors of North America and Eurasia. The continents then began to drift about on the underlying sima like icebergs floating in an ocean. Eventually the strains thus created split Gondwanaland apart into South America, Africa, India, Australia, New Zealand, and Antarctica, and sent the newly formed segments toward their present locations.

Wegener also believed that the movements of the continents induced a wandering of the geographic poles: that is, that such great variations in the placement of the land masses shifted the earth on its axis. In this way he explained the puzzle of the Permian ice age. During the Permian, he said, the South Pole had moved from Antarctica to a point just southeast of the present location of South Africa. This placed it in the middle of Gondwanaland and brought a glacial epoch to the still connected land mass that would one day become the continents of the Southern Hemisphere. The North Pole at this time was in the Pacific, so that the Northern Hemisphere enjoyed tropical or subtropical climates, and lush forests grew as far north as Spitzbergen, forming the coal deposits that exist there today beneath Arctic ice.

There were difficulties in the polar-wandering aspects of Wegener's theory, and about twenty years later the South African geologist Alex. L. Du Toit dispensed with that feature altogether. The poles had never varied from their place, said

Du Toit, but the continental drift had brought polar weather to different parts of the earth at different times. During the Permian all of Gondwanaland had drifted to the present site of Antarctica, while northern Europe lay at the equator, giving Spitzbergen its tropical climate. Later Gondwanaland broke up and most of its components drifted northward, leaving only Antarctica to endure perpetual ice; but at the beginning of the Pleistocene another continental drift caused the Northern Hemisphere to creep poleward to bring on the glaciation. To this Ewing and Donn added the Arctic Ocean hypothesis to explain the rhythmic fluctuations in the Pleistocene glaciation.

Many scientists find the notion of floating continents impossible to accept. Harvard's John Wolbach told the same 1954 gathering of climatologists at which he assailed the polar-wandering theory that the concept of continental drift "seems an objectional hypothesis, creating more problems than it solves." Others declared that the known forces that might send the continents sliding about were billions of times too weak for the job Wegener asked of them. As late as 1960, Wegener's theory and those related to it were considered not quite respectable—ideas more worthy of science fiction than of science.

But today's science fiction sometimes has an odd way of becoming tomorrow's science, and recent scientific developments have brought continental drift very much back into respectability. One such development springs from the analysis of the residual magnetism of rock. The earth is like a giant magnet, inducing a magnetic field with poles located near (though not at) the geographical poles. It is this magnetic force which draws a compass needle toward the ends of the earth. Investigations in the 1950's showed that rocks can be weakly magnetized by the earth's field at the time they are formed: igneous rocks as the lava they are made of cools, and sedimentary rocks as sedimentary particles settle in standing water. The particles of a rock mass orient themselves magnetically along the axis of the earth's magnetic field, to become what are essentially little compass needles frozen forever in place.

Analysis of residual rock magnetism has produced surprising

results. Rocks formed since the latter half of the Cenozoic have magnetic axes that follow the present orientation of the earth's magnetic poles; but older strata lined up in other ways. Measurements in the Permian rocks of Europe suggested that some 250 million years ago the north magnetic pole was located in the western Pacific east of Japan and the south magnetic pole midway between the tips of South America and Africa. Since the geographic poles and the magnetic poles are thought always to have been relatively close together, this seemed a confirmation of the wandering-pole hypothesis by which Wegener and others explained the Permian glaciation.

Magnetic studies in North America's Permian rocks turned up a contradiction, though: there the alignment of particles pointed to a north magnetic pole in China somewhat west of Peking and a south magnetic pole on the west coast of Argentina. The discrepancy could be reconciled only by assuming that in Permian times the relative positions of Europe and North America were not what they are today; since the magnetic axes of the rocks of both continents originally must have been pointing in the same direction, a continental drift is indicated. One reconstruction of the actual Permian state of affairs made in 1963 by G. W. Bain puts the Permian North Pole in the Pacific at 7½°S. and 165°W., an arrangement that has Africa in Antarctica's present position, the Americas, Antarctica, and Siberia along the equator, and Australia roughly where Siberia is today. This gives credence both to the continental-drift and wandering-poles hypotheses; but another reconstruction made in 1964 by D. Van Hilten, using the same paleomagnetic data, works on the assumption of stationary poles and drifting continents, and puts both Africa and Australia near the South Pole in Permian times. Other recent studies have likewise favored continental drift over polar wandering as an explanation of the paleomagnetic evidence.

A geological foundation for continental drift has been supplied by the discovery of a submerged oceanic ridge forty thousand miles long, running continuously from the Atlantic to the Pacific, indicating gigantic expansions and contractions of the earth's crust. Geologists generally concede now that the same vast forces that created this immense irregularity beneath the oceans would have been sufficient to push the continents around. The earth's crust is seen to be far more fluid than it was thought to be only a few years ago.

Lastly, radioactive measurements have proved that the resemblance of South America's Atlantic coastline to that of Africa is more than a geographical coincidence. West Africa is divided into two geological provinces of greatly different age, which meet along a sharply defined boundary. Tests with such new methods as potassium-argon and rubidium-strontium show that the rocks of Ghana, the Ivory Coast, and regions to the west are two billion years old, and that those of eastern Dahomey, Nigeria, and regions to the east are 550 million years old. The sharp boundary between these geological provinces appears to head southwestward from a point near Accra, Ghana. If South America and Africa are fitted together jigsaw-puzzle fashion, the eastern tip of Brazil slips into place under Nigeria, and the extension of the geological boundary line from Accra will run through the vicinity of São Luís, Brazil.

Geologists from the Massachusetts Institute of Technology reasoned that if Brazil and Africa had been joined at any time in the last half billion years, the rocks around São Luís would show the same age division as those of western Africa. With the aid of scientists from the University of São Paulo, Brazil, they collected rock samples around São Luís, subjected them to radioactive dating tests, and late in 1966 announced that Brazil, too, consisted of two adjoining geological provinces of greatly different age. The northern part of Brazil, going toward the mouth of the Amazon and the Republic of Guyana, is made up of rocks two billion years old. But eastern Brazil is composed of rocks 550 million years old. The boundary between the two formations runs right through the town of São Luís, as predicted; the older region is northwest of São Luís, the younger region southeast. This is the most convincing proof yet that Africa and South America once formed part of the same continent, drifting apart millions of years ago. This makes the continental-drift theory of the Permian glaciation seem possible and even probable; but no evidence exists as yet for the Pleistocene wandering of the continents to which Ewing and Donn attribute the onset of the last ice age.

What, then, made the glaciers come and go?

The flickering of the sun? The shifting of the earth in its orbit or on its axis? The migration of the poles? The birth of mountains? The joining of seas? The disappearance of carbon dioxide or the increase of volcanic dust in the atmosphere? Theories abound, as we have seen, and the resurrection of the concept of continental drift warns us to discard none of them as too imaginative. We are, perhaps, on the threshold of discovering an explanation for the ice ages that the majority of scientists will be able to accept; and the chances seem good that that theory, when we have it, will combine several of the current ideas, possibly embracing solar fluctuations, continental drift, mountain-building, and some variant of the Ewing-Donn or Simpson precipitation hypotheses. Our long search through scientific annals for an understanding of the prime causes of great climatic shifts ends, then, on an uncertain note, with a basket of theories and few certainties. Yet the clues grow ever more clear, and the detectives of science ever more skillful, and a solution to the mystery of the ice ages is likely to come—one hopes before the glaciers themselves are upon us once again.

4

Man and the Ice

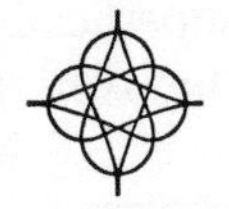

THE PLEISTOCENE, AN ERA OF CONVULSIVE MOUNTAIN-building and severe climatic change, was also the era in which the animal known as man evolved. The dramatic physical background of the Pleistocene, most scientists believe, was the anvil on which not only man's cultural traits but even his physical form was shaped.

That man has an evolutionary history was perhaps the most unsettling scientific discovery of the nineteenth century. When that century began, man was still considered to have been created in Eden and to have come forth in his final immutable shape. By the end of the century, perplexing evidence in the form of strange not-quite-human skulls provided troubling insight into what was suddenly a highly mutable past. Darwin's theory of evolution, made public in 1859, provided a scientific underpinning for the concept that species might change form over many generations in response to the prodding of external challenges and the winnowing process of natural selection; and the fossils of Neanderthal man and the Javan "ape-man" showed that man himself was subject to the Darwinian laws. Although that statement still is hotly disputed in certain rural areas, it causes no debate among scientists. Adequate proof exists that other species of men once walked the earth. Today, all human beings belong to the same species, which we have immodestly dubbed *Homo sapiens,* "Man the wise." *Homo sapiens* is divided into a number of races, differing from one another in such matters as body structure and skin color; but though these differences are superficially great, they are in fact trivial compared with those that distinguish us from our early ancestors.

Where the first manlike creatures evolved is not yet certain, but the latest evidence points toward Africa. In late Mesozoic times, when the first mammals appeared, one group of tiny tree-living animals developed whom we call the prosimians. Among them was the ancestor of man. The original prosimian stock divided into several branches; one scarcely evolved at all, and includes such creatures as the lemurs, man's most primitive living relatives, and the little goggle-eyed tarsiers. Another line evolved in the direction of the tailed, chattering, treetop-swinging animals we call monkeys. In South America the monkey line developed the use of the prehensile tail as a kind of fifth limb, but evolution went no further there.

Another tribe of tarsierlike prosimians began heading in the direction of the present-day apes. That is, they evolved toward a large-sized, tree-dwelling tailless animal with long arms and short legs, capable of using its feet and hands interchangeably. This line split away in the early Cenozoic; but South America and Africa must have been separate by then, for no apes evolved in the New World.

The main primate stock remained unspecialized throughout the Cenozoic. It consisted of small animals perhaps no larger than squirrels or cats, lacking in the tree-climbing adaptations of the monkeys and apes. The years produced evolutionary changes in these animals, and possibly the moderate cold spells of the Cenozoic had some role in guiding their development, but we do not yet know enough about that to make definite statements. Fossil evidence of this period in primate evolution is still scanty. An African primate of the Miocene, *Proconsul,* who lived some 20 million years ago, seems to be a chimpanzee ancestor, but had not yet evolved a chimp's long arms, and may also be on our evolutionary path. *Kenyapithecus,* found by the celebrated paleontologist Dr. Louis S. B. Leakey in 1961, dates from about 14 million years ago, according to potassium-argon radioactivity tests, and seems to show no apelike specializations; it, too, may be ancestral to man. *Oreopithecus*, a large primate of about the same era, may also belong on our family tree. The discovery of a nearly complete *Oreopithecus* skeleton in 1958 in Italy led its finder, the Swiss Dr. Johannes Huerzeler, to place it on the direct line between the unknown primate ancestor and modern man, though this is by no means universally accepted yet.

The fossil record has a large gap in it after these early primates. We have no idea what happened in human evolution for the next ten or twelve million years. When we pick up the evolutionary sequence, it is about two million years ago—on the boundary between the Pliocene and the Pleistocene—and Africa is inhabited by the creatures we call australopithecines, which are thought of by some scientists as manlike apes, and by others as apelike men.

Australopithecines began coming to light in South Africa in 1924. A workman conducting blasting operations in a limestone mine found the small skull of what appeared to be a monkey; but when it reached the Johannesburg anatomist Raymond A. Dart, he was surprised to find that its teeth were more like those of a human being than like those of any known ape or monkey, extinct or living. Regarding the fossil as belonging to "an extinct race of apes intermediate between living anthropoids and man," Dart gave it the name of *Australopithecus africanus*, "Southern Ape of Africa." In 1936 the skull of a somewhat different australopithecine was discovered, and a third type, much larger, came to light two years later. Six species of australopithecines have been identified to date. There is little scientific agreement on the relationship of these animals to one another or to modern man; but there is not much doubt that the australopithecines represent one of the earliest protohuman forms, even if they do not lie on our main line of evolution.

All the australopithecines were small, slender creatures who walked upright. One group was about four feet tall and weighed 40 to 50 pounds; the other may have been as much as a foot taller, weighing 100 pounds or more. Their teeth were human in pattern; their brains were small, for their skull capacity averaged about 550-600 cc., one third that of *Homo sapiens.* The general shape of their skulls was primitive, with some apelike characteristics—massive, jutting jaws, an absence of chin, a low skull vault, and a slanting forehead. There is some evidence that the australopithecines possessed a grasping big toe, as apes have today. Their elbow joints did not work like ours, and possibly they could not completely straighten their arms at all. In short, they seem to have been borderline cases, with larger brains and smaller teeth than the earlier primates, but still remote from anything we could consider human.

Whether the australopithecines deserve to be called the earliest humans depends to a great extent on how complex their culture was. Raymond Dart, who mistook manganese stains in an Australopithecus-occupied cave for the remains of charcoal hearths, wrote in 1948, "These intelligent, erect, and delicately proportioned little people were as competent as any other primitive human group in cavern life made comfortable by the use of fire, in the employment of long bones as lethal weapons, in the cunning and courage of the chase. . . ." But a year later the British anthropologist Wilfred E. Le Gros Clark declared, "The mental powers of the australopithecines were probably not much superior to those of the chimpanzee and the gorilla."

Tools, in the form of crude stone implements and pieces of what seem to be split and shaped antelope bones, have been found associated with australopithecine fossils. If the australopithecines did indeed chip pebbles so that they could be used as choppers, as many anthropologists now believe, we can hardly deny them at least the status of protohumans. Man is preeminently the toolmaking animal. Other animals, though, *use* tools not of their own making; apes and even monkeys have been known to pick up a handy stick or stone to help themselves in a fight or in getting food. But using tools is not at all the same thing as making them.

The possibility exists that some other species, far more human in physical makeup than the australopithecines, lived in South Africa at the same time and made the tools found with the australopithecine remains. In recent years Louis Leakey has turned up several fossils in Tanzania's Olduvai Gorge which he regards as representing the true main line of human evolution in Africa, the australopithecines being merely some evolutionary sideshoot. Leakey has dubbed this species *Homo habilis,* and places the ages of the seven specimens he has found so far at from about 1,820,000 years to about 1,000,000 years. He portrays *Homo habilis* as similar to the australopithecines in height and appearance, but with a larger brain, more "modern" teeth, and well-developed hands capable of fashioning tools. The verdict of most other anthropologists is that Leakey has probably been too enthusiastic on behalf of *Homo habilis,* and that it is simply another form of australopithecine.

We do not know how long ago the australopithecines evolved, since at present we have only the skimpiest of fossil evidence of their existence. All the specimens known so far—including the controversial Leakey fossils—are Pleistocene types, dating from the past two million years. These are thought to represent fairly well advanced examples of their kind. So although the australopithecines probably appeared in the Pliocene or even earlier, we are familiar only with those that existed in that period of drastic climatic upheaval that commenced at the Pliocene's end.

The Pleistocene glaciers, of course, left Africa untouched. Instead Africa was subjected to a series of pluvial and interpluvial periods which resulted in large-scale movements of vegetation belts. Rainfall in South Africa during the early Pleistocene varied from 70 percent to 150 percent of the present levels, according to the 1958 evidence of C. K. Brain; each shift toward the pluvial must have transformed arid areas into gardens, and each swing into an interpluvial must have caused widespread desiccation. Soil analyses conducted by Brain showed that at two sites where australopithecine fossils have been found, Sterkfontein and Swartkrans, the climate began like that of today, grew drier, then wetter, in the Pleistocene;

but the interval of drought was much more intense at Sterkfontein than at Swartkrans. At the nearby Kromdraii site the Pleistocene climate was at first wetter and then less wet than today.

The South African paleontologist J. T. Robinson has divided the australopithecines into two groups according to size, and believes that climatic shifts had much to do with their evolutionary pattern. The larger, heavier australopithecines he places in the genus *Paranthropus,* and he believes that these creatures were herbivorous, dwelling in a moist tropical or subtropical forest and living on roots and bulbs. The smaller australopithecines he puts in the genus *Australopithecus,* and argues from the large canine and incisor teeth of this form that this was primarily a carnivorous form. Robinson thinks that *Paranthropus* is the older group, having evolved in the warm, wet environment of the Pliocene, while *Australopithecus* represents an adaptation to the drier conditions of one of the early Pleistocene interpluvials. In a study published in 1963 he declared:

"Australopithecines living in areas which subsequently became semi-arid will have found that the dry season gradually became longer and drier. The critical time of the year, the latter part of the dry season, will gradually have become more difficult to cope with. It is reasonable to suppose that in these times of hardship insects, reptiles, small mammals, the eggs and nestlings of birds, etc., will have been eaten to supplement their diet. It is known that purely vegetarian primates will readily eat meat in captivity and that baboons, for example, will occasionally do so in the wild. Taking to a certain amount of meat-eating under environmental pressure could therefore occur fairly easily."

As the climate grew drier, Robinson believes, "It could be expected that population density will have dropped, probably to the vanishing point in the most heavily affected areas. But it is probable that in at least some areas the creatures will have adapted satisfactorily to the altering circumstances and adopted a certain amount of carnivorousness as a normal part of their way of life. That is to say, the originally vegetarian diet will have become altered by the addition of a certain amount of meat-eating to an omnivorous diet."

Robinson feels that the australopithecines were not tool-makers, though they were certainly tool-using, and that their use of tools was stimulated by the worsening climate: "For the vegetarian part of their food, implements for digging will have made possible greater exploitation of the larger number of bulbs found in drier areas. Implements for bashing, hitting, or throwing as well as digging, will have made capture and consumption of small animals much easier. Improved tool-using will thus have been favored by selection and any improvements in this respect will have improved adaptation, especially in respect of the carnivorous aspect of their diet. It is also obvious that improved intelligence will have been of great benefit in improving tool-using ability and dealing generally with the stresses of a somewhat hostile environment."

Environmental changes may have further stimulated australopithecine evolution by encouraging the migration of bands or "tribes." Seasonal migrations stemming from alternating wet ing in the exchange of genes that is so significant in evolution-and dry seasons could bring different groups together, result-ary change. However, extreme desiccation might bring the opposite effect. As the geographer Karl W. Butzer of the University of Wisconsin put it in 1964, "Wide dispersal of small bands in dry country, or increased isolation during the course of desiccation will favor inbreeding and genetic drift. Through premature death of certain individuals of a breeding isolate, certain blood groups or genes may be lost to a small population, whereas other biological traits may be accentuated. . . . In other words, certain environmental changes may enforce or favor group isolation and hence genetic drift, other modifications may facilitate gene exchange. . . . It is possible that alternating cross-breeding and genetic drift, motivated by alternating pluvials and interpluvials at the dawn of African prehistory, may have influenced and accelerated human evolution."

It is impossible to assert with any degree of conviction that the few australopithecines whose bones we have found represent the direct ancestors of *Homo sapiens;* but it seems increasingly likely that some sort of australopithecinelike creatures, their nature forged in the crucible of Pleistocene Africa, do hold an ancestral position on our family tree. But they were a long way from attaining any control over their environment, which is the hallmark of man. No evidence that they knew the use of fire has yet come to light, whether in the form of charcoal, charred bones, or discolored stones. (The oldest known traces of human use of fire come from the China of 360,000 years ago.) Thus they were deprived of the means of creating artificial warmth, and were confined necessarily to regions of moderate temperature. They had no likely way of constructing shelter, relying instead on caves where they could find them. They could not grow crops, nor did they have domesticated animals. They were primitive food-gatherers who grubbed for roots, scavenged the kills of larger carnivores for their meat, and themselves hunted, probably in an inefficient way, such creatures as crabs, lizards, birds, rodents, bats, fish, and young antelopes and baboons. With these limitations the australopithecines could not venture far from warm, well-watered areas with large animal populations; the temporary desert conditions of the interpluvials must have forced them to the boundaries of their ability to survive.

Nevertheless, they managed to cover a good deal of ground, radiating from their probable homeland in South Africa. Europe, which in Pleistocene times was first exposed to steadily diminishing temperatures and then seized by glaciers, was of course closed to them. But skeletal evidence of australopithecinelike creatures has come, in a sketchy way, from Palestine, China, and Java. This suggests that in the million or so years that they were earth's most clever creatures, the australopithecines succeeded in making their way north through pluvial Africa, following favorable climates into Ethiopia and somehow getting past the Red Sea, then eastward into southern China and the East Indies, which then were probably connected to the Asian mainland.

The distances covered in this migration are vast, but so are the time spans. If a tribe of primitive men (or australopithecines) moved onward at a rate of only one mile every two years, it could travel 5,000 miles in less than 50 generations. And about *40,000* generations separate the australopithecines from their successors, the pithecanthropoids, whom we think of as the first animals that indisputably must be classed as men.

The relationship of the pithecanthropoids to the australopithecines is uncertain. We have no right to say that the one group evolved directly from the other; perhaps, when the blanks in the fossil record have been filled in, we will see that both are descended from some common ancestor at present unknown, and evolved side by side along separate paths until one so exceeded the other in ability that it prevailed. All we can assert now is that in the middle Pleistocene the pithecanthropoids replace the australopithecines in the fossil record, and thereafter the australopithecines vanish from view.

Dr. Eugène Dubois, a fossil-hunting Dutch surgeon stationed on the island of Java, found the first pithecanthropoid remains late in the nineteenth century. In 1890 he discovered an odd-looking tooth and a battered lower jaw; about a year later he came upon a strange skullcap, shallow-vaulted but thick, with a heavy bony ridge above the eyes; nearby he found another tooth; and in 1892 he unearthed a fossilized thighbone near the site where the other finds had been made. The thighbone was undoubtedly human, he felt, since from its shape it had belonged to a creature that walked upright, after the manner of men, and not bent forward as apes walk. The skullcap, which almost certainly was from the same creature, indicated a brain capacity of 800 to 1000 cc., larger than an ape's but only about half that of modern man. At first Dubois christened his discovery *Anthropithecus erectus,* "Manlike Ape That Walks upright," but upon reconsideration he called it *Pithecanthropus erectus,* "Apelike man." He went on to find a variety of other *Pithecanthropus* bones; and in 1937 the German-born paleontologist Dr. G. H. R. von Koenigswald, also working in Java, produced a lower jaw with four teeth intact, another *Pithecanthropus* skullcap, and additional remains. We still have no complete skeleton of *Pithecanthropus,* nor even any of his facial bones, but nevertheless we have a good idea of what he looked like. He stood about five feet five, walked upright, and was probably of slender build. His face had an apish look, with a massive, underslung jaw, a sloping forehead, jutting brow-ridges, and a receding chin. His skull was oddly angular, and his teeth were huge. His brain was smaller than that of any normal modern human. He lived in Java and probably in surrounding regions between 1,000,000 and 300,000 year ago.

Another pithecanthropoid population existed in mid-Pleistocene China. This was shown by fossils uncovered beginning in 1927, near Peking: first a tooth, then skulls, jaws, legbones. Thousands of tools made of flaked pieces of quartz and chert were found in association with these remains, and also bits of charcoal and charred animal bones, indicating (though not proving absolutely) that these Chinese ape-men had the use of fire. Though quite similar in most important respects to the Javan pithecanthropoids, the Chinese fossils were placed in a separate species as *Pithecanthropus pekinensis,* or even in an altogether different genus as *Sinanthropus pekinensis,* "China Man of Peking."

In 1954 a third pithecanthropoid came to light in Algeria: the jaws, teeth, and some skull fragments of a primitive man whose discoverers placed him in a genus they called *Atlanthropus,* "Atlantic Man." Many contemporary paleontologists and anthropologists have advocated the discarding of the confusing and conflicting generic terms applied to these early men of the middle Pleistocene, urging that all be classified as members of the genus *Homo,* species *erectus,* "upright." The argument of this school is that the various pithecanthropoids, though undeniably different in many anatomical respects from modern *Homo sapiens,* are not so different that they merit exclusion from the genus that includes modern man; the lesser exclusion of placing them in a separate species is sufficient to distinguish them from ourselves. Nor are the differences between one primitive type and another great enough to warrant setting up species distinctions for the Javan, Chinese, North African, and other middle Pleistocene men; placing them all in *Homo erectus* is adequate.

Homo erectus did not dwell in tropical rain forests. He preferred open woodlands, subtropical or temperate, where the hunting was easier than in dense jugle. Though the Javan *erectus* lived in what is now rain-forest country, he inhabited it during an interpluvial period when it was much drier than it is today. All our known Asian and African specimens of *Homo erectus,* in fact, date from the long second interpluvial period. (According to the Zeuner-Milankovitch chronology formerly in general acceptance, this period began about 435,000 years ago and lasted 190,000 years. The newer Ericson-Wollin timetable places the start of the second interpluvial at 1,060,000 years ago and its duration at 640,000 years.) What *Homo erectus* did during the first two pluvial periods of the Pleistocene is still unknown; thus far only australopithecine fossils have been found in those levels. Possibly the alteration of wet and dry cycles stimulated migrations, tribal intermarriages, and other significant phenomena, but that must remain purely speculative until we have some proof of the existence of *Homo erectus* at all in the early Pleistocene.

While small bands of *Homo erectus* roamed the interpluvial woodlands of the tropics, chipping clumsy weapons and tools from stone, preying on wildlife, and possibly making war on the smaller and less able australopithecines, others were venturing into northerly regions where the australopithecines had never gone. The Chinese examples of *erectus* were found in a region that is far from tropical today, and which even in the relatively mild period between the second and third glaciations must have been quite cool. Analysis of pollen specimens found near the remains of "*Sinanthropus*" shows a forest made up 33 percent of pine, 28 percent of beech, 9 percent of alder, 4 percent of spruce, with scatterings of other predominantly cold-weather trees. The Chinese *Homo erectus* almost certainly had fire; his tools were good enough to permit the fashioning of crude garments from hides; his cave dwellings allowed him to survive winters far colder than anything the australopithecines had ever experienced. Man was beginning to conquer his environment and to emancipate himself from the tyranny of climate.

Not only in China did *Homo erectus* go northward. At a time much earlier than the heyday of the Chinese and Javan pithecanthropoids—perhaps even before the first of the Pleistocene ice ages—man had entered Europe. It was a hesitant invasion, carried out by so few that we have almost no skeletal evidence that it occurred. A single jawbone tells us of the arrival of *Homo erectus* in Europe; but he left many of his stone tools behind, and from them we can piece together a picture of painful progress and of the upheaval caused by the coming of the glaciers.

The oldest of these tools are artifacts so primitive that many anthropologists refuse to accept them as the product of human effort. They are called eoliths, "stones of the dawn," and they are nothing more than chunks of flint, fractured perhaps by man in search of a tool, perhaps by the action of nature. One French prehistorian says of the eoliths, "Man made one, God made ten thousand—God help the man who tries to see the one in the ten thousand." Beyond doubt many so-called eoliths unearthed by enthusiastic excavators, particularly in the nineteenth century, were mere fragments of flint fractured by frost or water, and never handled by man. But men may have picked up fortuitously shaped flints and used them as choppers or scrapers; and man may have smashed stones together to obtain the sharp-edged implements he needed.

Though most of the eoliths may be dismissed as accidents of nature, there is good reason to suspect that some actually were the work of manlike forms that entered Europe early in the Pleistocene. The most likely route for this migration was via a land bridge believed to have connected Tunisia and Italy. Man was not the only African animal to go north in this time of general warmth; the elephant, rhinoceros, antelope, hippopotamus, and saber-toothed tiger passed into Europe. Then came the glaciers, pushing southward for the first time and driving the African beasts back toward warmer country. Man gave way also, following the big game on which he preyed. When he returned to Europe after the first ice age (some authorities say he did not come back until after the second) he brought with him an important new tool: the hand ax.

These were simple pear-shaped implements three to six inches long, rounded at the butt end, pointed at the other. They were used for peeling away the hides of animals, butchering the kill, and scraping hides free of meat. Flint was the customary raw material; large flakes were knocked off along cleavage planes to produce the desired tapering at the business end. Archaeologists have identified several phases of the early hand-ax period, naming them for the French sites where the first discovery of each period was made. Thus the oldest of the hand axes are termed *Chellean,* after the town of Chelles, near Paris; a somewhat later and more refined type is sometimes classed *Abbevillean,* from Abbeville in northern France.

Artifacts of the Chellean type have been found in Africa, Asia, and southern Europe, but only at one site have human fossils been unearthed in association with them. In 1954 Louis Leakey discovered two large human baby teeth near Chellean artifacts in Tanzania's Olduvai Gorge; and in 1960, working about a hundred yards from that place, he found a skull. Because it came from the third of Olduvai's dozen known stage-levels of Chellean tools, he gave the skull the tentative designation of Chellean-3; no scientific name of a more formal kind has yet been proposed. The Chellean-3 skull is long and thick with large brow ridges, a low vault, and a capacity of about 1100 to 1200 cc. The facial bones are missing. Though it differs in some important respects from the known *Homo erectus* fossils, most anthropologists would place it in that species.

The most ancient human fossil found in Europe—the Heidelberg jawbone—may well have been a contemporary of Chellean-3. This massive relic came to light in 1907 in a gravel mine at the German village of Mauer, six miles from Heidelberg. Half again as big as a human jaw, formidably thick-walled, curiously square in shape, lacking any trace of a chin projection, it might have belonged to some extinct and ponderous ape, but for its teeth. The Heidelberg teeth were small, distinctly human in appearance, and arrayed in the curved dental arch characteristic of *Homo sapiens,* not the parallel-sided U of ape jaws; the canines were of modest size, while among apes these teeth are prominent fangs used as defensive weapons. The arrangement of the molars, the number of roots, the shape of the crowns—everything was quite similar to the modern dental plan.

Mainly on the basis of his teeth, Heidelberg man was regarded as human and was originally christened *Homo heidelbergensis;* today he is usually placed in *Homo erectus*. The gravel deposits in which the jawbone was found are known to have been laid down in the Günz-Mindel interglacial *, that is, the interval between the first and second Pleistocene ice ages. Thus he lived several hundred thousand years before the Javan and Chinese representatives of that species, whose known fossils are all post-second-glacial. The assumption is that Heidelberg man's tools were of the Chellean type, but no artifacts of any kind were found with the jawbone, nor any other parts of the skeleton. The huge jaw remains the solitary fragment of fossil evidence for human presence in Europe in the first interglacial.

However, Chellean tools have come to light in Italy, France, Spain, and southern England, showing that in this interglacial there was a considerable spread of man through southern Europe, wherever a sufficient supply of water and wild vegetables could be obtained and wherever the game animals roamed. The makers of the Chellean and the slightly more sophisticated Abbevillean hand axes lived in an almost subtropical Europe, with mild winters and hot summers. They followed the game trails through the deciduous forests along the riverbanks, as we know from the distribution of the sites where their tools have been found. The hand ax served them as an all-purpose tool, a combined hatchet, saw, knife, pick, and scraper. A strong blow with one could split an enemy's skull or kill a fairly large animal. Hand axes could not be used for hunting elephants, of course; but if the men of the first interglacial came upon a lone elephant they might try to

* One current school of Pleistocene geologists objects to such designations, asserting that Europe may have seen as many as seven major Pleistocene glaciations rather than the traditional four. By their system of terminology Heidelberg man dates from the Cortonian warm period that followed the second of the seven glaciations.

stampede it over a cliff, and then use their tools to cut it up for a feast. The axe was possibly employed to hack limbs from trees to use as clubs, to aid in preparing skins for clothing, or to split wood for burning. But these are all guesses. We do not know if the Chellean-Abbevillean men used fire, wore clothing, or made use of such materials as wood, bone, or horn. We know nothing about the culture of this period except the shape of the hand axes.

That shape scarcely changed over hundreds of thousands of years. One generation after another placidly pounded out tools exactly as they had been fashioned ages before. Such scant progress does not indicate dynamic minds or great adaptability; and when the glaciers of the second ice age began to roll down from the mountains, the Abbevilleans had no choice but to withdraw, like the hippopotamus and elephant, toward the warmth of Africa and the Near East.

In the first ice age, the primarily African fauna of warm-weather Europe had been replaced by cold-adapted animals from the north: the woolly rhinoceros, the mammoth, the reindeer, the musk ox, and other well-insulated beasts. This cold-weather fauna, forced southward itself as the all-engulfing glaciers made northern Europe uninhabitable even for typical Arctic animals, returned to southern Europe in the second glacial period. But this time human beings were on hand to hunt the shaggy creatures from the north.

As the warmth-loving Abbevilleans fled from Europe, a distinctly different culture called the Clactonian—named for the English town where its relics first were identified—arrived, perhaps from Asia. There was nothing swift about this double migration. It must have gone on for thousands of years as the European climate grew more bitter, with small bands of Abbevilleans filtering to warmer lands and small bands of Clactonians drifting into Europe. It is hard to see what made ice-age Europe attractive to the Clactonians, but perhaps they came because they were marginal folk being squeezed out of their own homelands by the entry of the Abbevilleans, or possibly they found the new pluvial conditions of Africa and Asia less to their liking than Europe's chill.

Since we have no fossils of Clactonian man, and only the Heidelberg jawbone to represent the Chellean-Abbevillean population, we are in no position to distinguish between one group and the other on a physical basis. By their tools alone can we tell a Clactonian site from an Abbevillean; but to a prehistorian the difference in tool types is immense and significant. The Clactonians did not use heavy hand axes. Rather, their tools were fashioned from slender flakes chipped off flint cores—the sort of flakes that the makers of hand axes threw away. Clactonian tools were apparently designed to serve as skinning-knives and hide-scrapers, which would be useful in a cold climate where fur clothing was a necessity.

Strictly on the basis of this distinction in tools, some prehistorians have indulged in an exciting speculation about human evolutionary development. At some point in the middle Pleistocene the basic *Homo erectus* stock split into two great evolutionary lines. One was the *Homo sapiens* line that culminated in modern man, with his well-developed chin, smooth forehead, and high-vaulted skull. The other line led to a related but markedly different human stock, characterized by thick bones, receding chins, and bulging brows. We call this stock, which has been extinct for at least 25,000 years, Neanderthal man. The Neanderthals—who do not appear in the fossil record until after the third ice age—fashioned their stone tools from flakes; the presumed ancestors of *Homo sapiens* long clung to the heavier core-derived tools. The Neanderthals tolerated cold weather; the early men of the modern type did not. If the analogy cold-flake–Neanderthal/warm-core *Homo sapiens* is extended back a few hundred thousand years to the beginning of the second ice age, a case can be made that the Clactonian flake-tool people were the ancestors of the Neanderthals, and that the Abbevillean core-tool people driven from Europe by the ice were our own forebears.

This is, as noted, pure speculation, unsupported by a shred of fossil evidence. But it has won some authoritative backing. The Clactonians, at any rate, held their own in the bleakness of England, France, and Germany during the second ice age, while the Abbevilleans enjoyed the pluvial weather of Africa and the Near East. The pluvial conditions in the tropical and subtropical zones created an effective barrier to migration: sea levels rose, lakes and rivers swelled. Across the Sudan and southern Sahara stretched a broad band of swamps and lakes which must have prevented any traffic between equatorial Africa and the north. The only remaining land access to Europe was cut off by a greatly expanded Caspian Sea and by a line of swamps south and east of the Urals. In Asia, on the other hand, the fall of sea levels as glaciers locked up the water created land bridges that may have united Japan with the Siberian mainland, and Tasmania and New Guinea with Australia. Another land bridge probably formed at the Bering Strait, so that it would have been possible to cross dry-shod from Siberia to Alaska; but glacial conditions kept mankind out of Siberia and no human beings entered the New World by this route or any other for hundreds of thousands of years, until the Pleistocene's last glaciation had nearly run its course.

Living in their pluvial isolation, the Abbevilleans who had never left Africa and those who had fled the second ice age developed improved techniques of fashioning tools, sufficiently advanced to warrant being placed in a new cultural period, the Acheulian. Acheulian hand axes were thinner, more delicately formed, and more evenly flaked than Abbevillean ones, with sharp, straight cutting edges. Though almost elegant in comparison with the tools of the preceding epoch, they were still clumsy implements, good for little more than cutting and chopping. The so-called *Atlanthropus,* the North African fossil of *Homo erectus,* is thought to be an early specimen of Acheulian man.

Eventually the ice relented again, producing the second interglacial in Europe and the second interpluvial in lower latitudes. The growing aridity of Africa and the Near East seems to have encouraged an Acheulian migration into Europe, which now was warm once more but not unpleasantly dry. So the hand-ax people, still following the most favorable climate, spread out over a wide area; the trail of Acheulian tools leads out of Africa toward southern England, and across central and eastern Europe to the Black Sea, Asia Minor, the Near East, and on to India. The Acheulians moved farther north in Europe than their predecessors, too: toward the end of the long warm interglacial period they reached the southern slopes of the Alps, judging by the presence of their artifacts in Austria and the Balkans.

This Acheulian culture that took form in Africa during the second glacial period and spread northward during the second interglacial/interpluvial was roughly contemporary with the pithecanthropoid fossils found in Java and China. But it appears that those two representatives of *Homo erectus* were cultural laggards, already hopelessly backward and primitive compared with the Acheulians, and heading for the evolutionary scrapheap. The tools found at the Chinese sites certainly indicate this. No tools have ever been found in connection with the bones of the Javan *Homo erectus*, though crude chopping implements discovered near the Javan sites have sometimes been linked to the pithecanthropoids. It is the prehistorian's misfortune that the most extensively known fossil men of the middle Pleistocene are not those who were carrying forward the development of human culture, but rather those of an obsolescent form.

The few fossils of Acheulian man that we do have suggest that not only a cultural but a physical evolutionary trend was at work in the second interglacial—that the Acheulians were well along the evolutionary road toward the form of modern man, *Homo sapiens*. In 1932 Louis Leakey unearthed an incomplete skull, fragments of other skulls, and bits of one legbone at a site called Kanjera, on the southern shore of the Kavirondo Gulf in Kenya. The bones were thick but the skull fragments showed no traces of the protruding brow ridges typical of *Homo erectus*. Leakey therefore declared that Kanjera man, found amidst Chellean and Acheulian hand axes and the bones of extinct animals that lived late in the second interpluvial or early in the third pluvial, was *Homo sapiens*.

Other scientists were dubious, since the Kanjera find would therefore have to be more than twenty times as old as the most ancient known *Homo sapiens* fossils of Europe. At that time, most paleontologists believed that the modern form of man had evolved quite recently, no earlier than the fourth glacial period. So Leakey's claim was generally rejected. It was said that the Kanjera bones must have worked their way downward into more ancient strata; and when chemical tests showed that they were of the same age as the fossils of extinct types of elephant and baboon found at the site, the skeptics argued that those animals may have lingered on in East Africa long after they disappeared elsewhere, so that the whole Kanjera site might be no more than fifty thousand years old.

There could be no debate, though, when in 1935 an English dentist and part-time prehistorian named A. Theophilus Marston discovered Swanscombe man in a gravel pit along the Thames. At a depth of 26 feet Marston found a human occipital bone; a year later, at the same depth and 23 feet away, he discovered a left parietal bone which fit into the other piece; in 1955 the right parietal was found at the Swanscombe site, completing the skullcap. Swanscombe "man" was actually a woman in her twenties, and she was almost certainly a member of our species. Though the skull wall is thick, there are otherwise no significant differences between it and a modern one; the skull capacity is about 1,325 cc., normal for a female of *Homo sapiens*. A jaw fragment might have clinched the case, but even with the skull cap that is all we have, it appears proper to consider Swanscombe man one of the oldest known fossils of *Homo sapiens*. Chemical tests indicate an age of more than 300,000 years for the skull, and this is supported by the presence at the site of some 600 Acheulian tools, along with the bones of warm-weather elephants and rhinoceroses of the second interglacial.

It seems, then, that somewhere in the second glacial/pluvial period man crossed at least one evolutionary threshold, perhaps two. The Acheulians, arising from the parent *Homo erectus* stock, evolved toward a kind of man with slender bones, a high-vaulted skull, and a jutting chin: *Homo sapiens*. It may be that North Africa's *Atlanthropus* (a *Homo erectus* Acheulian) and England's Swanscombe man (*Homo sapiens*) represent the polar points of this physical change; or perhaps *Atlanthropus* belonged to a band of the older human type that had learned to follow the new cultural style. Meanwhile, in Europe, the "cold-weather" Clactonian people, with their flake tools and fur clothes, were possibly evolving toward the thick-boned, chinless, big-browed type we call Neanderthal man. Lastly, in Java and China, other *Homo erectus* groups were not evolving at all, but were trudging toward the dead end of extinction.*

The role played by climate in inducing these and other physical changes in man deserves consideration. Two nineteenth-century rules reflect the relationship between climate and body type. Carl Bergmann, in 1848, proposed that warm-blooded animals which live in cold places tend to have greater body bulk than members of the same species living in warm places. J. A. Allen, in 1877, extended Bergmann's rule to hold that in a given species protruding body parts, such as ears, limbs, tails, or noses, will be shorter in the cooler parts of the species' range than in the warmer parts.

These rules are based on the physics of heat loss: the greater the surface area, the greater the radiation of heat from a warm body to a cooler surrounding atmosphere. Since volume is three-dimensional and area is two-dimensional, an increase in bulk is not accompanied by a proportional increase in surface area, and the heat radiation per unit of volume grows smaller with increasing body size (Bergmann's rules). The closer a body comes to being a perfect sphere, the smaller is its heat-radiating surface; projecting extremities are undesirable in a cold climate (Allen's rule). These rules do not apply to all species equally, for some, by hibernating or otherwise taking shelter, excuse themselves from the worst effects of cold; other species have modifications of fur or hair that help to deal with the heat-loss problem; and one, *Homo sapiens,*

* Several anthropologists, notably Carleton S. Coon, disagree with the belief that the Javan and Chinese pithecanthropoids reached evolutionary dead ends. Coon believes that each of the modern races of mankind was produced by a separate crossing of the *erectus/sapiens* threshold, with the Javan pithecanthropoids evolving into the Papuans and Australian aborigines, the Chinese pithecanthropoids becoming the Mongoloid race, and the Caucasians descended from Heidelberg man or some other European member of *Homo erectus.* This view, first made public in 1962, has not won much support.

is capable of transforming his environment by artificial heat and the use of shelter and clothing.

Nevertheless the Bergmann and Allen rules have considerable validity, as a survey of contemporary human populations shows. Even in man, the animal most in command of his environment, physical adaptations to climate are evident. In Europe northern peoples shows a greater average weight than those of the south: the Irish (157 pounds) and the Finns (154) are substantially heavier than the Spaniards (132 pounds) and the Berbers of Algeria (124). Northern Chinese average 142 pounds, Vietnamese 112. Indians of the northern United States and Canada average about 150, those of Mexico about 120, those of cold Patagonia 150. Along the equator some peoples have average weights of 100 pounds or less.

Associated with body size is general physique. Negroes of the Sahara and Sudan have unusually long arms and legs, slender necks, lengthy fingers; their bodies are constructed for maximum radiation of heat. Cold-weather people such as Eskimos are squat, burly, compact, with a far greater ratio of trunk length to leg length than tropical people. Accumulation of body fat helps to ward off the cold; polar and subpolar people have deep pads of subcutaneous fat, notably at the cheeks, wrists, and ankles, while dwellers in the tropics have almost none.

Skin color, the most conspicuous distinction among the races of mankind, is also thought to be a response to environment, and Carleton Coon and others believe that these distinctions may have been in effect even before the evolution of *Homo erectus* into *Homo sapiens*. The sun bathes the earth in ultraviolet radiation which weakens in intensity with distance from the equator, as well as varying from summer to winter in higher latitudes. Ultraviolet reacts with a substance in human skin to produce Vitamin D, which is essential to proper growth, particularly the development of the bones. A deficiency of Vitamin D leads to bowed legs, knock-knees, rickets, twisted spines, and other defects. However, excessive production of Vitamin D in the body can be equally dangerous, producing a condition known as hypervitaminosis D, in which the levels of calcium and phosphorus in the blood increase markedly, calcification of the soft tissues occurs, and a toxic condition akin to kidney stones may develop, often with fatal consequences.

Human skin has two mechanisms for guarding against the formation of an overdose of Vitamin D: production of substances called melanin and keratin, both of which serve as filters for ultraviolet radiation. Melanin is a pigment that darkens the skin; keratin, from which nails, claws, horns, and hooves are formed, toughens the skin and gives it a yellowish tinge. Negroes have such highly melanized skin that it is brown or black in color. Mongoloid peoples, who have little melanin, are well supplied with keratin. Thus Negroes and Mongoloids can live in equatorial regions, where ultraviolet radiation is at its greatest, without fear of producing too much Vitamin D; but white-skinned peoples, have relatively little melanin or keratin in their skins, are exposed to the full effects of the solar ultraviolet.

The biochemist W. Farnsworth Loomis of Brandeis University, in a study published in 1967, showed that under equatorial conditions untanned white Europeans would synthesize up to 800,000 international units of Vitamin D a day in six hours' exposure to sunlight, a toxic quantity. Deeply pigmented Africans under the same conditions synthesize 40,000 to 80,000 I.U. of Vitamin D; their skins filter out from 50% to 95% of the ultraviolet that reaches the skin layers that produce the vitamin. Thus Africans living near the equator and exposing nearly all their skin surface to the strong sunlight do not suffer from hypervitaminosis D; but dark-skinned people living in higher latitudes are prone to rickets and other Vitamin-D deficiency diseases.

Loomis believes that the need to control synthesis of Vitamin D affected human skin pigmentation in the Pleistocene when men first began to move far from the tropics. "Having originated in the tropics where too much sunlight rather than too little was the danger," he writes, "the first hominids had no difficulty in obtaining sufficient amounts of Vitamin D until they extended their range north of the Mediterranean Sea and latitude 40°N., where the winter sun is less than 20 degrees above the horizon and most of the needed ultraviolet is removed from the sun's rays by the powerful filtering action of the atmosphere through which the slanting rays have to pass. . . . The farther north one goes, the more severe becomes this effect of latitude on the availability of winter ultraviolet radiation, an effect compounded by cloudy winter skies."

He speculates that the earliest men "were probably deeply pigmented and covered with fur, as are most other tropical primates," and that one of the first evolutionary responses to lowered availability of ultraviolet light as they moved north was a reduction of fur. This, of course, can never be confirmed by fossil evidence, and some anthropologists are skeptical about portraying *Home erectus* as being as shaggy as a gorilla. In the northward migrations, he goes on, natural selection operated to eliminate the most deeply pigmented infants, who "must have been especially likely to develop the grossly bent legs and twisted spines characteristic of rickets, deformities which would cripple their ability to hunt game when they were adults." This favored the evolution of white, less pigmented skin, which would admit as much as possible of the greatly reduced available quantity of ultraviolet radiation—a process that reached its ultimate with the blond, fair-skinned people of Scandinavia. As early as the time of Heidelberg man, in the first interglacial, this process must have been at work, he asserts. The only exception to Loomis' rule that white skin is an adaptation to high latitude is the Eskimo, whose skin is swarthy and who nonetheless is wholly free of rickets. The explanation, first offered many years ago, is that the Eskimo diet consists almost entirely of fish oil and meat, which carry several times the minimum preventive dose of Vitamin D; an evolutionary bleaching of the skin to admit more ultraviolet was not needed in his case.

White-skinned people must also protect themselves from excessive doses of ultraviolet in the summer, when the intensity of solar ultraviolet is as great in the temperate zones as at the equator. For this they have the useful device of reversible suntanning: a deepening of the skin color through activation of keratin and melanin, producing a protective tan that will fade in winter, when ultraviolet levels are much lower. "It is significant," Loomis writes, "that both the keratinization and melanization components of suntan are initiated by the same wavelengths which synthesize Vitamin D, for it would be difficult to design a more perfect defense against excessive doses of Vitamin D than this reversible response to ultraviolet light of these particular wavelengths—a pigmentation response that is further protected by the painful alarm bell of sunburn, which guarantees extreme caution against overexposure to solar ultraviolet in untanned individuals suddenly encountering a tropical sun."

Following these ideas, we can picture relatively tall, slender, dark-skinned Acheulians entering Europe in the second interglacial and finding it inhabited by husky, fair-skinned Clactonians. Even if this picture of contrasts is correct, we need not imagine any violent collision of races. Human population in the middle Pleistocene was so scanty that there may have been only a few thousand people in all of Europe. Nevertheless, during the 190,000 years of the second interglacial (Ericson and Wollin say 640,000 years) the two groups did meet and, evidently, mixed. At a site in Suffolk, England, both hand axes and Clactonian flake tools have been found, and there is no way of knowing whether the craftsmen who made them were Clactonian-influenced Acheulians, Acheulian-influenced Clactonians, or some sort of hybrids.

Out of this mixing, perhaps, came increased control of environment. Another Acheulian site in Suffolk contains a layer of the pollen of weeds that appear only after the burning of a forest; this suggests deliberate forest clearance to encourage the growth of food plants, though an accidental forest fire may have been responsible. No sign of charcoal, charred wood, or charred bone appears, however, until near the close of the second interglacial. And as the glaciers advanced for the third time, some 230,000 years ago (Ericson-Wollin: 420,000 years) the Acheulians again began to withdraw toward Africa.

They did not entirely abandon Europe during this third ice age. Though they withdrew from England, France, and Germany, Acheulian people remained in the Mediterranean region. Those who stayed adapted to the colder weather. They learned how to make scrapers of flint as well as their traditional hand axes, so we can guess that they were using animal hides for clothing. Charcoal hearths start to appear in Acheulian sites. So do the bones of the mammoth, musk ox, reindeer, and other Arctic animals which had come south once more. So despite their long warm-weather tradition, the hand-ax people stayed on, at least to some extent, after the renewed onset of the ice.

The Clactonian flake-tool people, who had lived through the second ice age in Europe, stayed on for the third. Later in the glacial period the tools of a different culture, known as the Levalloisian, appear in the sequence. The Levalloisians also made flake tools, but by a sophisticated method in which a core of flint was carefully prepared by cross-flaking so that a complete and perfect tool could be struck from it with a single firm blow. It has been suggested that the Levalloisians were the former Acheulians who had borrowed toolmaking ideas from their Clactonian neighbors, improving on them to be able to face a rapidly worsening climate. But since the Levalloisians were much more hardy than the Acheulians, living far to the north and east of the Acheulian territory, it is equally possible that they were descendants of Clactonians who had learned a thing or two about craftsmanship from the Acheulians.

This is a cloudy picture, which grows no more clear at the end of the third ice age. As warm weather returns, about 170,000 years ago (Ericson-Wollin: 340,000 years), Africa is dominated by Acheulian peoples; western Europe is occupied by the Levalloisians; the Near East is the territory of Acheulians showing some influence of an eastern European flake-tool culture known as the Tayacians, whose tools were struck from disk-shaped cores. We know all three of these cultures almost exclusively from their artifacts; but in the warming Europe of the third interglacial appears a fourth culture, the Mousterian, which is amply documented both by artifacts and by skeletons of a striking nature.

The artifacts of the Mousterians and their fossilized remains both were discovered in the middle of the nineteenth century, but it was many years before the discovery of one in association with the other proved the relationship between them. The story begins in 1856, when workmen in a limestone quarry at a valley called Neanderthal, near Düsseldorf, Germany, found a startling human skull while cleaning out the mud floor of a cave. It was strangely brutish in form, with a sloping forehead out of which bulged an enormous ridge above the brows. The walls of the skull were much thicker than those of ordinary men. Thighbones found near the skull were so massive that they hardly seemed human at all.

At that time Darwin's theory of evolution had not yet been made public, and it was heresy to suggest that the Neanderthal skull might represent some prior form of man. Though a German scientist termed it "the most ancient memorial of the early inhabitants of Europe," the common scientific response was to dismiss it as the skull of a deformed individual whose skeleton had been distorted by rickets, arthritis, or some other disease. But in 1866 a jawbone came to light in Belgium, lying among the bones of mammoth, reindeer, and rhinoceros. It was curiously chinless and very thick, extremely primitive and apelike in appearance. The anthropologist E. T. Hamy leaped to the conclusion that the jawbone belonged to the same species of man as the Neanderthal skull, which had been found without its lower jaw. But there was no proof of the relationship.

The proof appeared twenty years later, in 1886. In a cave near the Belgian town of Namur, two geologists found five distinct layers of relics. Digging down carefully, they came upon the bones of ice age animals, stone knives and tools, and then—in the second layer from the bottom—the remains of three skeletons, huddled together as though in sleep.

They were Neanderthal skeletons. The geologists found two skulls, two lower jaws, some skeletal remains of one face, and a number of well-preserved leg bones. There could no longer be any doubt that a brutish-looking but undeniably human creature had once roved Europe, a sturdy, thick-boned man with a receding forehead, scarcely any chin at all, and huge eyes topped by protruding brow ridges.

Meanwhile, in 1863, the pioneering archaeologists Henry Christy and Édouard Lartet had excavated a number of caves in the Dordogne district of southwest France that showed signs of habitation by early man. Digging down, they found sequences of tools and animal bones showing changes both in craftsmanship and in prevailing fauna; and deep in a cave near the village of Le Moustier they came upon tools fundamentally different from those of higher levels. Whereas the tools near the surface of the cave floor were made of chips struck from flint cores, these older implements were fashioned from the cores themselves. Under a system of classification published later in the nineteenth century by Louis de Mortillet, director of the Museum of Prehistory in Paris, the artifacts of this culture were termed Mousterian. It was Mortillet who gave the name Acheulian to the much larger and cruder hand axes found below the Mousterian level in the cave of Le Moustier, and Abbevillean and Chellean to the extremely primitive tools found at other sites.

By the close of the nineteenth century Mousterian tools had been repeatedly discovered in association with Neanderthal skeletons; one of the finest Neanderthal specimens of all came from the cave of Le Moustier itself. Mousterian culture is recognized to have been that of Neanderthal man, who first appeared in the third interglacial and reached his peak of importance during Europe's fourth and last ice age.

Mousterian tools, which seem to have developed out of the Clactonian ones, were of many types; the Neanderthal tool kit far surpassed anything that had come before. It included knives and awls, scrapers and weapon points, each designed for its special function. A technique we call "retouching" was employed for greater efficiency: detaching tiny flakes or chips along the edge of the tool to provide a keener cutting surface. The complexity of Mousterian tools indicates a long period of development; and there are traces of Levalloisian influence as well as the much older Clactonian.

Neanderthal man's remains have been found at more than forty sites, mostly in western Europe but some in Asia Minor and the Near East. Thus we have a fair idea of how this not-quite-man looked. He was short and squat, not much more than five feet tall on the average, with a deep barrel of a chest and flat feet. His forehead sloped backward, his brow ridges were enormous, and he had no chin. His nose was broad and low-bridged and his mouth jutted forward like a muzzle. An early idea that he walked in a kind of shuffle, with his knees permanently bent or flexed, has been shown to be an error arising from the faulty reconstruction of one skeleton. A popular image of the Neanderthals as extremely hairy is also probably incorrect. His predominantly northern habitat argues against his having had a thick apelike pelt, following Loomis' ideas about Vitamin D, and we know that he clothed himself in animal hides to ward off the cold against which his heavy fur is popularly supposed to have protected him.

The Neanderthal was undoubtedly human. His brain was actually bigger than that of the average modern man; his wide variety of tools shows inventiveness; he seems to have had some sort of religion, cared for his sick, practiced a kind of rough surgery, and buried his dead. All these are human traits. Though he is classed by some anthropologists in a separate species, *Homo neanderthalensis,* on the basis of his physical differences from us, the modern school of anthropology insists that even those differences were not really so great, and prefers to move him right into our own species. They would place him in the subspecies *Homo sapiens neanderthalensis,* with modern man identified as *Homo sapiens sapiens.*

As we have noted, it has been proposed that the Neanderthals were the biological as well as cultural descendants of the cold-weather men of the second ice age, the Clactonians. Until we find a Clactonian skeleton, the truth of this proposition cannot be determined. Nor can we show a continuous pattern of Clactonian-Mousterian occupation of Europe running from the second ice age to the fourth, as such a theory would demand. Mousterian artifacts do not appear until late in the third interglacial. But it seems likely that a specifically cold-adapted type of human being began to split from the main human stock as early as the first ice age, and that as each ice age drove the Chellean-Abbevillean-Acheulian hand-ax people to warmer climes, the other stock remained, evolving in the direction of the Neanderthal.

For a long time it was believed that this sturdier type of man had Europe exclusively to itself until the abrupt arrival of *Homo sapiens* near the close of the fourth ice age. This idea was exploded by the discovery in 1935 of the *sapiens* Swanscombe man of the second interglacial, and was further demolished twelve years later when fossils of the modern human type were found in a third interglacial deposit. Caves in the valley of Fontéchevade, in west-central France, revealed the familiar artifact and faunal sequences of the fourth ice age, with Mousterian artifacts at the bottom; but in 1937 Mlle. Germaine Henri-Martin discovered a lower cave at Fontéchevade containing rhinoceros bones—not the woolly rhinoceros of the ice ages, but the tropical rhinoceros that had not lived in Europe since the end of the third interglacial. After the war, Mlle. Henri-Martin returned to work in the pre-Mousterian levels of the cave, finding more fossils of tropical mammals, and among them some flint implements of the Tayacian type. This culture, traces of which have been found from Palestine to France, is usually thought to provide a link between the Clactonians and the Mousterians. But in August, 1947, Mlle. Henri-Martin unearthed two fragmentary human skulls amid the Tayacian artifacts. They were without brow ridges, and in skull capacity and other characteristics were characteristic of *Homo sapiens.* What such men were doing in a Tayacian level is hard to understand, unless they were victims of a cannibal feast enjoyed by the Tayacian ancestors of the Neanderthals. But they prove the presence of *Homo sapiens* in nearly modern form in the Europe of the third interglacial.

The huskier cold-weather human stock of that period may not have been as different from *Homo sapiens sapiens* then as it later became. Fossils found with Mousterian tools of the third interglacial show few of the extreme Neanderthal specializations of the succeeding ice age. A skull found at Ehringsdorf, Germany, in 1925, was clearly associated with early Mousterian artifacts, but it lacked some of the features of the "classic" Neanderthal. Though it had big brow ridges, the forehead was well developed, the skull vault was high, there was the beginning of a chin, and the structure of the jaw was remarkably modern. Two skulls found in early Mousterian levels at Saccopastore, Italy, in the 1930's were also oddly non-Neanderthal in some respects: Though the foreheads sloped and the skull vault was low, the brow ridges were not particularly large and the teeth were small and modern looking. Another early skull, found at Steinheim, Germany, in 1933, likewise seems to be a Neanderthal specimen, with a low skull vault, big eye sockets, and a huge brow ridge, but the teeth and mouth structure are those of modern *Homo sapiens*. Since the Steinheim skull was discovered in a *second* interglacial stratum, it might conceivably be our only Clactonian fossil; but no artifacts were found with it to give cultural identification.

Many Neanderthal skulls of the third interglacial were discovered in Palestine in the 1930's. These came from caves in Mount Carmel, overlooking the port of Haifa, and, like the Steinheim, Ehringsdorf, and Saccopastore skulls, have been classed as "progressive" rather than "classic" Neanderthals, because of their many *sapiens*-like features. One skull found in 1932 had a retreating forehead and heavy brow ridges, but not the customary Neanderthal bulge at the back of the head. From a nearby cave came the skeleton of a man who stood five feet ten—much taller than the Neanderthal average—and had a high forehead, a rounded skull, a well developed chin, all *Homo sapiens* characteristics; but he also had massive, bulging brow ridges.

Some anthropologists suggested that the "progressive" skulls represented Neanderthals in the process of evolving into *Homo sapiens*. But the idea that such an evolution ever took place is now almost universally rejected: Neanderthals and modern man are seen evolving at the same time from a common ancestor, rather than the one from the other. The "progressive" skulls have also been explained as examples of crossbreeding between Neanderthals and *Homo sapiens*. This, too, has been dismissed in favor of the theory that the "classic" Neanderthal traits did not develop until the fourth ice age, and that the "progressive" Neanderthals of the third interglacial were generally much closer in appearance to *Homo sapiens* than were their apparent descendants.

The most vigorous exponent of this idea is Carleton S. Coon, who in his *The Origin of Races* (1962) proposed that most of what we consider the "brutish" aspects of the Neanderthals were late evolutionary responses to the bitter cold of the fourth ice age. He feels that the severe climatic conditions encouraged the development of thick-bodied, short-necked men with receding chins, low foreheads, and ever more prominent brow ridges. Even the big Neanderthal nose is seen as an adaptation to the cold. He points out that "the nose serves the purpose, among others, of warming and moistening the inhaled air on its way to the lungs. . . . Recent military research has shown that in very cold climates it is not so much the lungs but the brain that is in danger of chilling by inhaled air. The lungs are a long way from the nose. In arctic populations necks are generally short, skulls broad and low, and the distance from nose to lungs less than in many long-necked tropical peoples. . . . As the climate grew colder, Neanderthal men may have increasingly needed a large, projecting nasal 'radiator,' particularly as there is no archaeological evidence of cultural improvement that would help mitigate the severity of the climate."

The severity of that climate was great, but not beyond the capacity of primitive man to survive. In the north, the area that was mostly covered by the Scandinavian, British, and Alpine glaciers, a harsh Arctic climate prevailed; even in July the temperatures rarely rose above freezing. The ice-free corridor that ran across France, Germany, and eastern Europe between the Scandinavian and Alpine glaciers was a tundra, a bleak treeless zone where the ground was more or less permanently frozen; a calculation of probable temperatures during the fourth ice age ranges from a mean of 8°–10°F. in December, January, and February to about 50°F. for a short while in July. Along the rim of the Mediterranean was a cold-temperate forest zone, without permafrost, where the climate may have been something like that of Denmark or northern Germany today. All over Europe there was little precipitation the year around. The days were clear and cold. The westerlies blew 10°–15° closer to the equator than they do today.

The Neanderthals coped adequately with the deep freeze for hundreds of generations; though by our standards they appear coarse and almost bestial, they were superbly fitted for their rugged environment, and seem to have been endowed with courage, endurance, and no small degree of intelligence. In the southern half of France they staked out semipermanent territories, taking shelter in caves, swaddling themselves in furs, and hunting mammoths, rhinos, and smaller game; they had fire and approached the problems of food-gathering with ingenuity and determination. The northern Neanderthals were the first known men to take possession of a tundra environment; the evidence indicates that they followed the seasonal migrations of the herds of woolly beasts, moving northward in the summer almost to the border of the Scandinavian glaciers, retreating into the southern forests when winter came. On the wind-raked plains between the glaciers these Neanderthals of the marginal country may have lived in tents or wind shelters, though no trace of them survives. Never before in human history, at any rate, did men so ably meet the challenges of a hostile environment.

Then, for the fourth time, the ice began to retreat. It was no sudden thaw, but rather an infinitely slow process that saw the glaciers pulling back by a few hundred feet each year. There were many reversals of the trend, recaptures of ground. But the winters became less brutal; spring arrived earlier each year; summers were warmer. In the warm countries, in the Near East and North Africa, the future world-conquerors, our ancestors, had been biding their time while the Neanderthals hunted in glacier-covered Europe. As had happened in each of the ice ages previously, this evolutionary line had moved out of Europe when the glaciers came. Now roving tribes of *Homo sapiens,* seeking new hunting grounds, began to edge northward again. There was no instant rush into Europe. The invaders moved cautiously, camping for years in one place, then pushing onward. At last they were in France and Germany, some 30,000 years ago, perhaps as early as 60,000 years ago. This was the heartland of the Neanderthals. There came a collision of cultures and the swift disappearance of the hardier human stock.

The fate of the Neanderthals is unknown. It is most dramatic to imagine a terrible war of conquest, fought from cave to cave against the bleak backdrop of the frozen world. We can visualize Neanderthal blood staining the glacial snow as the tall invaders—more agile, more inventive—carried out their campaign of genocide. We can see the last few Neanderthals driven into the barren tundra, hunted down, starved out, taken as slaves. Or the conquest may have been more peaceful, a matter of intermarriage and the genetic absorption of the Neanderthals; but there is no fossil evidence to support this theory of mass hybridization. Perhaps the conquerors simply pushed the Neanderthals into ever more marginal environments until they passed a point of no return and were unable to sustain themselves. Whatever happened, the same grim story is told by the strata of nearly every cave of western France. Layers of sterile sand cover the Mousterian flake tools, and above them lie the deposits of a wholly different culture, which we call the Aurignacian, with objects of bone and horn and ivory, carved statuettes, flint tools of many shapes. With the replacement of *Homo sapiens neanderthalensis* by *Homo sapiens sapiens,* man's biological evolution reached approximately its present stage; but man's cultural evolution was really just beginning.

5

The End of the Ice

THOSE WHO SUPPLANTED THE NEANDERTHALS OF THE LATE fourth ice age in Europe are commonly called the Cro-Magnon men, but this is an oversimplification. The Cro-Magnons were only one of several *Homo sapiens* groups of their time. They were the most spectacular-looking, unusually tall, with strong cheekbones and wide faces; but actually the newcomers who took over Europe at this time were just about as varied in form as Europeans are today, and it is a mistake to think that they all had the striking Cro-Magnon physique. Some were short, stocky men with long arms and large feet; others were even shorter and quite slender. Whatever their differences, though, they were bound together by an underlying relationship of blood, by a fundamental similarity of form; all lacked the enormous brow ridges of the Neanderthals, all had well-developed chins, all differed in dozens of other skeletal features from the other human stock.

Louis de Mortillet, the great nineteenth-century classifier, called the cultural phase that now opened the Aurignacian, with the Cro-Magnon people of western France as its main representative. It has since become clear that the Aurignacian culture extended over Europe and parts of Asia and Africa, and that it must be subdivided into several subcultures, existing more or less contemporaneously.

The Chatelperronians, named for a site at Chatelperron in western France, seem to have been the first of the Aurignacian peoples to enter Europe. Their typical product was a large, curved flint knife with one end razor-sharp and the other blunt. This style of fashioning flints originated in southeast Asia, and perhaps the Chatelperronians had spent the worst of the glacial years in the Orient.

The next immigrants, the Aurignacians proper, were those we call the Cro-Magnons. Their flint tools were finer than any previous ones, with a wide range of types of knives and scrapers. They developed a method of striking long bladelike flakes from cores of flint which led to the introduction of new and highly useful tools like the chisel; and once in possession of chisels, the Cro-Magnons were able to begin fashioning tools from bone, a material previously difficult to work. They made polished bone pins and awls, and spearheads that could be fastened to wooden shafts. Thus one key invention touched off a cascade of progress, a common pattern in human development. We can trace the migrations of these Aurignacians by the trail of distinctive artifacts they left behind: from eastern Asia to the Crimea to the Balkans to central Europe to France. By the time they reached France they found the Chatelperronians already established there; doubtless there was some friction between the two cultural groups, but they seem to have managed to live side by side.

The third main Aurignacian phase is the Gravettian—named not for a site but for a type of tool, the *gravette,* a sharp cutting and engraving device shaped something like the blade of a penknife. The Gravettians roamed eastern and central Europe, reaching as far west as Spain, France, and England.

Europe was still relatively inhospitable when these peoples arrived. The fourth glaciation was past its first peak, and the big Arctic animals, the mammoth and the woolly rhinoceros, had withdrawn to the north; but a sheet of mile-thick ice still covered much of northern Europe, and south of this uninhabitable ice field conditions were little more cheering. The only forest trees were scrubby birches and alders that sprouted from the frozen earth. From every mountain there descended a glacier, a slowly flowing river of ice. Winters were long and harsh. Still, things were better than they had been in the times twenty or thirty thousand years before, when the Neanderthals alone had endured the cold. The hunting was good: the Arctic fox, the Arctic hare, and the reindeer grazed along the fringes of the retreating sheets of ice, the bigger mammals were still within reach, and the bison and the horse had come into western Europe from the steppes of southern Russia. And a man could see the climate changing during his lifetime—the weather was a little warmer than it had been in his grandfather's day, and would be warmer yet in the manhood of his grandchildren.

It was a time for the flowering of art. If there was any Neanderthal art, we do not know of it. A crude clay statue of a bear, found in a French cave, possibly is Neanderthal work, but there is no proof of that. The Gravettians, though, used their sharp blades to whittle bangles from the ivory of mammoth tusks, and carved the small, plump female statuettes, probably fertility goddesses, that we call "Venuses." In the caves of France, Aurignacian artists painted the brilliant, colorful scenes of charging bison and prancing horses and browsing mammoths that so astounded their nineteenth- and twentieth-century discoverers by their power and skill. The cave paintings, too, may have had religious significance; but they indicate that for the first time man was sufficiently the master of his environment to allow for the development of such luxuries as art. When a tribe must devote all its energy to the basic task of finding enough food to stay alive, artistic endeavors are left for some more congenial time.

The Gravettians, the core of whose territory was in eastern Europe, produced cultural innovations of a different sort. They painted no cave paintings, for they had no caves; but as far as we know they were the first human beings who constructed houses. The Gravettians were hunters whose hunting range was a narrow grassy strip, bordered on the south by the Alpine glaciers and on the north by the great Arctic ice sheet. The corridor between those two zones of ice was the grazing ground of vast herds of bison, reindeer, mammoths, and other cold-weather animals. In some parts of this range the game made seasonal migrations, with the hunters following them; in others, mainly in central Europe, the animal herds were present all the year round, and semipermanent human settlements sprang up.

Living on the open plains even in winter, the hunters were forced to devise shelter for themselves. Archaeologists working in Czechoslovakia, southern Russia, and Siberia have excavated a number of Gravettian houses dated by carbon 14 to 25,000 years ago—the oldest known man-made structures. They were large pit-houses, sunk into the ground and floored with powdered limestone. Heavy boulders were piled up to form walls. At some sites wooden roof supports remain, showing that the houses once were covered by branches, grass, or earth, very likely with an outer covering of skins weighted down by mammoth bones. One Gravettian house from Czechoslovakia reveals that these huntsmen knew the use of coal as fuel. Logs were scarce on the practically treeless plains, but outcroppings of coal lay near the surface; some prehistoric genius must have experimented with the black mineral in a fire, with happy results.

The warming trend that encouraged the Aurignacian migration into Europe and that fostered these cultural developments was only a cruel deception, however. After about five thousand years of steadily more favorable conditions, the trend reversed itself and the glaciers expanded again. In the period between 22,000 and 18,000 years ago, western Europe was exposed to a second upswing of the Würm glaciation, bringing a climate as severe as anything the Neanderthals had ever faced. This savage period of renewed cold checked and stifled the Aurignacian cultures, which made no further progress; but it also appears to have stimulated the birth of a new culture, the Solutrean, whose place in the archaeological record has long perplexed prehistorians.

Solutrean artifacts first were discovered by Édouard Lartet and Henry Christy during their pioneering work in the Dordogne in 1863. Above deposits of Aurignacian flint tools they found quite different flints, long, tapering, remarkably thin, with elegant retouching on both sides. Because these handsome blades were much longer than they were broad, they quickly became known as "laurel-leaf" and "willow-leaf" points; the culture of their makers was named for the type site of Solutré in eastern France. Solutrean artifacts have since been found above the Aurignacian over much of western Europe. The flat, startlingly attractive blades displayed impressive craftsmanship, and often craftsmanship for its own sake, since many Solutrean implements were too fragile or too bizarrely shaped to have had any practical use.

Archaeologists once spoke of a Solutrean "empire"—a conquered zone dominated by aggressive invaders who had come perhaps from North Africa, perhaps from Hungary (both places where flints resembling the Solutrean ones have been found) to sweep aside the Aurignacians. This view has recently been challenged by a Canadian archaeologist, Philip E. L. Smith of the University of Toronto, who in 1959 returned to the sites of the first discovery of Solutrean artifacts and began a study of the entire mystery. Smith concluded that the Solutreans had arrived at a time of intense cold to take possession of caves and rock shelters already abandoned by the Aurignacians. There was no actual invasion, then, but the entry of a new and unusual culture into a deserted area. They thrived and developed for some four thousand years; but about seventeen thousand years ago the trend toward colder weather once more halted, and western Europe's climate became unusually mild. The Solutreans, who had tolerated the long cold spell with apparent ease, were faced with a major problem when the woolly mammoth and rhinoceros on which they preyed moved northward out of a France that now was uncomfortably warm for them. As their sources of food grew scarcer, the Solutreans dwindled in numbers and relinquished their settlements, disappearing altogether in a short time. In their place is found a new culture of western Europe, the Magdalenian.

The Magdalenians were much closer in their ways to the old Aurignacians than they were to the Solutreans. Their cave paintings, their flint and bone tools, and their other artifacts all show descent from Aurignacian models. It seems as though the Solutreans were intruders who came, occupied, and vanished, leaving no heirs; the Aurignacian peoples must have continued to hold the regions bordering on the Solutrean dominion, and after the Solutreans had departed, the older culture-group returned, now in the guise of the Magdalenians.

Inasmuch as such labels as "Abbevillean" or "Acheulian" are applied to periods lasting hundreds of thousands of years, this quick succession of cultures in the latter part of the fourth ice age may seem like a failure of perspective: if we only knew the earlier periods in the same detail, we might also be assigning two or three cultural names for every few thousand years, instead of making a single one do for three thousand centuries. In part this is true; much of the early archaeological record is hidden or gone. But it is not only our greater wealth of knowledge about recent eras that makes the story become so much more detailed. The pace of progress itself had accelerated. Man became a quick learner. Where Abbevilleans patiently chipped hand axes in an unvarying way for inconceivable spans of time, new techniques now rushed upon one another with ever-increasing rapidity.

The ice ages had ceased to be major threats. In Europe the great glaciations had four times turned man into the toy of the elements. Whole populations had been driven into refuge, had returned thousands of years later, had been driven out again. But slowly man learned to cope with these powerful forces; fire, clothing, shelter provided some control over them; in each ice age a greater number stayed on, until by the fourth man was practically immune to the challenge of the glaciers. He was able to hold his own even in near-Arctic Europe. Perhaps as a direct response to this repeated challenge, Europe had replaced Africa as the center of human inventiveness and innovation.

Short-term shifts in the weather outlook continued to affect man's existence. A few decades of relatively warm weather would drive the woolly beasts to new pastures, forcing man to follow. A return to the cold meant a sudden revival of the habits and tactics of ice-age life. Tribes had to be able to adapt to these changes.

The Magdalenians, like the Solutreans and Aurignacians before them, were skilled hunters, adapted to a bitterly cold environment and living in caves, rock shelters, and open-air camps. More than fifteen thousand years had passed since the Aurignacian vanguards had entered Europe, and the Magdalenians were heirs to all the skills acquired in those years. They were superb artists, skilled workers in bone and ivory, inventors of such essential devices as the barbed spear, the harpoon, and the spear-thrower. From their base in southwest France and northern Spain they made their influence felt in Belgium, Switzerland, southern Germany, and Czechoslovakia. But their way of life, supremely successful on its own terms, was undone by the very factor that made it so glittering. The last of the ice ages was ending; each year was infinitesimally warmer than the one before. Food was plentiful, the climate was kind, and the Magdalenians had the leisure that is necessary to stimulate progress. A rush of new ideas, new methods, new accomplishments marked this golden age. Population increased also, for the improvements in hunting weapons and the milder climate permitted the growth of larger tribes.

But the Magdalenian skills, it soon became clear, were of little value in the changing world. The glaciers fell back, leaving bare plains of thawing ground. Birch and willow trees sprang up, and then pines. The ice-age animals could not survive in birch thickets; they were bulky grazers who needed open grasslands. The herds of mammoths, reindeer, bison, and horses migrated northward, or died out altogether in the shifting climate. The Magdalenians found themselves deprived of the big beasts that had been man's chief prey throughout the glacial periods. A time of transition opened; a great culture collapsed.

Those Magdalenians who were least adaptable followed the reindeer and mammoths northwood into the still-frozen steppe country of Germany and southern Scandinavia, becoming backwoodsmen carrying on an outmoded way of life. The ones who stayed behind in France and northern Spain developed a new pattern of culture based on trapping wild fowl and fish, digging up edible roots, and hunting the red deer and other smaller animals common in the new forests. Among these cultures are the Azilian and Tardenoisian of the Pyrenees, typified by the manufacture of delicate miniature tools and weapons known as microliths. These people produced arrow points that are little more than tiny slivers of flint, and made blades with complex cutting edges by inserting rows of little flint points into shafts of bone or wood.

Even in the north, the rapidly shifting conditions between 15,000 and 12,000 years ago caused problems for those who were unwilling to take up the forest life of the microlith people and become hunters of rabbits and squirrels. The giant Pleistocene tundra fauna became extinct in stages; the mammoth and woolly rhino died out, the musk ox fled to the inaccessible Arctic. No longer able to hunt such beasts, the backwoodsmen tracked the reindeer herds through almost barren grassland where dwarf birches and stunted willows alone broke the frosty monotony. With spears and harpoons they slew, and eventually some genius of the north added a deadly new weapon to man's arsenal by inventing the bow. So light a weapon as an arrow would have been useless against the huge woolly animals of the past, but now they were gone, and the new weapon was highly effective against the faster-moving but sparsely furred reindeer.

Small bands of these hunters moved over the naked landscape, killing swiftly in the short summer season before the long winter night. From June to September they hunted; then they settled down to endure the cold and wait out the winter. But not even the reindeer could tolerate the constantly more temperate climate. The zone of forests crept ever northward; one unusually warm interval that began about 12,000 years ago saw woodlands spreading into Scandinavia. The tundra regions that the reindeer preferred were confined to small areas in southern Sweden and Finland, bordering on what was left of the Arctic ice sheet. The reindeer-hunters, following their herds, were pulled onward into the remote north. In their wake came a different sort of people who settled in the new world that was opening up. These versatile folk expanded through the forests, keeping pace with the climatic changes and turning them to their own benefit.

Archaeologists have at their command several extraordinary techniques for determining the succession of events in this post-glacial epoch. They can reconstruct the botanical makeup of the forests, can tell whether the climate was warm or cold, and, most remarkable of all, can even set exact years to those prehistoric times when the glaciers pulled back.

This last feat is accomplished by a method known as varve-counting, developed late in the nineteenth century and perfected early in the twentieth by a Swedish geologist, Baron Gerhard de Geer. A varve is a ridge of sediment laid down in lakes along the border of continental glaciers. The spring thaw of the glacier sends water into the lake carrying suspended sand, clay, and fine particles of gravel, which gives the water the opaque, cloudy look that brings it the nickname "glaciers' milk." The coarser grains of this sediment settle first, while the finer material gradually falls to the bottom of the lake during the summer. Wave motion during the summer may keep the finest sediments from settling until the lake surface freezes over in the autumn. But the varve, which is the aggregate of the year's deposits, is distinct from those of past or later years, for a sharp contact zone divides each new springtime deposit of coarse sediment from that which accumulated the previous summer and fall. The thickness of the varve depends on the year's weather: a warm year produces a great deal of glacial runoff and a thicker varve than a cold year.

Geer, beginning his geological field work in 1878, was struck by the regularity of the glacial varves he found in different parts of Sweden, and sought to find some correlation between the varves of one district and those of another. In 1905 he led a team of students along a 120-mile line running north from Stockholm, measuring varves at intervals of less than a mile and charting them on strips of paper. The following year Geer and his field workers extended their coverage until it spanned 500 miles, from Sweden's southernmost tip to a point high in the northern mountains where the melting icecap had become divided into two sections, remnants of which still exist.

The southernmost varves were the oldest. By tracing the varve line northward, Geer was able to work out a sequence of glacial retreat covering thousands of years; each year had a varve of characteristic thickness, denoting that year's weather conditions. Of the more than five thousand varves that Geer charted in this way, one in particular was unusually thick. He interpreted this as the varve laid down in the year the icecap had split in two, for that must have released a great quantity of ponded-up water that had spilled out, rich with sediments. Geer termed this varve his "zero varve" and began his glacial chronology with it, marking all later years with a plus sign and the prior years with a minus sign.

He still could not assign specific years to any of his varves. Near the place of the splitting of the glacier, though, was the site of the former Lake Ragunda, which had accidentally been drained in 1796. Geer found some seven thousand varves in a hundred-foot section of Lake Ragunda's dry bed; near the bottom he saw his zero varve and other recognizable ice-age varves, while the upper end extended his series much closer to the present. However, varve formation had ceased in Lake Ragunda long before 1796, and it was necessary to patch recent varve sequences from northern Sweden into the chronology, matching them at their older end with the younger ones from Lake Ragunda, before the varve calendar was complete. By 1938 the job was done; specific dates could be reckond by counting back from the present; and before Geer's death in 1943 he was able to report that the splitting of the icecap and the deposit of the zero varve had occurred in 6839 B.C. The varve chronology now provides an exact year-by-year account of the retreat of the Scandinavian glaciers over more than 10,000 years, going back 1,400 years before the formation of the zero varve to 8239 B.C. In a less precise way it has been extended nearly 8,000 years back from that point to the depths of the last ice age.

The varve count not only serves as a prehistoric almanac,

but also shows us large climatic patterns, since several hundred consecutive thick varves can be taken as a sign of warm weather and rapid melting over a long span. The evidence thus obtained can be checked against another important source of information: the pollen count. Pollen analysis, which yields the most fundamental kind of climatic data, was the great contribution of a Swedish botanist, Lennart von Post, who began his work at the age of 23, in 1907.

Post's specialty was the study of the peat deposits that had filled Sweden's old glacial lakes. Peat is composed of plant debris—leaves, branches, seeds, stems—pressed down into solid form. Examining the preserved matter in a peat deposit tells what sort of plant life lived in that immediate vicinity. In particular, Post analyzed the microscopic, virtually indestructible grains of pollen embedded in the peat. Each type of plant or tree produces a distinctive kind of pollen, and a survey, or pollen "spectrum," of sediments or peat will indicate the nature of the plant life inhabiting a region at the time the ancient deposits were laid down. (Since wind-blown pollen can travel a hundred miles or more, pollen analysis gives a regional and not a local picture of the prevailing flora.) Though the pollen method has certain innate flaws (some species produce little pollen, or pollen that decomposes quickly), it provides a reasonably accurate profile of the forest succession of prehistoric times.

In 1916 Post established a series of pollen "zones," or strata, representing the botanical sequence of northwestern Europe over the last 13,500 years, and inferring the oscillations of climate that must have produced such a sequence. Though much modified, Post's system of zones is still in use and offers a useful key to the way Europe emerged, in fits and starts, from the deep freeze of the fourth ice age.

Areas covered by glaciers, of course, have no plant life and so no pollen deposits are laid down until the glaciers begin to withdraw. The Post sequence begins with the first postglacial period, the Older Dryas, so named after a characteristic plant found in tundralike environments. During the Older Dryas, which began some time prior to 13,500 years ago in the northern areas Post studied, the land newly freed from the ice was a barren, forlorn, treeless terrain gripped by an Arctic climate; the pollen record shows grasses, dwarf willows and birches, a few pines, and small plants. About 13,500 years before the present, the chill of the Dryas was interrupted by a warm period known as the Bölling, which lasted about a thousand years and saw the growth of birch forests in the former tundras. Then, about 12,500 years ago, the Arctic conditions of the Dryas returned; the glaciers expanded southward, and the forest zone retreated.

This lasted five or six hundred years, and about 12,000 B.P. there commenced an extraordinary warm period, the Alleröd, in which temperatures were close to what they are today. The pollen spectra of Alleröd times show pine woodlands in the southern half of France, southern Germany, and northern Poland; pine and spruce farther to the southeast; northern France and northern Germany were covered by a birch woodland with some pine; Denmark and the British Isles (which then were joined to continental Europe) had birch forests. Only in upper Scandinavia was there a tundra strip. Glacial melt had proceeded so far that world sea level was less than a hundred feet below where it is today, though this still left many land bridges above water; the Baltic Sea region, which had been completely covered by a glacier in the last ice age, now became a large freshwater lake, connected to the Atlantic only by a narrow gap at its western end. Through this opening the overflow of water from the melting glaciers of Alleröd times could escape, but otherwise this Baltic Ice Lake was dammed by the remaining ice masses and was totally cut off from salt water.

The congenial Alleröd might be thought to have been a time of great human expansion, but actually this warm interval seems to have been a period of crisis for the hunting peoples of Europe. The last of the mammoth herds now were extinguished; the reindeer vanished to the remote north and did not come south even in winter, leaving only small forest game as a source of meat. There is some evidence that the human population dropped steeply with the warming weather, until at last in the late Alleröd food-gathering techniques suitable to the new environment were generally in use and population growth could resume.

Such growth as there was, though, was cut off sharply about 10,850 B.P. by the abrupt return of the Arctic conditions of the Dryas, which threw the forest folk of the Alleröd into chaos. This so-called Younger Dryas brought a sudden and severe deterioration of the climate; glaciers advanced, sea level dropped by twenty to thirty feet, mean temperatures fell drastically, from a July average of about 56°F. in the Alleröd to about 42°F. in the Younger Dryas. Vast forest tracts were killed and converted into bleak tundra in less than a century; man was driven back hundreds of miles to the south and forced to resume his discarded hunting tactics.

Conditions turned again in the Preboreal, beginning about 13,500 years ago. For reasons not yet understood, the climate grew warm once more, permitting colonization of the tundra by such cold-tolerant trees as pine and birch and willow, and a hesitant northward movement by animals and men. The archaeological record shows almost uninterrupted improvement in the European climate now, permitting the development of a typical northern forest succession. In the early cool, dry years of the Preboreal, the birch and pine did well, pushing aside such previous colonists of the tundra as juniper and aspen. But the environment continued to grow warmer, and botanical migrants from the south entered the forests, marking the transition from the Preboreal to the Boreal about 9,500 years ago. The arrival in the forests of the hazel, a shade-loving shrub that does well under birch and pine, is considered to denote the formal boundary between Preboreal and Boreal. Soon oaks, alders, and elms found places for themselves beside the hazels spreading through the Boreal woods, and the birches and pines thinned out and started to disappear. This was in part a reflection of the warming trend, which made conditions more favorable for mild-weather trees than for birch and pine; but also it was the result of a normal forest succession, for hazel tends to stifle the growth of young birch trees, and as the older forest population was crowded out, the newer trees from the south were able to take possession.

Many lively, inventive cultures flourished at this time, of which the Maglemosean, which ranged over much of northern Europe in Preboreal and Boreal times, is typical. The rediscovery of this culture began in 1900, when a team of archaeologists from the National Museum of Denmark began to dig at the Magle Mose, or "great bog," on the Danish island of Zealand. Near the surface of the site lay flint tools, and deeper in the bog were implements of bone and wood. The Maglemoseans were forest-dwellers who occupied the lowlands along large lakes; they pitched their camps in one place for a few years, until their hunters and fishermen had thinned the food supply past the level of support, and then moved on to some other area where game and fish were more abundant. They were expert carpenters who made excellent use of the plentiful wood of the new forests. One important Maglemosean innovation was the true ax with attached handle—a flint blade mounted on a shaft made either from wood or a deer antler. They also had drills, gouges, chisels, and the highly useful adz, which is an ax with its blade mounted at right angles to the shaft so that it can be used for scraping and hollowing logs.

The Maglemoseans built boats, and fishing now became an important activity of man for the first time. In the past, there had always been a little trapping of river fish, and some cultures of the Spanish coast had depended to a certain extent on what they could catch along the Atlantic shore. But the Maglemoseans, equipped with nets, hooks, and other fishing gear, went to sea regularly. Their boats ranged for great distances, permitting the wide and rapid spread of their way of life. On land they hunted the red deer in the forests. They were mobile even in winter, for they had invented the sledge, and their runner-equipped wooden vehicles, hauled by manpower in the absence of domesticated horses or sledge dogs, made winter's snows less of an impediment to getting about than ever before.

During the Boreal times when the Maglemoseans thrived, Europe's climate was of the kind called continental: severe winters, hot summers, and prevailing easterly winds that brought only sparse rainfall. The summer temperatures now went well beyond the highest levels of the Alleröd, with means of 60° F. or more even in the north, but in the winter much harsher conditions were experienced. The chief reason for this was the landlocked nature of northern Europe; in place of the Baltic Sea, which could have conducted the warmth of the Atlantic Ocean to the coasts of Germany, Poland, and Scandinavia, there was the cold Baltic Ice Lake, its western outlet blocked by a dam of ice. This huge body of fresh water acted as a refrigerator for an area covering thousands of square miles.

A combination of events helped to bring about the replacement of Europe's continental climate, with the great temperature range and general lack of precipitation, by a gentle oceanic climate typified by mild winters, cool summers, and heavy rainfall. The transformation of the Baltic Ice Lake into the Baltic Sea was essential to this process. It began in the Preboreal when warming temperatures caused the dam of ice plugging the lake to break up. This happened, according to Geer's varve chronology, exactly 1,073 years before the dividing of the Scandinavian icecap: that is, in 7912 B.C. As the dam gave way, the penned-up waters of the Ice Lake rushed out into the North Sea, flooding the low-lying plains and giving northern Europe approximately the coastline it now has. The level of the lake itself fell by some sixty feet, which left an unmistakable mark in the varve record. Now there was direct communication between the Atlantic and the Baltic, but the climate did not at once grow warmer, for there still was ice along the Baltic's northern shore, more than sufficient to counteract the effects of the influx of sea water. Archaeologists call the Baltic in this phase of its development the Yoldia Sea, after a type of subarctic mollusk that lived in it. On the north shores of the Yoldia Sea the climate remained frigid, while along its southern rim there was only a slight warming effect.

Midway through the Boreal the Baltic became a lake again as a result of the general lifting of the coasts of Germany and Denmark. This geological upheaval cut the Yoldia Sea off from the ocean and turned it into a body of fresh water with its surface about ninety feet above the present sea level. At this stage it is called the Ancylus Lake after a different genus of mollusks that flourished in its waters. The presence of the Ancylus Lake served to reinforce the continental climate. Since the mean temperatures were still rising, northern Europe now had parched, dusty summers. Even though the winters were cold, the low precipitation starved the glaciers, so that they were unable to replenish what had been lost in the warm months. The shrinking of the Scandinavian icecap had been going on for thousands of years, but now it accelerated, and by 6839 B.C.—the year of Geer's zero varve—it split in two, an event which Geer and others regarded as the precise moment when the last Pleistocene ice age reached its end. When the icecap had been larger, it had been covered by a more or less perpetual high-pressure area, and this lingering glacial anticyclone had helped to keep northern precipitation low. Now, the contraction of the glaciers broke up the high-pressure zone; the belt of westerlies swept over northern Europe, carrying moist air from the Atlantic that created heavy cyclonic storms.

The effects of this change were enhanced about 7,000 years ago by the end of the Ancylus Lake. The southern shore of the lake settled, allowing water to flow from the North Sea, an arm of the Atlantic, by way of Denmark. This created what is called the Litorina Sea, after a species of snail that occupied it then. No longer was the warm water of the Atlantic shut out; no longer was there a Scandinavian icecap to keep the Baltic cold; and the result was the ushering in of a period of warm, extremely humid and rainy climate of an oceanic kind. The presence of the oceanic body of water to the west acted as a stabilizer, eliminating extremes of temperature from season to season, and serving as an evaporation sink feeding the rainfall-bearing winds.

This period of warm, wet climate is known as the "Atlantic." Forests of oak and elm spread rapidly; and within a thousand years after the formation of the Litorina Sea Europe entered a time known variously as the "postglacial thermal maximum," the "hypsithermal," and the "climatic optimum," in which temperatures throughout most of the world averaged several degrees higher than those of today. During this period, which was at its peak from 6,000 to 4,000 years ago, the icecaps of the Arctic diminished greatly and perhaps vanished altogether in many places. Forests increased; in Great Britain trees grew at altitudes 600 to 1,000 feet above the contemporary timber-line, and there were forests in such northern isles as the Orkneys and Faeroes, now treeless.

The growth of these lush forests forced a radical change in the living patterns of the Maglemoseans. When their culture had taken form, some 10,000 years ago, the forests had consisted of straight, slender birches and willows, well suited for hunting. But now gigantic oaks filled the woods, surrounded by a dense undergrowth of hazels and alders. Not even with their axes could the Maglemoseans clear paths through these tangled thickets. Finding and pursuing the red deer now became impossible; crowded out of their forests by the flourishing trees, the Maglemoseans were compelled to settle along the sea-coast and collect oysters and shellfish as their main source of food. Their great mounds of discarded shells, the "kitchen middens" of archaeology, testify to this migration from the forests to the shore roughly 5,000 years ago.

This kitchen-midden culture, which archaeologists term the Ertebølle culture after the type site in Denmark, stretched all along the coasts of northern Europe from England to the Baltic. Inland lay thick, impassable forests of oak and linden and elm, and in the shelter of these big trees thrived the forest animals, the red deer and roe deer, the wild boar, the wild ox. The Ertebølle men still hunted these animals as their Maglemosean forebears had done, but they did not pursue them very far into the woods.

No traces of Ertebølle houses have been uncovered, but we can guess that their shoreside settlements were composed of skin tents or branch shelters, a few dozen to a camp, with a constantly growing mound of refuse at the downwind side. The communities were busy ones, each person with an assigned task. There was as yet no farming, no raising of livestock; this was purely a food-gathering society in which the men hunted and the women, children, and old people waded in the sea at low tide to harvest shellfish. Fishermen went out regularly to cast their nets and lines; hunters with harpoons sometimes killed the seals of the coastal waters; archers using sharp, flint-tipped arrows thinned the flocks of birds soaring overhead. The Ertebølle people were the first in northern Europe to make pottery, producing rough, dark, lumpy ware. Pottery offered new opportunities. Seeds and nuts could now be stored safely where rodents could not reach them; stews, porridges, and soups became part of the diet; boiling food, formerly a complex business involving dropping red-hot stones into leather vessels containing water, now became a simple matter. Certain plants that could not be eaten unless boiled now became staples of the meal.

But the dwellers on the kitchen middens were hardly the vanguard of civilization with their flint tools, their crude pottery, and their food-gathering ways. Western Europe once had been a fertile source of new ideas, the intellectual capital of the ice-age world, and now it was a backwoods region of cultural laggards, and the center of progress had shifted elsewhere. In the Near East, an entirely new way of life had developed as a result of what is called the Neolithic revolution. Technically, "neolithic" is a term that describes nothing more than the replacement of chipped stone tools by polished stone tools; but the real importance of the Neolithic innovations lay in the new ways of obtaining food. While Europe still was thawing out from the ice age, more than 10,000 years ago, and its inhabitants still depended on hunting, fishing, and the gathering of seeds and nuts, certain outposts in the Near East were taking the giant step toward independence from nature's whims. They learned how to grow crops and how to domesticate livestock. They discovered that useful grains like wheat and barley could be raised by planting seeds in cultivated soil, and by watering and weeding and tending. They mastered the art of making pottery, and learned that wild pigs and sheep and cattle could be tamed and kept close at hand to serve as permanent sources of meat and milk. Settlements of a lasting nature sprang up next to the best grazing and farming lands. The first villages were born. The new ease of obtaining food permitted a sudden and dramatic expansion of population. A flood of new inventions followed—the loom, the plow, the sickle—and mankind was set on the path that took it to the city-building stage, the great civilizations of Egypt and Mesopotamia, and the birth of our modern world.

6

Farmers and Cities

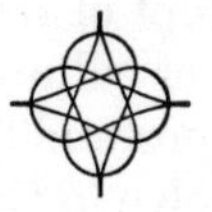

IN THE PAST TEN THOUSAND YEARS HUMAN LIFE HAS CHANGED more profoundly than in the previous ten thousand generations. The rate of progress has increased spectacularly since the time when it took 50 millennia to effect a small change in the style of chipping stone axes. Farming, pottery, houses, cities, steam power, electrical power, automobiles, atomic energy, supersonic planes—the innovations come tumbling one over the other at an ever more rapid pace.

One group of geographers and historians attributes this surging development largely to climatic factors. Climate, they say, provided the stimulus and created the necessary environmental conditions; after that, progress was cumulative and steady. These environmental determinists hold that climate shapes man and his society, and that only in the right kind of climate can a technological society such as ours evolve. The opponents of environmental determinism argue that the theory is vague, simplistic, superficial, and—in some of its manifestations—capable of being used as a justification for racial prejudice.

That environment is relevant to culture has never been seriously doubted, only the degree of the relationship. In the nineteenth century many historians studied the influence of geographical factors on the growth and expansion of societies, coming to the obvious conclusion that great empires do not flourish in hostile surroundings or in an overly comfortable environment. Following Darwin, whose theory of evolution was based largely on the concept of response to environment, they looked for shaping forces of culture in wind, rain, and temperature. It took no great profundity to prove that a farming society was unlikely to evolve in Greenland or a tribe of fishermen in the Sahara; but the environmental determinists quickly moved away from such extreme cases to consider how the main stream of human society had been influenced by climate.

The American writer Ellen Churchill Semple (1863–1932) devoted much of her career to these problems. In such books as *American History in its Geographic Conditions* (1903) and *Influences of Geographic Environment* (1911) she sought climatic explanations not only for technological and cultural developments, but even political ones. "The most fruitful political policies of nations have almost invariably had a geographical core," she wrote, giving as examples "the colonial policies of Holland, England, France and Portugal, the full-trade policy of England, the militantism of Germany, the whole complex question of European balance of power and the Bosporus and the Monroe doctrine of the United States." The political aspect of environmental determinism has a lively history of its own, but it lies largely outside the scope of the present book. Miss Semple, a good Darwinian, gave credit to influences other than thc climatic: the people of the Auvergne, which she called a European "misery spot," are weak, she said, due "in part to race" and also to a harsh climate and poor food, as well as to a "disastrous" emigration of the taller and more robust individuals. She showed how climate shapes cultural assumptions: the desert-dwelling Old Testament Hebrews pictured Hell as a place where one is eternally fried, the Eskimos as a place where one is eternally frozen.

Ellsworth Huntington (1876–1947) was the best known of these theorists. Originally a geologist, the Illinois-born Huntington turned to climatology at the beginning of the twentieth century. Field work in the canyons of the Euphrates River in

1897–1901 showed him dramatically how changes of climate can weaken a civilization, and this became even more apparent to him on expeditions to central Asia in 1903–04 and 1905–06, in which he saw clear evidence of a widespread pattern of desiccation. In 1907 he published *The Pulse of Asia,* his first statement of the theory of climatic "pulsations" or cycles with which his name is associated; and during a long career spent mostly at Yale University he produced twenty-eight more books, collaborated on twenty-seven others, and wrote hundreds of articles, all exploring climate and its relation to human activities, the distribution of civilization, and the nature of geological and historical change. Among his most widely read books were *Civilization and Climate* (1915) and *Mainsprings of Civilization* (1945), the latter of which is still in print and used at many colleges.

When Huntington began his work, the idea that global climate patterns were subject to large-scale change was not at all firmly established; even the existence of the ice ages was still the subject of some controversy, and much of the evidence for subsequent climatic changes was yet unknown. Therefore he found it necessary to expend a great deal of effort simply to prove that climatic shifts were possible and had taken place many times during historical times. He dealt with records of floods and droughts, with encroachments of ice on medieval Europe's shores, with the rise and fall of civilizations in marginal areas. He was a great believer in cycles of many kinds, and felt that these great climatic upheavals repeated themselves in a periodicity that he hoped could be detected and analyzed. "The whole history of life is a record of cycles," he wrote. "In the vast geological periods plants and animals of one great order after another rose to importance, flourished, and declined. In prehistoric times successive species of manlike creatures passed across the stage. In the historic period nations have risen and fallen; types of civilization have grown great and decayed; science, art and literature have been full of vigor and originality only to fall into deadly weakness and conventionalism. In modern business few things are more disturbing than the cycles which seem to become more extreme as time goes on. In each of these examples some form of existence or type of activity starts in a certain condition, goes through a series of changes, and comes back to essentially the same condition as at the beginning."

Huntington isolated scores of cycles ranging in periodicity from a few days to thousands of years. Ransacking archives of every sort, he asserted that European weather has a 35-year cycle from oceanic climate, with wet, cool, stormy summers and mild, moist winters, to continental climate, with dry, sunny, warm summers and cold, clear winters. He found that insect pests in Europe had reached a maximum about every 36 years since 1700. He cited a 7.54 year cycle in barometric pressure, the 11-year sunspot cycle, an 8-year cycle of crop growth, a 41-month cycle of stock market prices, a 150-year cycle of Nile River floods, a 340-year precipitation cycle, and many more. (The records on which some of these cycles were based have since been shown to be in part faulty.) Huntington pursued his obsession with cycles to the point of asserting that almost every human manifestation from the yield of bonds to the migration of nomads can be shown to be geared to a climate-related cycle. "It will be a vast boon to mankind," he wrote, "when we learn to prophesy the precise dates when cycles of various kinds will reach definite stages." But he admitted that such a time was unlikely to come soon: "Investigators have described cycles of hundreds of kinds and with scores of different lengths. Aside from such things as the wavelength of light, practically no cycle is absolutely uniform in length. Even the day and year fluctuate a little, although always returning to a length that can be predicted far in advance." One cycle can interfere with another, frustrating attempts at prediction; he cited "the effect of weather on crops, crops on animals, animals on man, and then of both crops and animals on prices, and weather on health."

The key to Huntington's teachings is the idea that combinations of climatic cycles occur, bringing first to one region and then to another the uniquely favorable environmental conditions that he believed were required for the development of civilization. His generalizations on the invigorating effects of certain kinds of weather are the most controversial features of his work. Progress and intellectual activity, he said, occur most readily in areas with a well-defined seasonal pattern, frequent changes of weather, alternation of warmth and cold, a regularity of cyclonic rainstorms, and no unusual extremes of temperature. Inheritance and training were important to the growth of civilization, he agreed, but climate was basic. "For the production of good fruit," he wrote in 1915, "the three factors of good stock, proper cultivation, and favorable climatic conditions are absolutely necessary. Are they equally essential to the fruit known as civilization? We all admit that race and the thing which for lack of a better name we call cultivation or training are of vital importance, but it is also true that man cannot rise to a high level except where the climate is propitious? . . . We realize that a dense and progressive population does not live in the far North or in deserts simply because the difficulty of getting a living grinds men down and keeps them isolated. We know that the denizens of the torrid zone are slow and backward, and we almost universally agree that this is connected with the damp, steady heat. We continually give concrete expression to our faith in climate. Not only do we talk about the weather more than about any other one topic, but we visit the seashore or the mountains for a change of air. We go South in winter, and to cool places in summer. We are depressed by a series of cloudy days, and feel exuberant on a clear, bracing morning after a storm. Yet, in spite of this universal recognition of the importance of climate, we rarely assign to it a foremost place as a condition of civilization."

The world at present has very few "areas of high climatic efficiency," according to Huntington. Such an area, he suggested, must have a mean temperature that rarely falls below 38°F. or rises above 65°F., for beyond either extreme people are debilitated or stupefied. Even where the temperature is ideal, though, lack of fluctuation fails to provide sufficient stimulus: he dismissed Los Angeles as a potential center of civilization, for example, because of its unvaryingly mild climate, saying that the change of temperature from day to day "seems to be second only to that of the mean temperature of the seasons" in its effect on human activity. Cyclonic storms were also vital factors. They "encourage progress by presenting a challenge which is great enough to be highly stimulating, but not great enough to be permanently discouraging. The challenge can be met without undue difficulty if people are energetic and use their heads. For example, on fair days in regions of frequent storms the farmer must hurry with his plowing and planting because rain will soon interfere. He must cut his hay with an eye to drying it before the next storm. When it is drying he must be constantly alert to rake it up or store it away before it gets wet. . . . In such ways and many others the frequent and sudden changes of weather accompanying the meeting of opposing air masses and the shifting winds of cyclonic storms act as a stimulant. They challenge the farmer and others to greater alertness and activity than in the far more extensive regions where changes of weather are usually more gradual. . . . They also encourage the growth of a social system in which great stress is laid on the dynamic qualities which are needed to meet such difficulties." He went so far as to claim that "this cyclonic climate may be too stimulating," linking it to such alleged American traits as "excessive eagerness for action without due planning, boisterousness among children, and the prevalence of degenerative diseases among older people."

In the United States, Huntington found an area of high climatic efficiency in the Northeast from the Atlantic seaboard to the Great Lakes, and one of lesser degree in the Rocky Mountain region. The southern states he regarded as doomed to backwardness by a muggy climate. "One feels it everywhere," he wrote, "for on the trains, at the railroad stations, and at the newsdealers it is generally difficult to find the higher grade of magazines. Time and again during a recent journey of three months in the southern states I tried to get such papers as the *Outlook, Independent, Harper's, Atlantic,* the *Review of Reviews, The Century,* and so forth—but all that I could find was trashy story magazines. The dealers rarely keep the better magazines because people will not read them. Lack of training surely has something to do with the matter, but mental inertia due to lack of climatic stimulus seems to be at least equally important." Huntington also gave his accolade to Japan, New Zealand, Australia, South Africa, Argentina, and most of western Europe from southern Scandinavia to northern Italy as suitable for the growth of a technological society, which he regarded as the highest human endeavor. The rest of the world was either too hot or too cold, too dry or too humid, too hostile or too congenial in environment to stimulate the growth of civilization, although he recognized that certain ingenious peoples—the Eskimos, the Bedouins—might make remarkable adaptations to unusually formidable conditions, without, however, developing the resources or the inclination to expand beyond their home territory.

Huntington believed, although he grew steadily more cautious about saying it, that it was helpful to belong to the white race and perhaps to be Protestant or Jewish. Jews, he said, achieved great things because their thousands of years of persecution had acted as a Darwinian selection, producing a people of resilience, determination, and ability. Protestants were guided by an ethic of expansion and hard work. He did not make it clear whether he felt that race and religion themselves were governed by climate—that the Protestant ethic had in some way necessarily sprung from western Europe's stormy, fluctuating weather—or if they were simply supporting factors in the general advance of civilization. In 1915, when it was still possible to make blandly racist statements even in a book published—as most of Huntington's were—by the Yale University Press, he proposed that Negroes were fundamentally and ineradicably inferior to whites in intelligence: "So far as I am aware, every exact test which has been made on a large scale indicates mental superiority on the part of the white race, even when the two races have equal opportunities. . . . As the plum differs from the apple not only in outward form and color, but in inward flavor, so the negro seems to differ from the white man not only in feature and complexion, but in the workings of the mind. No amount of training can eradicate the difference. . . . We have tried to convert the black man into an inferior white man, but it cannot be done." The essential qualities of Huntington's "Teutonic race" (represented by the white man of western Europe and North America are "initiative, versatility, and the power of leadership. . . . Good humor, patience, loyalty, and the power of self-sacrifice give flavor to the negro. With proper training he can accomplish wonders." In a book written thirty years later, after Huntington's most Teutonic Teutons had dealt the world a terrifying lesson in the dangers of believing in the innate superiority or inferiority of races, he was not only willing to dignify the Negro with a capital letter but to retract much of the innocent and casual racism of his earlier works: "At first Negro inferiority was rarely ascribed to physical environment or cultural deficiency. Race was to blame. Four years of devastating civil war ensued, but the idea of racial superiority still dogs our steps incessantly. . . . No reputable scientist knows of evidence that would reveal a causal connection between the family-line heritage ("race") of a population and its language, culture, mental or emotional makeup."

Huntington thus abandoned his earlier belief that, as he put it in *Civilization and Climate,* "the brain of the white man is more complex than that of his black brother," but he remained convinced that climate and cultural traits ("upbringing") had much to do with the kind of civilization an area develops. Sociologists today prefer not to look at the cultural differences between nuclear physicists and the slash-and-burn farmers of tropical rain forests in terms of the superiority of one group or the inferiority of the other, but none would deny Huntington's oft-repeated assertion that "the energetic area of western and central Europe has been the great center of civilization for a thousand years. From it have gone forth more new ideas than from all the rest of the world combined. Its manufactures have flooded all parts of the earth. Politically it dominates about 60% of the earth's surface. Socially its domination is much greater." (Huntington sees the United States, settled mostly by western Europeans and in large measure having a European climate, as simply an extension of the European cultural zone.)

Though he spent his life proving that a variable, stormy temperate-zone climate had been essential in the birth of western European culture, which he regarded as mankind's highest achievement, Huntington was never a dogmatic environmental determinist. "The theory of climatic efficiency," he wrote, "must not be stretched to cover non-climatic matters. High climatic efficiency does not provide inventive brains; it merely stimulates such brains. It does not supply natural resources, even though the climates that are best for human energy are also admirable for agriculture and animal husbandry, and happen in some cases to be located in regions well supplied with minerals. Climates which promote efficiency merely help in developing the possibilities provided by the geographical environment. In short, not even the most stimulating climate insures the presence of a high civilization. It merely aids in the attainment of such a civilization." The example that proved the rule was the American Indian culture of New York, which never got beyond a stone-age level even though it was a product of the same hearty climate that spawned the towers of Wall Street and the intellectual acropolis of Morningside Heights. The Indians "were notable for their activity and alertness" as a result of living in such a stimulating climate, and in their social, military, and political achievement far surpassed the Indians of less favorable environments; but it remained for the first European settlers to create the sophisticated and complex civilization Huntington so greatly admired. "The absence of civilization [among the Indians] was due to a variety of reasons, some of which can only be guessed," he wrote. The lack of animals suitable for domestication was one, apparently; the New York Indians could not use animals "for wool, milk, plowing, and transport, because no wild animals fit for these purposes existed anywhere near them. Even if the bison had not lived far away, it was too big and stupid." The lack of metal tools hampered the development of agriculture, and Huntington could not say whether the failure to have such tools was "due to innate lack of inventive ability or to mere accident." Implied in all this, of course, is the unstated assumption that the Indians simply were not equipped by genetic heritage to take full advantage of the opportunities of their climate, and that the whites were. Modern anthropologists would take issue with that assumption, for they do not regard technological civilization as something finer than primitive life, merely as something more complex; they do not share Huntington's puritan belief that a society that covets and builds automobiles or bombs is morally as well as technically superior to one that shows no interest in "progress."

Technological civilization was not born in Europe, though, and Huntington knew that the test of his ideas on climate and civilization lay in their applicability to great centers of civilization of the past. What of Mesopotamia and Egypt, where the first urban cultures took form more than six thousand years ago? What of the somewhat later civilizations of China and India, and of the subsequent great societies of the Mediterranean? Did all of these cultures spring from Huntington's optimum combination of "people of great energy" inhabiting a region where cyclonic storms brought stimulating changes of weather from day to day? If so, how can one account for the present state of most of those countries, past glories forgotten, many of their people torpid peasants with no discernible ambitions or attainments?

Huntington was able to argue with some justice that none of the great civilizations of the past had arisen in truly tropical places; Thebes and Babylon both lay well north of the Tropic of Cancer, and despite the prevailing heat of the Near East there is considerable fluctuation of temperature through the year. Why, then, did the peoples of these historic lands have in ancient times "a virile energy which they do not now possess," Huntington asked? "Many authorities attribute the loss of this to an inevitable decay which must overtake a nation, as old age overtakes an individual. Others ascribe it to the lack of adaptability in various institutions, to increasing luxury, to contact with inferior civilizations, or to various other factors, all of which are doubtless of much importance." By 1911 he had arrived at an explanation of his own: climatic cycles, or pulsations, which shift the temperate zone of cyclonic storms back and forth, alternately toward and away from the equator.

This is Huntington's famous "pulsatory hypothesis," which, in his words, "holds that although in general the past was moister than the present, the changes have taken place irregularly in great waves. Certain centuries were apparently drier than today, while others were moist." The proof of this he saw almost everywhere: "In many parts of Asia, Africa, and America ruins of towns and cities are located where now the supply of water seems utterly inadequate. Old roads traverse deserts where caravans cannot now travel; traces of dry springs are seen; bridges span channels which carry no water for years at a time; old fields are carefully walled in places where now the rainfall is too scanty to permit agriculture and where no water can be brought for irrigation." Such shifts in climate sent people migrating from arid lands to stormy ones, in which they experienced the invigorating effects of variable weather and proceeded to develop far beyond their earlier performance. Huntington's example of this is the Semitic invaders from the desert who swept into Babylonia some four thousand years ago: "The invaders had done no great things in their original homes so far as we know, but when they came to Babylonia they blossomed into people of inventive minds full of new ideas which caused the arts to rise to higher and higher levels." On the other hand, a movement of the belt of westerlies away from an already established great nation would be its undoing, according to Huntington, both through the effect of growing aridity on agriculture and through the loss of the vital stimulation of the cyclonic storms. Progressive desiccation through climate change, he maintained, was at the core of the breakdown of the first civilizations of the Near East; and then, spurred by climatic pulsations, civilization moved northwestward from Babylon and Thebes to Athens and Rome, to Paris and London, to New York and Chicago. "If the pulsatory hypothesis is true," he declared, "the relationship between historic events and climatic vicissitudes is even greater than has been supposed."

Many of Ellsworth Huntington's favorite concepts fall apart

under close examination, or have been exploded through the replacement of shrewd speculation by archaeological fact. Environmental determinism is in poor scientific repute today, despite or perhaps because of its espousal by such popular historians as Arnold Toynbee, whose "challenge-and-response" ideas, so tempting to the layman, seem to provoke professional scholars into fits of wrath. Though nearly everyone is willing to concede that great shifts in climate can affect civilization (i.e., that an ice age in Europe brought certain cultural and even evolutionary responses, or that a prolonged drought in an agricultural region will produce famine and lead to migration), most of Huntington's attempts to show relationships between rainstorms and factory production in New England now are lightly regarded, as are the theories he and others offered in explanation of the effects of climate on the rise and fall of whole civilizations. He frequently overstated his case or generalized from unreliable sources; nevertheless, it does seem likely that Huntington may be due for a rehabilitation. His specific examples must in many instances be discarded, his statistical tables are outmoded, and his fondness for discovering cycles seems a little ludicrous, but his underlying thesis—that climate shapes civilization—will probably survive the assaults of his detractors.

The difficulty of determining the relationship of climate to man in any situation more subtle than the onset of an ice age is shown by the inquiry into the causes of the greatest single cultural advance in human history—the Neolithic revolution. The basic Neolithic achievement was the transition from a food-gathering to a food-producing society, which is the foundation for the enormous edifice of progress that has been reared in the succeeding hundred centuries.

The exact site where farming was born has not been determined, nor can a precise date be assigned to the moment when man took the momentous step toward the self-sufficiency of an agricultural economy. But beyond much doubt the Neolithic revolution began in Syria, Palestine, Iraq, or Asia Minor, about eleven thousand years ago or even earlier—that is, at a time when Europe was finally emerging from the ice and moving from a big-game-hunting tradition to a small-game-hunting tradition. Probably the evolution from a hunting economy to a Neolithic farming economy took place more or less simultaneously in several parts of the Near East, and led to the relatively rapid expansion of humble camps into substantial permanent communities.

One of the oldest Neolithic sites excavated thus far is Jericho, which lies near the Dead Sea in what was until the war of June, 1967, part of the kingdom of Jordan. Modern Jericho is a pleasant town in an oasis of palms and banana trees, surrounded by the harshness of a desert as wild and as barren as any badlands of the American West. About a mile from the town, beside a spring known since ancient times as Elisha's Fountain, is a mud-colored mound called Tell es-Sultan, which is the site of biblical Jericho. Archaeologists have been prowling in this high, irregular, unprepossessing mound since the middle of the nineteenth century, most of them looking for the famous walls overthrown by Joshua. To their consternation they discovered a whole series of Jerichos, one atop another, and were unable to determine satisfactorily which, if any, might be the Jericho conquered by the Israelites.

The matter remained unsettled until the British archaeologist Kathleen Kenyon began work there in 1952. She sent shafts through the mound to the bedrock and virgin soil below the oldest layers of human occupation, and produced a result disappointing to those who seek for archaeological confirmation of biblical events: "Of the town walls of the Late Bronze Age, within which period the attack by the Israelites must fall by any dating, not a trace remains." Erosion had completely obliterated them. She could find nothing of that Jericho but a part of the kitchen of a single house and a lone clay dipper that might have been dropped by a panicky housewife when the trumpets of Israel sounded. The lower levels of the mound, though, held much of great value. Deep in Tell es-Sultan lay the oldest known city of mankind, Neolithic Jericho. It dates from a time when the use of metals was unknown, when even pottery had not yet been developed. Flint knives, borers, scrapers, arrowheads, and sickles abounded. There were stone querns for grinding corn, tools of bone, hammers and pestles of stone. The carbon-14 method gave dates of about 5850 B.C. and 6250 B.C. for charcoal fragments found in one of the higher levels of the Neolithic zone; organic matter from a lower level produced a date of about 6800 B.C., nor was this the bottom of the mound, though no datable material could be found in lower strata. The results showed that Jericho had existed as a town more than nine thousand years ago.

Fifty centuries before Egypt's pyramids were built, then, Jericho was a large fortified community where crops were raised and animals domesticated. At that incredibly early date, when virtually all the world was a hunting ground for simple nomads, Jericho was a self-sufficient and fully organized settlement of cooperating citizens. It covered at least eight acres, was surrounded by massive stone walls, and may have had a population of as much as three thousand. Within the town was a ponderous circular stone tower almost thirty feet in diameter, pierced by a sloping staircase—perhaps the most complex architectural achievement of its era. Certainly the community that built the great walls and massive tower of Neolithic Jericho must have had purposeful leadership and a host of skilled craftsmen. Only a well-developed system of agriculture could possibly have supported this ambitious program of public works; the fertility of Jericho's oasis must have been important in fostering this agriculture, though it would have been necessary for the ancient farmers to devise a network of irrigation channels in order to raise crops sufficient to keep so large a village fed. This, too, is testimony to Jericho's precociousness.

In the lowest levels of the Jericho mound, with an estimated age of 10,800 years, were found stone artifacts of a type known as Natufian, characteristic of Palestine's pre-Neolithic culture. The Natufians were a transitional people, nomadic hunters who originally lived in caves, gradually emerged to create semipermanent communities in the open, and in some places experimented with primitive agriculture. At Jericho, an interconnected chain of circumstances permitted the nomadic Natufians to settle and develop a town: a good location, a dependable supply of water, intelligent leadership, the willingness to join in common endeavors, the creation of irrigation works, the raising of abundant crops, all were part of the sequence of progress that culminated in the walled town of Jericho. The Natufian flint tools at the bottom of Tell es-Sultan provide the link between Jericho and its pre-Neolithic predecessors, such as the Natufians who lived in the caves of Mount Carmel, near Haifa. These people hunted gazelles, goats, squirrels, deer, and many other animals, mostly small ones, according to the debris of bones scattered on the floor of their caves. The presence of mortars, pestles, and flint sickles indicates that they reaped and ground such wild grains as wheat and barley and other plant foods, though there is no evidence of actual agriculture; the Natufians were probably highly specialized food-gatherers rather than farmers, harvesting the grains that grew on the hillsides all about them. Eventually some Natufian settlements moved from this intensified food-collecting to the stage of cultivation.

Wild wheat and barley are native to high land, and the desert oasis of Jericho lies nearly a thousand feet below sea level. It would seem, then, that the Natufian hunters learned to harvest grain in the hill country and brought their knowledge with them to Jericho, where unusually favorable conditions allowed the flowering of their way of life into a true Neolithic culture. Archaeologists have looked to the uplands for the beginnings of agriculture, investigating not only the Natufian caves of Palestine but the sites of a roughly contemporary and similar culture of the Kurdish hills of Iraq, known as the Karim Shahirian. The Karim Shahirians, who, like the Natufians, flourished between nine and twelve thousand years ago, also had access to wild wheat and barley, the most useful of the wild grains. Grinding and pounding tools in their sites show that they made use of them. Wild sheep and goats also were available to them, and at one Karim Shahirian site, Zawi Chemi Shanidar, there is evidence of the domestication of sheep about 8900 B.C.

Two early Neolithic towns, contemporaries of Neolithic Jericho, have been excavated so far in Iraq. They are Jarmo and

Tepe Sarab, 120 miles apart on the inward slopes of the Zagros mountain crescent in Kurdistan. Robert J. Braidwood of the Oriental Institute of the University of Chicago, who began work at Jarmo in 1948 and at Tepe Sarab in 1960, believes that they were inhabited between 7000 and 6500 B.C., and that many sites of the same age await discovery in the Kurdistan hills. "Tepe Sarab," he wrote, "may have been occupied only seasonally, but Jarmo was a permanent, year-round settlement with about two dozen mud-walled houses that were repaired and rebuilt frequently, creating about a dozen distinct levels of occupancy. We have identified there the remains of two-row barley (cultivated barley today has six rows of grain on a spike) and two forms of domesticated wheat. Goats and dogs, and possibly sheep, were domesticated. The bones of wild animals, quantities of snail shells and acorns and pistachio nuts indicate that the people still hunted and collected a substantial amount of food. They enjoyed a varied, adequate and well-balanced diet which was possibly superior to that of the people living in the same area today."

Why did the transition from food-collecting to food-producing occur when and where it did, in Palestine, Iraq, and the rest of the so-called "fertile crescent" of the Near East, some eleven thousand years ago? According to the environmental determinists, the motivating stimulus was a sudden shift from pluvial to arid conditions at the end of the last glaciation. Regions in North Africa, the Near East, Arabia, Iran, India, and Central Asia that had enjoyed heavy rainfall while the glaciers covered Europe now became deserts; and the hunters who had lived in those regions were compelled to invent a new way of life in order to survive.

This concept was first put forth by the American explorer Raphael Pumpelly, who had led the Asian expedition on which Ellsworth Huntington's theories of desiccation were formed, and who had excavated a Neolithic site at Anau, in central Asia. Pumpelly wrote in 1908,

> With the gradual shrinking in dimensions of habitable areas and the disappearance of herds of wild animals, man, con-

centrating on the oases and forced to conquer new means of support, began to utilize the native plants; and from among these he learned to use seeds of different grasses growing on the dry land and in marshes at the mouths of larger streams on the desert. With the increase of population and its necessities, he learned to plant the seeds, thus making, by conscious or unconscious selection, the first step in the evolution of the whole series of cereals.

V. Gordon Childe of the University of Edinburgh, an important archaeologist and an influential archaeological writer, made use of this theory in such books as *New Light on the Most Ancient East* (1934) and *Man Makes Himself* (1936). In the latter he wrote,

> The period when the food-producing economy became established was one of climatic crises adversely affecting precisely that zone of arid sub-tropical countries where the earliest farmers appear, and where the wild ancestors of cultivated cereals and domestic animals actually lived. The melting of the European ice sheets and the contraction of the high pressures or anticyclones over them involved a northward shift in the normal path of the rain-bearing depressions from the Atlantic. The showers that had watered North Africa and Arabia were deflected over Europe. Desiccation set in. Of course the process was not sudden or catastrophic. At first and for long, the sole harbinger would be the greater severity and longer duration of periodical droughts. But quite a small reduction in the rainfall would work a devastating change in countries that were always relatively dry. It would mean the difference between continuous grasslands and sandy deserts interrupted by oases.
>
> A number of animals that could live comfortably with a twelve-inch annual rainfall would become a surplus population if the precipitation diminished by a couple of inches for two or three years on end. To get food and water, the grass-eaters would have to congregate round a diminishing number of springs and streams—in oases. There they would be more exposed than ever to the attacks of beasts of prey—lions, leopards, wolves—that would also gravitate to the oases for water. And they would be brought up against man too; for the same causes that would force even hunters to frequent the springs and valleys. The huntsman and his prey thus find themselves united in an effort to circumvent the dreadful power of drought.

This "enforced juxtaposition," Childe wrote, "might almost of itself promote that sort of symbiosis between man and beast signified in the word domestication," and this, along with the development of techniques for cultivating the previously wild grains, would bring "emancipation from dependence on the whims of the environment." Toynbee, too, saw the onset of desiccation as the "physical challenge" that spurred the evolution of agriculture in the Near East, and other historians have continued to make use of the idea.

However, the archaeological record seems to show that the food-producing revolution did not take place in the deserts but in the hill country of western Asia, which is unquestionably the native territory of the ancestral forms of wheat and barley. Childe assumed that these wild grains also grew in the lowland oases, and that when desiccation had driven animals and the men who hunted them out of the hills and into the oases, the art of cultivation was invented there. Such hillside cave-dwellers as the Natufians, he said, were probably not the progenitors of agriculture but "just a backward tribe who adopted some elements of culture from more progressive cultivators elsewhere," meaning the lowlands. Modern research has shown him wrong on all counts. The early wheats and barleys did not grow in the lowlands until man planted them there, and by that time he was already an agriculturalist. Nor did post-pluvial desiccation drive animals and men from the hills to the lowlands. The zoologist Charles Reed has pointed out that any increase in aridity would have caused the wild goats and sheep to climb higher into the hills, not to descend into the desert, so that the hunters would have been pulled away from, not toward, the lowlands where Childe thought agriculture began. Furthermore, such desiccation as occurred after the pluvial did not, evidently, have much effect on the hill country, where numerous streams continued to provide abundant water even while the grasslands below were shriveling into deserts.

If Childe is wrong that "incipient desiccation . . . would provide a stimulus towards the adoption of a food-producing economy" and that man's enforced concentration near oases spurred the development of agriculture and domestication, what did bring about the Neolithic revolution of the Near East?

Robert Braidwood, one of those who most strongly opposes the environmental determinist approach, feels that "there is no need to complicate the story with extraneous 'causes.' The food-producing revolution seems to have occurred as the culmination of the ever increasing cultural differentiation and specialization of human communities. Around 8000 B.C. the inhabitants of the hills around the fertile crescent had come to know their habitat so well that they were beginning to domesticate the plants and animals they had been collecting and hunting. At slightly later times human cultures reached the corresponding level in Central America and perhaps in the Andes, in southeastern Asia and in China. From these 'nuclear' zones cultural diffusion spread the new way of life to the rest of the world."

Certainly there were changes of climate in the Near East in the post-glacial/pluvial period. Rainfall fell and temperatures rose during the time that corresponds to the Bölling and Alleröd warm spells of northern Europe; during the relapses of cold during the Older and Younger Dryas, the weather in the fertile crescent was generally cooler and moister. One of these moist periods evidently coincided with the time of the Natufian culture (9000–7000 B.C.) and seems to have come to its end about the time the first known Neolithic villages were being founded. Braidwood does not think that these climatic shifts were particularly pronounced or that they were major determining factors in the development of agriculture; the Neolithic revolution happened, he says, as a natural advance unrelated to environmental conditions.

How this may have come about has been suggested by the Danish botanist Hans Helbaek, who took part in the Braidwood excavations. Helbaek proposed in 1959 that agriculture necessarily arose in the highlands of the fertile crescent, since in no other place did both wheat and barley grow wild. (Barley alone occurred in wild form across much of Asia and Europe, but no early agriculture was based just on barley.)

Pre-Neolithic man gathered and milled the seeds of these two wild grasses, perhaps practicing a kind of unintentional selectivity. The grains of wild grasses drop easily from the seed-holding spike, so that the seeds can be widely scattered; but when early man collected seeds he naturally chose to reap plants with tough spikes and intact heads. This encouraged the persistence of a recessive gene that produces seed-retentive plants, which are precisely those needed for farming. When the idea of deliberately planting a crop of wheat or barley arose, it was these seeds that happened to be on hand to be used.

In this way the domestication of the wild grasses began, leading to the emergence of a kind of grain that did not reproduce well in nature, but which—with proper cultivation, weeding, and watering—could meet human demands. Soon it became advantageous to move down from the hills and plant the crops on level ground near a reliable water supply, and so wheat and barley left their original home (from 2,000 to 4,300 feet above sea level) and were raised beside streams and springs in such lowland sites as Jericho. The entire process, according to Helbaek and Braidwood, could have taken place without the need to postulate the stimulus of desiccation.

The desiccation theory has also been invoked to explain the spread of Neolithic ideas into Europe. The movement of these ideas away from their Near Eastern birthplace has been the object of much study in recent years, and many sites along the route have been excavated, among them, Catal Hüyük and Haçilar in Asia Minor, Khirokitia on Cyprus, and Nea Nikomedeia in northern Greece. These sites all date from 6000 B.C. or earlier, and indicate the early traces of what is thought to have been a large influx of Neolithic peoples into Europe from the Near East. They moved into a continent that was nearly empty, inhabited only by wandering hunting tribes. One group of Neolithic colonists evidently traveled through Bulgaria and Northern Greece, plunging onward generation after generation along the valleys of the Danube and Rhine rivers and still more northward, until, hundreds or thousands of years later, they reached Scandinavia, while a second Neolithic thrust followed a sea route westward through the Mediterranean, from the Greek islands to Malta and Sicily, into southern Italy, then to the south of France, the east coast of Spain, and ultimately north to Great Britain. The agriculturalist concepts of these migrants were watched and imitated by the hunters, who in time adopted Neolithic ways themselves.

Childe believed that the same increasing aridity in the post-glacial Near East which had inspired the birth of Neolithic concepts eventually became so severe that it drove some Neolithic peoples to seek new territory in the moister lands of Europe. This idea no longer has much support, since it has been shown that the most extensive expansion out of the Near East into Europe came after 5000 B.C.—at a time when desiccation had halted in the fertile crescent and most of the world was enjoying the moist climate of the Atlantic phase of the post-glacial period.

Whatever the reasons for the development and expansion of Neolithic ways, they brought man an immense new freedom from the dictates of his environment. An economy based on farming and herding provided a larger and more dependable food supply; domestic animals could be used for meat most of the year, while grain could be stored for consumption long after the harvest. It was no longer necessary to move whenever the local supply of game or wild plants was exhausted. Droughts, cool summers, or unusually harsh winters still would have their effects, but given reasonable conditions, settlements could remain at one site for an indefinite time. Man had ceased to be wholly at the mercy of his environment, and in fact the environment was beginning to be at *his* mercy, as fields of cultivated crops replaced woodlands or grasslands. Soon such new environmental problems as erosion and soil deterioration would be posed, but these stemmed from man's own deeds, not from the impersonal dictates of the invisible gods of storm.

One region where there can be no doubt of the effects of post-pluvial desiccation was the Sahara. Today it is the world's largest desert and the world's least populous area, aside from Antarctica: less than two million people inhabit its 3,089,000 square miles. Stretching across North Africa for 3000 miles from the Atlantic Ocean to the Red Sea, it covers an area not much smaller than the United States. Its average rainfall is under ten inches a year, and that includes the comparatively moist highlands. Over most of the Sahara the annual precipitation is about four inches a year; great patches see an inch or less a year, on the average; large regions may have no rainfall at all for a decade or more at a time. Summertime temperatures often reach 120°F. in the shade. The Sahara's sparse population is confined mainly to the highlands, though the presence of occasional oases and the use of that almost indestructible beast of burden, the camel, has made possible nomadic exploitation of the desert proper.

Beneath the sands of this inhospitable wilderness, however, are seven tremendous rock basins that hold one of the world's greatest reservoirs of groundwater. Together they have a capacity of some 15 million million cubic meters of water, an astonishing resource that may someday be tapped to sustain human settlement and to turn barren places into productive fields. Some of this subterranean water seeps into the Sahara at the edge of the desert, where the rainfall is ten times as great as it is at the center, and where there is a flow from rivers coming from more fortunate parts of Africa. But this inflow travels through the basins at a speed of half a mile a year or less; in some places it moves only a yard or two a year. Hence the underground water in the heart of the desert attained its present location thousands of years ago—when the Sahara was a tropical region of heavy rainfall, large rivers, and abundant vegetation, and had widespread human habitation.

The Sahara may never have been a tropical paradise; even at the best of times it seems to have had tracts so parched they were incapable of supporting life. But during the pluvial periods of the Pleistocene, rainfall over the Sahara was greatly increased both in the north and in the south, leaving only an arid zone between. One reason for this was the displacement of the northern westerlies toward the south by the high-pressure zone that formed over the European ice sheet. The glaciers, radiating cold into the atmosphere, maintained a perpetual cover of dense, frigid air, and this immovable anticyclonic mass forced the storm-bearing cyclones laden with Atlantic water into the Mediterranean region; thus North Africa had pluvials while Europe was having glacials. At the same time, the "caloric equator"—the zone of heat that usually lies near the geographical equator—shifted north by about five degrees of latitude during the glacial periods, according to the calculations of Milutin Milankovitch. This changed equatorial evaporation patterns and brought heavy rains to the lower Sahara instead of to the jungle regions of central Africa that receive them today.

An inland sea covered some 250,000 square miles at the southern end of the Sahara; nothing remains of this but Lake Chad, which has an area of less than 10,000 square miles and is still shrinking rapidly. (A town which was on the southern border of the lake in 1850 was twenty miles from it by 1905.) Such animals as elephants, giraffes, rhinos, hippos, and deer lived in places now fit only for camels. At elevations of 2,000 feet or more, trees such as juniper, cedar, cypress, and olive grew; still higher were large forests of pine, evergreen oak, and cedar; the low-lying areas that contain nothing today but sand dunes were lush grasslands.

The ghosts of rivers tell us of that lost Sahara. The French archaeologist Henri Lhote, who has done much important work in North Africa, traced the course of one of the desert's "fossil rivers" by automobile in 1959–60. The expedition traversed what Lhote called "one of the most desolate regions in the whole desert—the Ténéré—where, for more than six hundred miles, from north to south, you never see a human being or come across a water-hole. The flora, with the exception of a few grasses that shoot up after the very infrequent rains, is confined to one single, solitary tree, growing almost in the center, that has been adopted as this desert's geodetic point and appears as such on the maps. The general aspect of the Ténéré is one of a pebbly plain stretching as far as the eye can reach. From this flat surface little peaks or eroded ridges jut up here and there. . . . When, in great gusts, the sand-storms begin to blow and you can see but a few paces before you, the scene assumes an apocalyptic grandeur."

But once through the Ténéré there flowed a river 750 miles long; and once, Lhote wrote, there might have been heard "the cheerful shouts of men returning from a good day's hunting, when chattering women gathered around cooking-pots steaming from messes of fish and meat. . . ." Of the river hardly a trace remains except deposits of fishbones and shells visible here and there; the sands have blotted out the bed for hundreds of miles. Along that ancient riverbed, however, Lhote found crude pebble-tools, nothing more than stones from which a few flakes had been struck off at one end to form a sharp point; he believes they were made by australopithecines who lived in the Sahara when the lost river still flowed, half a million years ago or more.

During the oscillations of the Pleistocene the Sahara now was rainy, now was dry; but not even in the interpluvials, apparently, was it the terrifying desert of today. After the makers of the pebble-tools came the makers of the more advanced Chellean hand axes, and then those of the Acheulian type. In Acheulian times Africa was a world leader in Stone Age innovation, but while Europe went on to develop many new tool styles and techniques in the later Pleistocene, Africa remained loyal to the now obsolescent Acheulian toolmaking tradition. These late Acheulians of Africa still flourished as late as 60,000 or 70,000 years ago, perhaps a quarter of a million years after the abandonment of Acheulian styles in Europe. They inhabited a pulvial Sahara, hunting the elephant, hippo, and other large tropical mammals. A warm interlude in Europe's Würm glaciation some 60,000 years ago produced aridity in the Sahara, evidently with devastating effect on these hunting and seed-gathering Acheulians; rainfall diminished by 50 percent in the Sahara, forcing the Acheulians to concentrate at waterholes and springs. One group of archaeologists believes that this change of climate provided the stimulus for a long-overdue burst of progress in North Africa; after millennia of making hand axes, the inhabitants of the Sahara at last started to fashion scrapers and blades from light flakes of flint struck off specially prepared cores. These new tools resemble the Levalloisian and Mousterian artifacts of Europe. However, other prehistorians think that the sudden appearance of Levalloisian-Mousterian implements in the late Pleistocene of Africa is a sign not of progress or imitation of European modes but of an actual invasion of Neanderthals from Europe. These Neanderthals supposedly crossed during one of the cold peaks of the Würm glaciation, in which the sea level was so low that Europe and Africa were connected by many expanses of land now covered by water. So far there is one bit of skeletal evidence to support this idea: the jawbone of a Neanderthal child, found near Tangier and given a carbon-14 date of 38,750 B.C. ± 500 years.

Not enough is known yet about Saharan prehistory to permit an adequate explanation of Pleistocene events in North Africa; but it is clear that the Acheulian tradition did disappear in stages from the Sahara and that it was replaced by a tradition derived from the Levalloisian-Mousterian styles of Europe's Neanderthals. It seems likely that there was a considerable Neanderthal emigration to Africa during the latter part of the fourth ice age, and some romantics have suggested that this was a flight of "refugees" before the advance of *Homo sapiens*. Perhaps so. In any event, the general warming that set in at the close of the Würm glaciation caused sea levels to rise and cut the African Neanderthals off from Europe. They dwelled in isolation in North Africa, developing a variant of the Mousterian culture known as the Aterian, characterized by tools with a tang or shank at the butt end to facilitate attachment to a handle or shaft. Aterian artifacts have been found from Tunisia and Algeria southward to the beginning of the West African grasslands; they have been dated variously from 30,000 to 20,000 years ago, and fragmentary Neanderthaloid remains have been found in association with some Aterian deposits.

These Neanderthals lingered long after their European cousins had wholly disappeared. Their ultimate fate is unknown. The Sahara was subjected to severe aridity beginning about 15,000 years ago—as the Würm glaciers of Europe commenced their final retreat—and this may have forced them out, but it is equally likely that they survived at oases for another five or ten thousand years, desert-dwelling remnants of a doomed species.

After what may have been a hundred centuries of dryness broken only by short spells of moist climate, the Sahara once again began to enjoy heavy rainfall about 7,000 years ago. In Europe at this time the dry continental climate of the Boreal was giving way to the humid conditions of the Atlantic phase; the splitting of the Scandinavian glacier and the opening of the Baltic Sea had ushered in the "climatic optimum" there, with almost unparalleled warmth and moisture. Simultaneously the Sahara's climate shifted into what was, if not a true pluvial level, at least subpluvial.

This seems paradoxical. If, during the Pleistocene, the Sahara had had pluvial periods while Europe was having glacials, why should a *warm* epoch in Europe coincide with a wet one in the Sahara? If Europe now had the full benefit of the rain-laden westerlies, why was the Sahara not smitten by "horse-latitude" dryness as it is today? As the British climatologist H. H. Lamb has observed, "There seems to be something meteorologically curious about the conjuction of pluvial times and conditions for life in the Sahara with the warmest post-glacial epoch in the temperate zone. Explanation in simple terms of a poleward shift of all the climatic zones would hardly be adequate. . . . Perhaps, however, a good deal is explained by higher ocean surface temperatures than now and correspondingly increased moisture in the atmosphere. The Sahara seems to have been still relatively the driest zone."

There is no doubt that the Sahara of 5000 B.C. was a green and pleasant place, at least in comparison to what it is today. Pollen grains from strata that can be dated to that time show evidence of lotus, hackberry, tamarisk, wild olive, cypress, pine, and evergreen oak. The stumps of ancient sycamore and acacia trees still rise from the sand in what now is lifeless desert west of the Nile. In the Aïr highlands of the southern Sahara there stands a living olive tree more than twenty-five feet in diameter; it may be as old as three or four thousand years, and is the lone survivor of what formerly was an extensive grove.

This, according to Henri Lhote, was "the real epoch of the fertile Sahara, when the human communities were so numerous that the density of population was probably greater here than in almost any other region of the world at that time." He tells of successive waves of immigrants invading the area, perhaps wiping out the last of the Aterian Neanderthals: "'Europoids' occupied the northern region; Negroes arrived from the south, and other populations, possibly copper-colored and of Ethiopian type, poured in from the east. . . . Hunters were also food-gatherers; fishers dwelling in villages by the side of rivers and lakes lived on aquatic fauna—fish, mollusks, and even hippopotamus. Later, food-gathering gave way to agriculture carried on with stone hoes in the flood-plain by the side of lakes and streams. Finally came the pastoralists, first with sheep and goats and afterwards with cattle. We can say with confidence that at this period there was an astonishing culture in the Sahara, astonishing both for its variety and for the high quality of its stone artifacts. . . ."

The most vivid testimony both to the quality of culture in the Sahara then and to the nature of the environment comes from the glorious rock paintings now being discovered in some of the most remote regions of the desert. The best known of these are the paintings of the Tassili, a forlorn and colossal wasteland plateau in the southeastern corner of Algeria, where on sandstone escarpments deeply eroded into fantastic pillars and pylons by the action of wind and vanished streams a galaxy of fantastic creatures was depicted by ancient artists. Today only a few Tuareg herdsmen occupy this part of the desert, but thousands of years ago it was the home of a talented people that produced what Henri Lhote has called "the greatest museum of prehistoric art in the whole world."

The Tassili paintings were deeply engraved in outline form into the rock, then colored with rare subtlety, using mineral pigments found nearby. Lhote, who in 1956 led a group of French archaeologists into a region never before penetrated by Europeans in order to make copies of the paintings, declared, "What we saw among the maze of the Tassili rocks goes beyond the bounds of imagination. We copied hundreds upon hundreds of painted walls on which were depicted human and animal figures in their thousands. Some of the figures stood alone, others formed complex groupings. . . . We were astounded by the diversity of styles and subjects and by the great number of overpaintings. Side by side with little figures, a very few inches high, we came across others of gigantic dimensions such as are unknown among prehistoric pictures elsewhere. Then again, there would be archers struggling for the possession of flocks and herds, figures of warriors armed with clubs, of hunters chasing antelopes, of men in canoes hunting hippopotamus. There were dance scenes, representations of libations, and so forth."

The rock paintings of the Tassili comprise a brilliant chronicle of a lost world now withered by heat and dryness. The most ancient ones, which date from 5000 B.C. or earlier, show round-headed people adorned with horns or feathers. Lhote sees resemblances in this work to styles of art known from Black Africa, and regards it as the product of a Negroid population in the Sahara; but it is overlain with art of what Lhote calls a "Europoid" population, meaning Caucasian, and perhaps having affinities with the early Egyptians. The art of these two styles is quite different, but the fauna portrayed is the same, and shows us a Sahara as teeming with life as the great plains of central Africa are today. Giraffes, elephants, rhinos, hippos, ostriches, horses, and other beasts are shown, in life size or even larger than life; some pictures of rhinoceros are nearly 25 feet long and one group of giraffes is more than 26 feet high. Some of the animals shown are now extinct, such as *Bubalus antiquus,* a huge buffalo with exceptionally long, curving horns.

About 3500 B.C., perhaps a few hundred years earlier, pastoralist invaders entered the Sahara, probably from the direction of Ethiopia. The first wave of these herdsmen came only with sheep and goats, but later ones raised cattle of two species, one with long, lyre-shaped horns and the other with thick, curved horns. The herdsmen were the most prolific artists of the Tassili, and their favorite subject was the ox. "There can be no doubt that these pastoralists' whole life turned on this animal," writes Lhote. "In one scene you can see cattle, surrounded by herdsmen, coming back from pasture. In another there are calves tied with a rope. A third scene shows milking in the encampment near the huts where women are tending their children, and so forth."

The lakes and rivers of the Sahara were beginning to shrink by the time the Tassili pastoralists arrived, and some of the big tropical beasts were starting to move southward into better grazing areas. The African elephant requires 300 pounds or more of green fodder a day; the rhinoceros and hippopotamus need upwards of 200 pounds. Such immense quantities of greenery were ever more difficult to obtain in the Sahara, though it was still a region of more than normal rainfall with ample grazing grounds for the cattle, goats, and sheep of the herdsmen. The early pastoralists were also hunters, as is shown by such paintings of their period as one of men in canoes chasing a hippo; hippopotamus bones have been found not far from the Tassili which can be dated by carbon 14 to the time of the herdsmen. But eventually most of the huge animals were gone from the Sahara, heading either into the plains to the south or into the highlands of Africa's Mediterranean coast. (Elephants survived in the Atlas Mountains of Morocco and Algeria well into the Christian era; Hannibal of Carthage used them in warfare, leading them across the Alps in his invasion of Italy in 218 B.C.; later the Romans slaughtered North African elephants by the thousands for circus entertainment.) The Tassili pastoralists now depended much more completely on their cattle—using them for meat, not for milk, according to the rock paintings, which show cows with poorly developed udders—and supplemented their diet with the seeds of wild grasses.

By about 2000 B.C. the postglacial climatic optimum was drawing to its close; in Europe the weather was becoming cooler and drier, and in the Sahara vegetation zones were shifting under the impact of reduced precipitation. The generally Mediterranean flora of the wet millennia—Aleppo pine, olive, evergreen oak, and such—now was limited almost entirely to the highlands; below, shrubbery was giving way to grassland, and grassland to desert. This growing aridity had its effects on the herdsmen, who became increasingly nomadic as they sought water and pasture for their animals. A fledgling Neolithic farming economy, based on agricultural ideas transmitted at second or third hand from the more fertile regions to the east, was choked off almost before it had an opportunity to become established. Yet even this newly parched Sahara had its attractions, for about 1200 B.C. invaders came once more: a warlike people riding in horse-drawn chariots and carrying javelins and shields. Whether these newcomers drove the pastoralists out, or whether the deterioration of the climate had already done the job, is not known; but at the point that the first paintings of the chariot-people appear on the rock walls of the Tassili, the pastoralists vanish without further trace.

These invaders came from the north, probably from the direction of Tripoli and Cyrenaica; they left a trail of paintings of chariots all down the Sahara to the Niger River. That they came at a time of climatic change is shown by the complete absence of hippopotamus or rhinoceros from their paintings; they show giraffes and antelopes, which are better able to withstand aridity, and elephants, which survived in the highlands, but the beasts of rivers and lakes were gone. Early Greek and Latin writers refer to the horsemen as "Libyans" or "Garamantes," and speak of them as lawless and belligerent. By 500 B.C. they had learned to ride their horses, and had given up their chariots; by this time they occupied what had become a somber desert, and were mastering the arts of making do with little that typify the Tuareg tribesmen of the Sahara today. Herodotus, writing about 450 B.C., relates that in his day the inland parts of North Africa contained a tract "which is wholly sand, very scant of water, and utterly and entirely a desert." Strabo, a Greek geographer born about 63 B.C. who toured North Africa, told how the desert dwellers must carry water-skins when setting out on long journeys.

By then the Sahara had passed into the hands of the Romans,

who had seized it at the climax of their generations-long war with the city of Carthage in modern Tunisia. For more than a century they made no use of North Africa, but in the time of Augustus colonies were planted in what now are Tunisia, Algeria, and Morocco, and in gradual stages Roman influence spread deep into the desert. Some ten million acres were under cultivation that now are abandoned wastes; thousands of miles of roads were built, and splendid stone cities sprang up which today offer the best preserved and most exquisite ruins of the Roman era.

The flowering of the Sahara under the Romans had nothing to do with climatic change. It seems certain that there have been no major shifts in Saharan precipitation levels in the last four thousand years; the terrible desiccation that set in about 2000 B.C. never relented, and the vast reservoirs of groundwater beneath the sands of today's Sahara represent "capital" deposited long ago. What the Romans accomplished was a triumph of man over environment; hard work and not the vagaries of meteorology made the Sahara habitable for them. They built their desert outposts beside springs or wells wherever possible, but as they pressed southward they came to places where the groundwater was inaccessible. There they made use of wadis, or ravines—dry gulches carved by ancient streams or cut by rainfall erosion. By damming the wadis the Romans were able to catch what little rainfall there was, diverting it by terraces, retaining walls, barricades, and ditches into storage cisterns before it could run off and soak into the parched ground. Irrigation channels led from the cisterns to the fields; superb aqueducts carried water for great distances from outpost to outpost; the entire intricate system took maximum advantage of a minimally congenial situation and permitted farms to flourish and support a large population. As late as A.D. 400 Roman Africa still thrived; but the collapse of the mother country deprived the settlers of military protection against bandits; the troubles at home drained population from the colonies; and the wondrous irrigation systems fell into disrepair, so that the beautiful stone cities had to be abandoned and the desert reclaimed what had been wrested from it.

Nothing has changed significantly in the Sahara since then: only in our own day has there been an attempt to duplicate through modern technology what the Romans achieved twenty centuries ago.

The withering of the Sahara in the past four thousand years is one of the most emphatic possible demonstrations of the effects of climatic change. The Tassili rock paintings show a world of life and gaiety and prosperity; the bones of hippos conjure incredible images of swampy lakes where dunes now dominate; the hidden reservoirs testify to a time when heavy showers kept the fields green for great flocks and herds. Probably at no time in the past, not even in the relatively arid interpluvial periods, has the Sahara been as inhospitable as it has been since the breakup of the pastoralist cultures about 2000 B.C.

Why? Is it entirely a matter of shifts in the location of high-pressure zones? Henri Lhote feels that the vast and impersonal forces of meteorology have had a good deal to do with what has happened to the Sahara, but that man himself has played a part in bringing about this unfavorable modification of the climate. "We are well aware," he writes, "that any change made by man in the balance of nature may have disastrous consequences. And, in the case of the Sahara, the ancient pastoralists themselves may have been, at least partly, responsible for the spread of desert conditions, just as in our own times the Tuareg, the Mauritanian, the Arab and Tippu pastoralists by cutting down the few remaining trees—either for fuel or to feed the higher branches to their beasts—unceasingly help on the desert's expansion."

The development of agriculture in the Near East led by a roundabout route to the next great advance in human history: the emergence of city-building civilizations. This occurred, however, not in the regions of Palestine and Iraq where the first farming villages had evolved, but rather on the alluvial plain between the Tigris and Euphrates rivers and in the valley of the Nile—two places which the gospel of agriculturalism had not reached until it had been practiced for some thousands of years at Jericho and Jarmo.

Since both Egypt and Mesopotamia have had hot and far from temperate climates for as long as modern weather records have been kept, Ellsworth Huntington found it necessary to postulate an explanation for their awesome achievements of the past that can neither be proved nor disproved. Riding his hobbyhorse, he argued that the birth of the great civilizations of those two nations must have been the work of a now-vanished belt of cyclonic storms which swept over them at the end of summer, so that "during the early fall and late spring conditions would be about as they are in the homes of our Connecticut factory operatives during cool summers such as 1912 or 1913. For the remaining five or six months the average temperature would range from about 55° to 65° F., there would be a constant succession of cool waves, and the conditions would be almost ideal for great physical activity. Thus, even though the summers were distinctly bad, the total debilitating effect would be little greater than that of summer and winter combined in Connecticut."

The obsession of this great scientist with stormy weather and New England factory output seems amusing; but in fact the only detailed record we have of ancient Egyptian weather, that of the geographer Ptolemy from A.D. 127 to 151, shows many rainy days then in Egypt in April, May, June, September, and October, which are dry months today. (Cairo goes through whole years without any rain at the present time, and had no precipitation at all between 1909 and 1916.) But Ptolemy lived less than two thousand years ago, and is closer in time to us than he is to the builders of the pyramids, let alone to the unknown founders of Egyptian civilization twenty centuries or more before the pyramids were erected. Whether cyclonic storms afflicted and stimulated Egypt in the formative years of her civilization is something we are not likely to discover.

The civilization of the Nile, though, was born at a time of radical change in climate, and one does not need to be an environmental determinist to see a possible connection. Egypt today and for at least the past six thousand years has been a narrow strip of a country, six hundred miles long and in places only a few miles wide, following the bed of the Nile and flanked on both sides by fearful deserts; the demarcation line between the rich black soil of the fertile river valley and the barren red sand of the desert is sharp and precise. But things were not always this way.

The Nile is a colossus of rivers, 4,160 miles long, draining a million-square-mile region of desert, swamp, jungle, and valley. Its main stream, the White Nile, has its source below the equator in Lake Victoria, the world's second-largest lake; in the Sudan it is joined by the Blue Nile, which descends from the mountains of Ethiopia carrying torrential masses of water. Through more than thirty degrees of latitude the Nile flows northward, emptying into the Mediterranean. The immense quantity of water it carries has its origin in the South Atlantic, two thousand miles west of Egypt; here evaporation lifts vapor to the sky, to be carried eastward by cyclonic winds and dumped on equatorial Africa from March to August in an almost unending shower. The runoff from the mountains feeds the Nile.

Two or three million years ago, in the Pliocene, there was no Nile. The Mediterranean was 500 feet or more above present levels, and an arm of the sea projected onto the Nile Valley at least as far south as Aswan. Heavy rainfall created powerful streams that fed into this body of water, carrying great amounts of gravel, sand, and silt torn by erosion from the Red Sea hills to the east and the plateaus on the west and south. Gradually this debris filled the gulf and drove the sea arm back, a process that was assisted by the uplifting of the land at the beginning of the Pleistocene and a corresponding drop in sea level.

This left Egypt covered from north to south by a dreary wasteland of errosional deposits, hundreds of miles long, several hundred feet thick, and much wider than the modern Nile Valley. During the pluvial periods of the Pleistocene, rainfall runoff from the south spilled across this gigantic flood plain, cutting down through it to form the ancestral Nile. At each interval of maximum rainfall the river gained in intensity, slicing deeper into the accumulated debris to form an ever deeper and narrower channel. Above the present river, terraces can be traced successively at 300, 200, 150, 100, 50, 30, and 10 feet, each indicating an old bed of the Nile, and showing how what had been a broad plain over which sheets of water ran had been transformed into the existing deep valley between deserts.

The geologists K. S. Sanford and W. J. Arkell undertook a survey of the prehistoric Nile Valley in the 1920's and 1930's under the auspices of the Oriental Institute of the University of Chicago. Their report, published in 1933, described a rainy Pleistocene Egypt strange to anyone who has visited that land more recently:

> The dry wadies of the desert were running streams, and the landscape was pleasantly diversified with forest and grassland, over which wandered troops of wild animals. Reaching far beyond its present bounds, the ancestral Nile flowed rapidly over a pebbly bed, augmented on its journey northward by a host of tributaries draining the surrounding country. The Nile of the present day is but a dwindled shadow of the original river. Constantly choking itself with fine silt where formerly it hurried down large pebbles, and winding languidly through deserts without receiving additions from any tributary for 1,200 miles from its mouth, it diminishes in volume as it approaches the sea, owing to loss by evaporation and absorption.
>
> . . . Of greatest interest . . . are the traces of the mighty Nile which then flowed high above its present level. For many miles the hills bounding the valley are terraced at remarkably constant heights. In the frequent cliffs the strata composing them can be seen to undulate and to vary in hardness, but nevertheless they are all planed off evenly at about 50 feet, 100 feet, 150 feet or greater heights above the present valley floor. Often these abandoned Nile beds are still, like their smaller counterparts in the tributary wadies, covered by the gravels brought there by the river; and rolled among them may be found also the stone implements of Man.

The oldest stone tools appear in the 100-foot terraces: flint hand axes of the Chellean-Abbevillean style. Acheulian tools show up at the 50-foot level and again at the 30-foot level, indicating the long persistence of this tradition. The 30-foot implements display traces of the Levalloisian flake-tool technique, and the next terraces down, ten feet above the present level, show a complete disappearance of hand axes and the triumph of the Levalloisian methods. Archaeologists have tried without much success to correlate the Nile terraces to the Günz-Mindel-Riss-Würm sequence of glacials and interglacials detected in Europe; the Egyptian sequence is more complex, apparently, though the alternation of pluvials and interpluvials seems to follow in a broad way the larger contours of the European sequence. The 10-foot-terrace stage appears to have been reached about 25,000 years ago, during the peak of Europe's final glaciation; by then the Nile had assumed approximately its present dimensions, though downcutting continued for another few yards.

After this time the climate of Egypt grew slowly but steadily more dry. This is shown not only by the Nile terraces but by two oases west of the Nile: the Fayum, just south of Cairo, and Kharga, west of Luxor. The Fayum in the Pleistocene was the site of a large lake built up by Nile floods; in the oasis of Kharga wind erosion cut down to the water table, causing springs to rise in an otherwise barren area. During pluvial times, Stone Age hunters camped along the shores of the Fayum and beside the hundred-mile-long row of springs at Kharga; but the contraction of the water supply at the end of the Pleistocene forced a withdrawal in some places, and ancient tools have been found in the gravels of ravines now utterly dry.

The Nile tributaries were the first to show the effects of the changing climate. Those along the last thousand miles of the river, from the Sudan to the Mediterranean, dried up one by one; the Nile itself, diminished by their loss and by greater evaporation, no longer moved as swiftly. Downcutting ceased, and a reverse process began as the sluggish river of twenty thousand years ago choked on the silt it was transporting from the south. In some places the deposits of silt grew so thick that the river rose to the level of the old 100-foot gravel terraces.

On these high silt terraces have been found the sites of a culture known as the Sebilian, typified by small flint flake-tools. The Sebilians were hunters who roamed the plains beside the river, preying on the large herds of animals that occupied what was still a comparatively favorable environment. Later—about twelve thousand years ago—they became a semi-sedentary people, living in campsites along the Nile and gathering fish, shellfish, turtles, and occasionally crocodiles, while continuing to hunt some game; the existence of many grinding stones in Middle Sebilian sites of this period shows that they were seed-collectors as well. They were not nearly as close to an agricultural economy, though, as were their contemporaries, the Natufians of Palestine and the Karim Shahirians of Iraq. Not until 4500 B.C. or slightly earlier did Neolithic communities appear in Egypt. By that time Jericho was already ancient and Jarmo had been abandoned.

Prehistorians are as divided over the birth of the Neolithic in Egypt as they are over explaining its origin in Palestine and Iraq. One group holds that it resulted from increased aridity that transformed the Nile Valley from a marshy jungle to an area suitable for farming; another faction asserts that the jungles of the Nile never existed, and that agriculture was a natural development out of the food-gathering economy that preceded it; still another group, not necessarily opposed to the first, believes that the Nile Valley did indeed have nearly impenetrable thickets in Sebilian times, but that they were removed more by the actions of man himself than by a major change in climate.

Thus the Egyptologist Cyril Aldred has written, "The early settlers found a valley full of swamps and pools left by the uncontrolled inundation of the Nile every year, in which vast thickets of reeds and sedge grew over a man's height and acted as cover to every kind of pond fowl and freshwater fish, besides hippopotami and less desirable creatures such as crocodiles. The elephant, lion, ass, ibex, Barbary sheep, antelope, wild ox and smaller desert game frequented the wadis that flanked the river, since up to late historic times these ancient water courses still resembled parkland with low shrubs and flowering meadows. . . . It is probable therefore that there was not much compulsion on these first settlers to change their way of life radically, and they doubtless enjoyed a mixed economy, trapping birds and fish among the pools, hunting for game in the wadis and exploiting such marsh vegetation as papyrus and the wild Abyssinian banana. . . ." Jacquetta Hawkes, in an account of prehistoric times published in 1962, wrote, "Progressive desiccation marked the period from perhaps 7000 B.C. onward, turning the plateaus from grassland into steppe and ultimately into desert, while making the swampy valley itself more habitable." Miss Hawkes declared that the first farming communities appeared near the mouth of the Nile, spreading along the Mediterranean coast from Natufian Palestine, and that Neolithic ways advanced up the river as the swamps of the south disappeared. But two years later Karl W. Butzer of the University of Wisconsin denied the existence of "the jungle-thickets and endless papyrus swamps commonly postulated in the archaeological literature. The extent of perennial swamps and lakes in the Nile Valley was limited in prehistoric times, and as today, the greatest part of the plain consisted of seasonally flooded basins. Groves of acacia, tamarisk, sycamore, and Egyptian willow crowned the levees which were always available for permanent settlement. Papyrus swamps and quiet expanses of standing water with lotus, sedge, and reeds, and teeming with hippopotamus, crocodile, and a host of aquatic birds, were available. But these only constituted a small segment of prehistoric Egypt." In his view the Egyptian climate had reached its greatest dryness at the end of the Pleistocene and there was no accelerating desiccation afterward.

All parties to the controversy agree that the technique of planting and harvesting crops were transmitted to Egypt from a western Asian source, probably Natufian. But the kind of farming that developed along the Nile was quite different from that practiced in Palestine and Iraq. In the wooded hill country of the earliest farming communities, planting was done in time for the winter rainy season; but there was no real rainy season at all in Egypt, and farmers had to coordinate their work with another phenomenon altogether, the annual flood of the Nile. The winds of the summer monsoon bring heavy rains to Ethiopia in May; the waters of this deluge drain into the Blue

Nile and rush northward toward Egypt, stripping away tons of topsoil en route. By July the flood reaches Egypt and the mud-laden water spreads out over the valley of the Nile, reaching a peak of inundation in September. When the flood waters retreat in October, a marvelous coating of fertile mud remains on the fields of Egypt. The Egyptian farmers, having waited out the season of flood, need do little more than enter the fields and scatter seed. Miraculously, almost of its own accord and with little care, the seed sprouts, the mud of the Nile brings forth crops in abundance.

Butzer and others maintain that this sort of simple alluvial cultivation was possible in Egypt at almost any time since the Nile had adopted its present outlines, and that it was only necessary for someone to think of the idea of planting seed for agriculture to become established. Those who, like Jacquetta Hawkes, see the early Neolithic as a time of rapidly increasing aridity, think that such agriculture was impossible until the drier conditions had converted the swamps into an open plain. Cyril Aldred implies deliberate removal of the swamps by the early agriculturalists, who drained the marshes in order to plant wheat and barley. Whatever the case, the marshlands disappeared along a far-reaching front, though they remained (and remain) in the south. In the Fayum, one farming settlement has been dated by carbon 14 to 4437 B.C., within a probable margin of error of 180 years. These people grew wheat and barley, raised flax and wove it into linen, kept cattle and sheep, and made pottery and basketry. They also still hunted and fished, with the hippopotamus among their prey. Other Neolithic communities appeared about the same time near the delta of the Nile and at Tasa in southern Egypt.

The advent of the Neolithic revolution brought special problems as well as new advantages. More food now was available, allowing a great increase in population; but usually the growth of population outstripped the growth of the food supply, forcing an upward spiral of development: more land had to be cultivated to grow more grain to feed the greater population. This certainly stimulated drainage of marshes, even if climatic changes were not involved. Large herds of goats, grazing on the grasslands beside the river, may have hastened the spread of desert conditions in the marginal areas by devouring all the vegetation in reach.

The need to expand the cultivable zone into the swamps on the one hand and the encroaching deserts on the other was complicated by the unpredictability of the Nile itself, on which the yearly bounty of fertility depended. In some years the river's flow was skimpy, and the farming communities suffered. In other years, heavy rains in the south turned the Nile into a savage monster rather than a benevolent bringer of rich earth, and the fierce river burst its banks with sudden force, engulfing not only the farmlands but the villages that lay beyond. Only through building dikes and dams to hold back the waters in years of unusual flooding, reservoirs to store surplus water against time of drought, and irrigation canals to carry water to fields outside the normal flood zone, could the struggling communities survive and prosper.

The need for such cooperative action was a spur to the development of urban civilization in Egypt as the isolated settlements, attempting at first to control the river by individual action, found the task too much. Groups of scattered villages coalesced into towns; towns affiliated themselves into provinces; by 3500 B.C. the provinces were organized around two polar points into the kingdoms of Upper Egypt (in the south) and Lower Egypt (in the delta). A central government could best direct the river work, and by 3200 B.C. Egypt was unified under a single monarch, the first of the Pharaohs; legend gives his name as Menes.

In a thousand ways the Nile prodded the Egyptians into a more complex way of life. Swamp drainage may have been the first communal activity, practiced on a town-by-town basis. Later came basin irrigation, in which a series of reservoirs was created, either by using natural depressions or by throwing up embankments at right angles to the river's course; short canals conveyed the water from one basin to the next, providing a supply that could be tapped in dry seasons. But under the unified monarchy more impressive engineering feats were achieved, for Pharaoh had the power to levy a huge working force for any specific project; carefully placed levees and dikes were built, a network of bureaucratic functionaries presided over the job of predicting the extent of the coming season's flood and readying the irrigation system to deal with it; calendars were devised so that the changing of the seasons could be comprehended, and, because it was necessary to watch the heavens to know the seasonal changes, astronomy came into being. The variable nature of the Nile made some sort of record keeping necessary; the Egyptians invented a system for writing things down, and many of the most ancient inscriptions are concerned primarily with the level of the Nile. Life took on a new complexity as population expanded: there now appeared kings and nobles, soldiers and slaves, priests, scribes, engineers, metalworkers, architects. How much of all this was the result of the rapid desiccation of what had been a vast marsh, and how much was the cumulative effect of human ingenuity and resourcefulness, remains in dispute; but the outcome was a powerful and elaborate society that dominated much of the world for twenty centuries.

About a thousand miles to the east and north of Egypt, another great civilization developed in what is now Iraq, but which was long known by its Greek name of Mesopotamia—"The Land Between The Two Rivers." Those two rivers are the Tigris and the Euphrates, and on the plain between them arose an urban culture now recognized as older than that of Egypt, and probably the inspiration for much of what the Egyptians achieved.

Like Egypt, Mesopotamia is a land of little rainfall, and—the cyclonic-storm notions of Ellsworth Huntington to the contrary—probably has been for most of the last ten thousand years. But the challenges confronting the early villagers of Mesopotamia were quite different from those of Egypt.

In the north, the region drained by the Tigris, the land is hilly and not very different from the region a short distance to the east where Jarmo, Tepe Sarab, and the other early Neolithic villages developed out of the Karim Shahirian culture. By 500 B.C. the Neolithic ideas were spreading down the valleys into such sites on the upper Tigris as Hassuna, near modern Mosul. In the thousand years that followed, the Neolithic constellation of farming, pottery, and domestication of animals spread widely through northern Mesopotamia. Simultaneously a new culture was coming into being in the lower reaches of the Tigris-Euphrates valley, in a flat alluvial lowland subject to periodic flooding. This culture is called the Ubaidan, after the type site of al'Ubaid.

Where the Ubaidans came from is not known, though the Iranian highlands is one likely place of origin. In the course of their migration to the Mesopotamian flood plain they acquired Neolithic ideas, which they attempted to put into practice in an environment that bore little resemblance to anything they had known before. Their first task was to drain the land, for it had all been built of silt carried southward by the two rivers, and was little more than a reedy tangle of marshland when they arrived. (The familiar debate is heard here: did a dramatic change of climate about 7000 B.C. render lower Mesopotamia dry enough to be fit for cultivation, did the Ubaidans transform it into cultivable land wholly through their own heroic effort, or was most of the land suitable for use all along?) Certainly they did a great deal to improve the land, even laying out platforms of reeds to catch silt and hasten the transformation of swamp into dry land.

In raising their crops they had the benefit, like the Egyptians, of fertile silt brought by river floods. But in Mesopotamia the annual floods are unpredictable in arrival and highly variable in volume from year to year; and they come at an awkward time, between April and June, for they are generated from the melting snow of the mountains of Asia Minor in the spring. Thus farming becomes impossible in Mesopotamia during the best growing months, since the fields are flooded then.

However, the climate is warm enough the rest of the year to permit agriculture; the problem then is that the rivers are low and there is no rain. The Ubaidans solved this at the cost of immense labor, by constructing an intricate system of reservoirs, dams, and irrigation canals. When the full rush of flood water came late in spring, as much of the excess as possible was carried off into reservoirs, which were tapped after the flood. This stored supply was enhanced by canals leading from the Euphrates itself; the Tigris was of no value for irrigation because its bed was too deep, lying so far below the farmlands that canals would be useless without pumps, which of course the Ubaidans did not have.

Triumphant over the difficulties of their environment, the Ubaidans successfully drained, dammed, canalized, and farmed their muddy plain, expanding into new territory as the delta grew and as dry land was formed, until by 4000 B.C. they were so productive that their agriculture could support full-scale cities. A loosely federated kingdom of city-states, known as Sumer, came into being.

Whether they were descended directly from the Ubaidans or, as some scholars have suggested, represent a hybrid between the Ubaidans and an invading group known as the Uruk people, the Sumerians created an extraordinary civilization. In their irrigated fields they raised wheat, barley, and the date palm; they drew prodigious supplies of fish from the marshes and streams; they had large flocks of domestic animals, sheep, goats, donkeys, cattle, pigs. By about 3400 B.C. they had invented the earliest form of what was to become their wedge-shaped cuneiform writing. Shortly there were a dozen or so important Sumerian cities, some with fifty thousand inhabitants. Among the inventions of the Sumerians were the wagon wheel, the plow, and the sailboat. They had measuring instruments, surveying tools, and the potter's wheel. They worked in bronze and copper, manufactured paints and leather, cosmetics, perfume, drugs. They had a well-developed science of medicine, the beginnings of an astronomy, and a mathematics. They had sculpture, strange and highly individual. They had music, for harps and lyres were found in the tombs of the Sumerian city of Ur, and mention was made in their cuneiform inscriptions of drums, tambourines, and flutes. All in all, they seem to have been a highly intelligent, ambitious, and capable race of pioneers, endlessly resourceful and inventive. Even before Egypt, Sumer attained an elaborate, well-balanced urban economy—the impetus for which came, it is possible to believe, from the challenges offered by the unusual environment of the Mesopotamian flood-plain.

Fairly early in Sumerian history that flood-plain was subjected to an environmental event that left its mark in the literature of more than one religion. The story of a catastrophic deluge that destroys nearly all civilization is familiar to us, of course, from Genesis, with its tale of Noah and the Ark. One of the archaeological sensations of the nineteenth century was the announcement in 1872 of the discovery of fragmentary clay tablets from Mesopotamia that told a story much like the biblical one. The tablets, which dated from about 700 B.C., related the epic adventures of a hero named Gilgamesh, who in his wanderings encountered an old man called Utnapishtim—the Mesopotamian Noah. From Utnapishtim, Gilgamesh learned how the gods had warned of a flood that would wipe out sinful mankind, and how Utnapishtim had been instructed to build a great ship on which to take all that was to be spared from destruction. Utnapishtim declares:

> All that I possessed of the seed of life I gathered together, the whole I made to enter into the ship; all my servants, male and female, the tame animals of the fields, and the wild animals of the plains, and the young men of the army, all these I made to enter. And Shamash [the sun-god] caused a great flood, and he spoke, speaking in the darkness of the night: "I will cause it to rain from the heavens abundantly; enter within the ship and close its door."
>
> I entered into the ship and shut its door. . . . The fury of the tempest arose in the morning. Destruction marched over the mountains and the plains. . . . The waters destroyed all life from the face of the earth. Six days and six nights passed: the thunder, the storm, and the winds reigned. In the middle of the seventh day the tempest ceased. . . . I was borne over the sea. Those who had done wickedness, all the human race who had turned to sin—the bodies of these floated like reeds.
>
> The ship was borne to the country of Nizir, and came to rest on the mountains of Nizir. On the seventh day afterward, I sent forth a dove, and it departed. And the dove flew away, and sought a place of rest; but it found none, and it returned. I let loose a raven. The raven flew forth, and it saw the bodies on the water, and it ate them; and it wandered a great way off,

> and it returned not. I let go the animals to the four winds; I poured out a libation; I built an altar on the summit of the mountain.

The first fragments of the Gilgamesh tablets had turned up in the 1850's during the excavation of the library of the palace of the Assyrian king Sennacherib, at Kouyunjik, near Mosul in northern Mesopotamia. Nearly twenty years had passed before the British Museum philologist George Smith had translated these tablets and recognized their importance to biblical studies. In 1873, after making public his find and causing an immense sensation—for the relationship between the Assyrian myth and the account in Genesis was too close to be denied—Smith went to Kouyunjik and successfully uncovered the tablets containing most of the missing parts of the story.

Sennacherib, who ruled from 704 to 681 B.C., is himself a prominent biblical figure—the half-mad, bloodthirsty king whose ferocity had been felt by the children of Israel. But, like many other Assyrian kings, he was something of an antiquarian, a collector of the literature of the people who had inhabited Mesopotamia before its conquest by the Assyrians; for in Sennacherib's day the Sumerians had been gone for nearly two thousand years. It developed that the tablets translated by George Smith were merely copies of a much older Sumerian poem, one which had already been ancient when Sennacherib's scribes had themselves translated it from Sumerian into Assyrian, a language akin to Hebrew. This put the tale of the Mesopotamian deluge into a new light—for now it was clear that it had first been set down long before the time of Abraham, and that the deluge section of the Old Testament, at least, had probably been borrowed intact from the Sumerians.

Toward the end of the nineteenth century this theory was confirmed when part of the original Sumerian text of the Gilgamesh epic came to light during excavations at Nippur, Sumer's holy city, which was at least 4,500 years old. Other tablets also made mention of the deluge, such as the Sumerian "king list," composed about 2100 B.C., which purports to be a list of all the dynasties of Sumer from the earliest time, and after naming the eight kings of five cities that existed "before the Flood," goes on to say, "The Flood swept over everything. After the Flood swept over everything, and kingship had [once again] descended from Heaven, [the city of] Kish became the seat of kingship."

All this remained in the realm of biblical scholarship and comparative mythology until 1929, when the great British archaeologist Sir Leonard Woolley produced what seemed to him conclusive evidence that the various Sumerian flood-accounts were not myths but echoes of an actual catastrophe. He was digging in the cemetery of Ur, one of the oldest of the Sumerian cities; and after having removed from the cemetery some of the most handsome and exciting works of art ever found by an archaeologist, he drove a shaft less than five feet square into the soil underlying the area. As the shaft descended it passed through about a yard of the ordinary debris of an ancient civilization: ashes, bits of mud brick, pieces of pottery. But then, Woolley wrote, "it all stopped—there were no more potsherds, no ashes, only clean, water-laid mud, and the Arab workman at the bottom of the shaft told me that he had reached virgin soil; there was nothing more to be found, and he had better go elsewhere." Some intuition led Woolley to have the man go on digging. Reluctantly the workman cut down through eight feet of clean soil free of any trace of human presence—and suddenly, immediately below, there appeared tools and vessels of the Ubaidan type! Surely this thick layer of mud atop a stratum of human occupation had been laid down by some immense flood. "No other agency could possibly account for it," wrote Woolley. "Inundations are of normal occurrence in Lower Mesopotamia, but no ordinary rising of the waters would leave behind it anything approaching the bulk of this clay bank: eight feet of sediment imply a very great depth of water, and the flood which deposited it must have been of a magnitude unparalleled in local history." In the seasons that followed, Woolley sank fourteen shafts at Ur, some of them down to sea level, and in each he discovered a deposit of clean, water-laid soil above the Ubaidan strata. From this he concluded that he had found the mark of the event that had inspired the Sumerian flood myth and was the indirect ancestor of the story of Noah.

More recent archaeologists take a less romantic view: they point out that the flood at Ur must have taken place no later than 3500 B.C., perhaps fifteen centuries before the writing of the Gilgamesh epic. Though it was undoubtedly a great deluge, Woolley's flood was not necessarily *the* deluge. Mesopotamia has always been prone to floods; one in 1954 sent the Tigris over its banks to cover hundreds of miles of low-lying plains, and threatened to destroy the city of Baghdad. A flood layer at the Sumerian city of Kish was discovered in 1928 lying above a level that can be dated from 3200 to 3000 B.C., while in 1931 a similar flood deposit was found at the Sumerian city of Shuruppak, which, incidentally, the Gilgamesh epic gives as the native city of the Mesopotamian Noah, Utnapishtim. It appears likely that the story in Genesis is a rewritten version of the oldest known human account of a natural disaster, but that the tale of Utnapishtim reflects only one of many terrible floods that afflicted Sumer in its time of greatness.

Some archaeologists have speculated that these floods may have facilitated the periodic entry of invaders into Sumer. Thus Woolley wrote in his last book, published in 1962, "The city of Ur itself, standing as it did on a mound already fairly high, survived [the flood]; but numerous village sites of the al Ubaid period show no signs of later occupation and must have been completely destroyed; the mass of silt deposited against the Ur mound implies a flood of a depth sufficient to drown the entire delta, and it is easy to believe that the bulk of the population perished. Naturally the land was too valuable to be left untenanted, and a horde of immigrants flocked into it from the north and settled down side by side with the survivors of the old stock." Later cultural changes in Sumer may be explained the same way. What brought the magnificent Sumerian civilization to its end, though, was not flooding nor any other environmental disturbance, but rather warfare among its cities, which left it vulnerable to barbarian invasion. The chronicles of Sumer record a dreary series of fratricidal wars, with each city-state in turn attaining a temporary supremacy after having sacked and burned its neighbors. And about 2400 B.C., barbarians from the west, speaking a language of the Semitic family, entered Sumer under the leadership of the warrior Sargon, who conquered not only Mesopotamia but much of western Asia. The Semitic language Sargon brought with him joined the Sumerian tongue as an official language of the region; both were written with the cuneiform script that the Sumerians had invented, and the absorption of the Sumerians by their Semitic conquerors commenced.

Sargon's empire lasted only a century; then new barbarians from the mountains of Persia overran Mesopotamia, and in the confusion that ensued the Sumerians enjoyed a brief return to power in their own land. But the barbarian invasions continued for centuries, until the old Sumerian stock had been completely engulfed by Semites. The name of Sumer itself was forgotten, though the new people adopted the ways of Sumerian technology and even kept the Sumerian language alive for religious use, much as the Roman Catholic Church preserved and used Latin long after it had ceased to be a spoken tongue. By about 1800 B.C., the region that had been Sumer now was the kingdom of Babylonia, with its capital at Babylon, which had been an unimportant town in Sumerian times. To the north arose the kingdom of Assyria, more warlike and less civilized than that of Babylonia; and these two realms, both founded by Semitic barbarians making use of the advances of an older civilization, struggled for more than a thousand years until Assyria's ultimate triumph.

The circumstances that brought repeated waves of nomadic invaders into Mesopotamia were basically climatic, according to Ellsworth Huntington and his followers. He saw a pattern of pulsations, impossible to trace archaeologically, which emptied nomad hordes out of two great human reservoirs—the deserts of central Asia and the hills of Iran—into the fertile lowlands of Sumer. At the hot, dry part of the cycle, the pastoralists of the desert are unable to feed their flocks, and migrate in search of better territory; this accounts for Sargon and his desert-dwellers. But when a cold, rainy climatic cycle has begun, heavy snow in the Iranian mountains covers the pastures, driving the highlanders westward; this, said Huntington, brought in the mountain men who overthrew Sargon's empire. Another pulsation several centuries later was responsible for the arrival of the desert Semites who founded Babylonia, and so on, cycle after cycle, explaining each of the political convulsions that swept the troubled land between the two rivers.

Since there is no doubt that all these nomads did invade Mesopotamia, and since such climatic shifts as Huntington describes may well have put them on the move, this seems a reasonable, though of course speculative, theory. More tenuous is the characteristic Huntington explanation for the success of the nomads in mastering urban life once they had reached Mesopotamia: that they found the Mesopotamian climate so stimulating, because of hypothetical periodic cyclonic storms, that they were able to transcend their earlier low level of accomplishment. Since no evidence of a storm belt in Mesopotamia in ancient times exists, it is more plausible to assume that prolonged contact with a defeated but culturally superior people had an uplifting effect—by cultural osmosis, so to speak.

In time the Assyrian kingdom, heir to all the Mesopotamian civilizations that had preceded it over thousands of years, decayed and collapsed; and after a final burst of glory in Babylon in the seventh century B.C., the Persians under Cyrus conquered Mesopotamia. Babylon itself, which had been rebuilt into the most glorious city of its time under Nebuchadnezzar, was delivered to Cyrus by traitors in 539 B.C. Xerxes, a later Persian king, destroyed the city after a rebellion, and it was not rebuilt. The splendid irrigation works of Mesopotamia no longer were maintained, and that neglect, rather than any particular change of climate, turned the area into a desert. Sand and silt thrown up by the Euphrates swallowed the cultivated fields; the great cities of antiquity became shapeless abandoned mounds rising above barrenness; a sparse peasant population scratched out of a living where there had been a magnificent civilization. Nor has much changed there since the time of the downfall of Babylon, twenty-five centuries ago.

The third of the three great urban civilizations of the remote past emerged on the subcontinent of India, in the valley of the Indus River, about 4,500 years ago. Thus it came into being somewhat later than those of the Egyptians and Sumerians; but it maintained contact with the other major centers of urban life, and probably was influenced by them.

The existence of the Indus Valley civilization—which is also called the Harappan civilization, after one of its chief sites—was unknown until the twentieth century. Previously, historians had thought that Indian civilization dated from about 1500 B.C., when tall, fair-skinned invaders who called themselves Aryans burst into India from the north, conquered the short, dark-skinned, primitive natives, and began to found cities. No ruins of pre-Aryan cities had ever been discovered in India, which seemed to demonstrate that this theory was correct. However, evidence to the contrary could be found in the *Rig-Veda,* a collection of Sanskrit hymns and poems composed by the Aryans themselves not long after their entry into India. The Vedic hymns, which have come down virtually unchanged across more than two thousand years, describe the Aryan victory over people with "deftly-built defenses" and forts "with a hundred walls." A hymn in praise of Indra, the Aryan god of war, declares:

> With all-outstripping chariot-wheel, O Indra, thou far-famed, hast overthrown the twice ten kings of men
> With sixty thousand nine and ninety followers . . .
> Thou goest on from fight to fight intrepidly, destroying castle after castle here with strength.

The references to "castle after castle" indicated that the Aryans had overthrown a substantial civilization; but to exaggerate the strength of the enemy is the easiest way to inflate one's own accomplishments, and historians long dismissed the Vedic hymns as self-serving legends. In 1921, though, an Indian archaeologist named Rai Bahadur Daya Ram Sahni began to excavate at a great mound near the village of Harappa in what was then northwestern India and is now part of Pakistan. Workmen building the East Indian Railway between Karachi and Lahore had plundered that mound in the middle of the nineteenth century, finding in it admirably made bricks that served well as ballast for the foundations of the railroad tracks. Those bricks, and the little antiquities that had turned up in the mound as it was ripped open, showed that the mound must be the site of a ruined city. But nothing was done to examine it until the 1921 excavations.

The truth was apparent then: the city at Harappa was older than anything yet unearthed in India. Another great mound was located about 350 miles away, near the town of Mohenjo-daro, on the Indus River. In 1922 a second team of archaeologists under R. D. Banerji began to work there, and soon it was clear that this was the twin of Harappa. Sir John Marshall, the Director-General of Archaeology in India, excavated at Mohenjo-daro from 1922 to 1931; in 1933 and 1934 he dug at Harappa, and another British archaeologist, Ernest Mackay, resumed the Mohenjo-daro dig in 1935 and 1936. After the interruption caused by the Second World War, a new expedition under Sir Mortimer Wheeler explored the Harappan region for several seasons beginning in 1946. Extensive work at both sites has continued, most recently an important 1964–65 project conduced by the University of Pennsylvania. The results have been phenomenal. An entire civilization, forgotten until 1921, has been rediscovered—a civilization that flourished for more than a thousand years and in its heyday was one of the mightiest on earth. It is still a civilization of many mysteries, however, and most of the puzzles have to do with climate.

The heartland of the Harappans was a vast, irregularly triangular plain 950 miles long and up to 750 miles wide, running from the foothills of the Himalayas to the shore of the Arabian Sea, and from the Gulf of Cambay, near modern Bombay, westward to the Pakistan-Iran border. Through this region runs the Indus River, which rises in the Baluchistan hills and flows diagonally across the Sind Plain into the sea. Except for a green strip bordering the river, where artificial irrigation systems have been built in modern times, this plain is a forbidding sandy desert, one of the least appealing regions in the world.

How could a great civilization ever have established itself here? In the summer the temperature rises to 120 F. in the shade. The soil is salty, and as the summer heat bakes the plain, the salt rises to the surface of the land, so that, as the archaeologist Stuart Piggott has put it, "It has a brittle shining crust that crushes beneath the step like a satanic mockery of snow. The whole landscape is whitened, and forms a dead background to the ugly stunted trees and grey-green bushes that stud the plain." Yet here the two great twin cities we call Mohenjo-daro and Harappa were built, housing some 40,000 inhabitants apiece; and there were 60 to 100 smaller cities as well, covering an area more than twice as large as that of Sumer or ancient Egypt. Scarcely any rain falls there—less than six inches a year. For most of the year the Indus flows feebly, and dust-devils dance in the parching wind. Only in the spring is the river swollen by the floods caused by melting snow in the Himalayas.

The evidence that the Indus region had a different and far more favorable climate five thousand years ago is great. Sir Mortimer Wheeler has written of marshes and jungles on the Sind Plain then, and of great fertility renewed by annual floods. The cities themselves tell of heavy rainfall, for they were built of brick—not the simple brick made of dried mud that was used to build the cities of Sumer, but burnt brick, kiln-baked brick. This is a costly building material, and Harappa and Mohenjo-daro are not small cities; each is more than three miles in circumference. The effort of producing kiln-baked brick in such quantity must have been tremendous, and can be justified only if the cities were subjected to torrential rains; for in a heavy downpour sun-dried brick turns back to mud, but kiln-baked brick remains intact. The elaborate drains in the two cities seem intended to carry away rainwater running through the streets.

The layouts of both cities are similar. From the beginning, they were planned in rectangular superblocks, each about 400 by 200 yards, divided by wide main streets. Adjoining this residential area in both is a citadel, on a separate brick platform 40 to 50 feet high. The streets themselves are blank and featureless, for the houses have no windows in their outside walls; within the superblocks are mazes of little lanes and alleyways, but the outward appearance is one of grim, almost inhuman organization and severity.

For a thousand years, beginning about 2500 B.C., these cities flourished. High on the citadel, slaves labored in municipal granaries, milling wheat into flour. In the lower city, weavers, potters, jewelers, bead-makers, and other craftsmen had their quarters; brick-makers sweated over their kilns, and smelters of metals toiled over their furnaces. Beyond the rigid gridiron of the city lay the farms, where grain, melons, dates, and cotton were grown. Cattle, sheep, pigs, and poultry were raised, and the river supplied an abundance of fish. Harappan voyagers departed regularly for distant lands, as we know by the presence of Indus beads and pottery in Mesopotamian cities of the time of Sargon and later, and of Mesopotamian artifacts in the Harappan sites. Perhaps the Harappans learned the idea of writing from Egypt or Sumer, although the Harappan hieroglyphic script, consisting of some four hundred signs, has resisted all attempts thus far at decipherment.

Evidence of contact between the Harappan culture and Sumer vanishes about 2000 B.C. There are traces of trade between the Indus cities and Persia until perhaps 1500 B.C., and a bead dating from 1600 B.3., found at Knossos in Crete, seems to be of Harappan manufacture. But after 1500 B.C. there is no longer any sign of trade between the Indus cities and the outside world. Since that date matches the traditional date of the Aryan invasion of India, does it mean that Mohenjo-daro and Harappa fell to the invaders then?

The end of the Harappans has been the subject of a great deal of archaeological discussion, and has given rise to a host of theories. The simplest, and the least favored today, is that a prolonged series of attacks by waves of barbarians so weakened the two cities that at last they fell and their inhabitants were massacred, as the *Rig-Veda* claimed. Ernest Mackay, who worked at Mohenjo-daro in 1935–36, asserted that he had found evidence of the final slaughter. One room contained the skeletons of thirteen men and women and a child who seemed to have perished under tragic and violent circumstances. In another part of the city nine skeletons were found huddled together as though for mutual protection, or perhaps just out of fear. Five of them were children. Mackay suggested that they were "the remains of a family who tried to escape from the city with their belongings at the time of a raid but were stopped and slaughtered by the raiders." Nearby two skeletons were found on a flight of stairs, "evidently lying," according to Mackay, "where they died in a vain endeavor with their last remaining strength to climb the stairs to the street."

On the basis of these and other skeletons—thirty-seven in all—some writers imaginatively reconstructed the last stand of the Harappans and the triumph of the Aryans, seeing the cities aglow in the fires set by the barbarians. "Indra stands accused," wrote Sir Mortimer Wheeler, of the death of the Harappan civilization. But Mackay's image of a massacre was questioned even in his own day, and is almost universally rejected today. Sir John Marshall, Mackay's superior, believed that the skeletons were mostly burials dating from several hundred years before the abandonment of Mohenjo-daro rather than victims of any cataclysmic invasion. This idea was taken up by George F. Dales of the University of Pennsylvania, who regards the whole story of an Aryan invasion and massacre as a myth arising from improper analysis of archaeological evidence. "Scholars and laymen alike," he wrote in 1964, "have always delighted in being able to boo and hiss the evil villain, the murderous invader, the barbarian hordes." But a mere thirty-seven skeletons are no evidence of massacre, he went on, especially since most of those do not seem to have been left unburied in the streets (as Mackay thought) but were uncovered by erosion long after Mohenjo-daro was a dead city. "There is no destruction level covering the latest period of the city, no sign of extensive burning, no bodies of warriors clad in armor and surrounded by the weapons of war. The citadel, the only fortified part of the city, yielded no evidence of a final defense."

Most contemporary archaeologists believe that the Harappans were already a decaying culture when the Aryans arrived, and that no clash was necessary; it may even have been the case that the Aryans moved into a land that had already been depopulated, and that their hymns of conquest and triumph are as fictional as once was thought. In that case, though, what was the undoing of this great civilization?

Environmental changes were, according to the latest research. Even Sir Mortimer Wheeler, who had tentatively accepted Mackay's massacre theory, felt that the Aryans had merely given the last shove to a tottering culture. "One thing is clear about the end of Mohenjo-daro," he wrote in an essay published in 1961: "The city was already slowly dying long before the ultimate *coup de grâce*. Houses, mounting gradually upon the ruins of their predecessors or upon artificial platforms in an incessant endeavor to out-top the Indus floods, were increasingly shoddier in construction, increasingly carved up into warrens for a swarming lower-grade population. To a height of thirty feet or more, the tall podium of the Great Granary on the fringe of the citadel was engulfed by rising structures of poorer and poorer quality. Economic decline is everywhere apparent. . . ." Wheeler believed that the Harappans had worn out their environment through misuse. They had cut down trees for a thousand years to feed the furnaces that baked their bricks, perhaps to the point where whole hillsides were deforested. A forest breathes; it gives off water vapor, which collects in the atmosphere and returns in the form of rain. Did the Harappans break the precipitation cycle by stripping away the forests, and turn their valley into a desert?

Reid A. Bryson, the head of the Department of Meteorology at the University of Wisconsin, suggested in 1967 a different way for deforestation to have brought aridity to the Indus Valley. The air over the Rajputana desert of northwestern India—which borders on the Indus region—is far from dry, as Wheeler had supposed. "If all the moisture in the air over northwestern India were to be precipitated out," Bryson wrote, "it would make a layer of water about four centimeters deep. In most deserts it would be about one centimeter. In the wettest place on earth, the depth would be about five centimeters. The Rajputana desert is strange because in the air above it there is as much moisture as there is above Panama, or the Amazon Valley, or the Congo, notorious sites of heavy rain. Why, then, is this Indian desert a desert?"

The air above the Rajputana comprises a high-pressure zone; it is continually sinking, which compresses the air and causes it to grow warmer, increasing its ability to retain moisture. Bryson could not understand why this sinking and compressing of the atmosphere should take place as it does, until he flew over the region in 1962 and observed the great quantity of dust in the air. Measurements taken later showed 5½ tons of dust suspended over every square mile of northwestern India. "This amount of dust," he wrote, "is greater than the amount over the smokiest, haziest, foggiest city on earth. It is enough to explain about a 50 percent increase in the sinking rate of the air."

The source of this dust, said Bryson, is the desert itself; there is no grass cover, and the wind skins the surface of the land, sending soil particles aloft. Farmers in the desert manage to grow some 30 pounds of grain per acre per year, a minimal subsistence level. But once this region was the site of the vast agricultural empire of the Harappans. "Suppose," Bryson wrote, "the Harappans moved into an area of grassland and started farming it. They got good yields and their cows had enough grass on which to graze. We know that they raised cows and pigs and grew grain. The Harappans flourished and their population grew—the people farmed more area more intensely. They destroyed the grass cover of the land and the wind blew the dust into the air. . . . The dust changed the rate at which the atmosphere subsided, and with this change the area became more desert-like. As the climate gets drier, any people tries a little harder to grow enough food to supply the population if the population is dense and not very mobile. This means tearing up more of the surface and loosening more dust to blow into the air.

"Around 1500 B.C., the Harappans disappeared. . . . I would guess that the Harappans misused their land and turned it into a desert."

The University of Pennsylvania group that is the most recent to have excavated at the Harappan sites has a different theory: that the Harappans did not necessarily wear out their environment, but rather were worn out by it. A series of disastrous floods may have broken the spirit of the Harappans and shattered their civilization.

Deposits of river silt had long been observed at Mohenjo-daro, but these had been considered signs of nothing more important than brief seasonal overflows of the Indus. In 1940 an Indian paleontologist, M. R. Sahni, had noticed similar silt deposits far above the level of the Indus flood plain near the city of Hyderabad, and had suggested that what had taken place was no mere overflow, but the formation of a gigantic lake by a geological upheaval that had dammed the river for many years.

Little attention was paid to this idea until 1960, when a hydrological engineer, Robert L. Raikes, began to study the geological history of the Indus Valley. Raikes believed that the high level of silt deposits indicated that Sahni's dam-and-lake hypothesis was basically correct, and found a site ninety miles downstream from Mohenjo-daro where he thought the trouble could have started. If a geological disturbance had thrown up a barrier of rock or mud across the river's course there, the waters of the Indus would not have been able to reach the sea, but would have backed up behind this natural dam, obliterating the lowland settlements and eventually reaching Mohenjo-daro. Perhaps the city-dwellers could build dikes and barricades to keep from being inundated, but their fields and lower streets would be invaded, perhaps for several decades. Eventually the dammed water would flow over the top of the obstruction and begin to cut it away, the Indus would resume its normal flow, and the lake would disappear; but repeated cycles of this kind would weaken the city and possibly make life impossible in it.

Raikes joined the 1964–65 University of Pennsylvania expedition as hydrologist and helped to search for signs of such extensive and long-lasting flooding. Test drilling at Mohenjo-daro showed that the total depth of occupation at the examined part of the site was 74 feet—35 feet above the level of the plain, and 39 feet below it—of which the bottommost 24 feet is waterlogged by groundwater and cannot be excavated until the area is drained. This in itself indicates a sharp rise in the water table since the earliest days of the city, but is not necessarily the result of flooding.

At plain level, a massive platform of mud brick faced with more durable kiln-baked brick was found fronting the city to a height of at least twenty-five feet. This vast embankment, a thousand feet long and many feet thick, seemed too colossal to have been a defense against armed attack; it could be more satisfactorily explained as a structure designed to protect the city against slowly rising flood waters. Other evidence showed that after the lake had engulfed Mohenjo-daro the lower levels had been abandoned and new sections were built directly above them. At the highest part of the mound, just beneath its surface, the archaeologists found what George F. Dales, the expedition leader, described as "a thin, poorly preserved level which suggests a squatter-type occupation. The buildings were crudely constructed of secondhand, often broken bricks. . . . No trace of foreign objects which could indicate the arrival of invaders or non-Harappan peoples was found. The few examples of pottery found in place on the house floors are of standard Harappan types. . . . Architecturally it is important to note that before the building of this latest squatter-level the abandoned rooms and alleyways of the previous occupation were completely filled in with rubble and grey dirt. Also, crudely made packing walls were constructed to face portions of these fillings. When such fillings were removed during our excavation it was found that these structures so filled in were still in fairly good condition and should have been adequate for habitation. Why then did the last occupant of the city go to the trouble of packing these areas with from three to four feet of fill? If the overall picture we are obtaining from our other studies is correct, it becomes obvious [that] this elaborate filling and platform making was . . . the last of several attempts on the part of the Mohenjo-daro population to artificially raise the level of the city to keep above the height of the flood waters."

The various levels of silt deposit show that the cycle of dam-forming, lake-filling, and city-flooding may have occurred five or six times. Each time, a reservoir more than a hundred miles long could have been formed and filled up with silt until the river was able to top the dam and begin eroding it away. Though the citizens of Mohenjo-daro had ample opportunity to protect themselves against the encroachment from downstream, the constant need to erect flood barriers must have sapped the city's resources; and perhaps at some phase of each cycle the city had to be abandoned altogether for a period of months or years. In the end, Dales suggests, "Not only Harappan prosperity but also the Harappan spirit was being mired in an unrelenting sequence of invading water and engulfing silt."

The twin city of Harappa, far upstream from Mohenjo-daro and located on a tributary of the Indus, shows no sign of flooding at all, yet it, too, was abandoned at about the same time occupation ceased in Mohenjo-daro. Dales thinks that the decline in the southern city may have weakened Harappa too; possibly the climatic changes brought on by deforestation had begun to make Harappa's surroundings a desert, and this, coming atop the repeated disasters at Mohenjo-daro, sent the Indus people into a despondent migration to some other part of India where they lived on a reduced scale until the appearance of the Aryans.

This revised picture shows the Aryans not as all-destroying conquerors but as the inheritors by default from a tired and weakened people beaten by their own environment. The archaeological record after 1500 B.C. in the Indus region gives evidence only of an impoverished culture of squatters. There is no continuity with the great urban civilization of the Aryans that flowered after 500 B.C., nor did the Aryans choose to build their cities near the Indus, in that terrible desert where human society could no longer thrive.

While cities were rising in Egypt, Sumer, and the Indus Valley, Europe was struggling toward lesser attainments in a time of unsettled weather. During the warm, moist "climatic optimum" from 6,000 to 4,000 years ago, Neolithic concepts had been spreading across Europe, transforming a continent of small-game hunters into a continent of farmers. Glaciers had almost entirely disappeared, except near the summits of the Alps and in sub-Arctic Scandinavia; summer temperatures were four or five degrees warmer than they are today; great forests of oak, elm, and alder in the west and pine in the east covered much of Europe.

One thrust of Neolithic peoples was moving out of Asia Minor into Bulgaria and Greece, and on through the valley of the Danube into central Europe. The best known of these farming cultures is the Danubian, dating from the fifth and fourth millennia B.C. and centering on the region just south of the moraine deposited by the Würm glaciers in Germany, Poland, Austria, Czechoslovakia, and Hungary. The Danubians cultivated wheat, barley, lentils, flax, beans, and other crops, and raised cattle and pigs; but they also hunted such animals as deer, wild boar, and the now-extinct bison known as the aurochs. They lived in long, rectangular houses, and their villages had 200 to 600 inhabitants. Heavy rainfall and a generally mild climate encouraged the growth of these farming settlements, which were generally confined to lowland plains or river terraces, avoiding the dense forests.

While this column of Neolithic settlers was making its gradual way across eastern Europe toward Scandinavia, a parallel movement was under way in western Europe. These western Neolithic peoples had traveled the length of the Mediterranean before turning inland through France and Spain, which had been the heartland of the Aurignacians and Magdalenians thousands of years before. The farmers advanced steadily, building villages, clearing forests, raising crops, tending herds. They cultivated the olive and the grape. They knew how to spin and weave. They made good pottery. They had excellent stone tools, carefully ground and polished to a keen edge.

The western Neolithic folk who moved northward across the Alps into Switzerland during the climatic optimum built their villages by the shores of lakes. These settlements were rediscovered beginning in 1854, following an unusually cold, dry winter and a late spring. Mountain streams did not produce the usual bounty of the thaw that year, and the level of the Swiss lakes dropped sharply. Lake Zurich in particular suffered; the shoreline shrank inward, exposing great stretches of rocky beach that had not been laid bare for as long as anyone could remember. The retreat of the shoreline exposed a curious forest of wooden beams, four to six inches thick and three to five feet long, which had been sharpened at one end and driven vertically into the lake floor at distances of about a foot from each other. These wooden piles covered a wide zone stretching twelve hundred feet along the shore and extending out toward the deep water; and in the mud about them were unusual artifacts, tools fashioned from bone and stone, an extraordinary bronze ax-head, and other treasures of the past. Swiss archaeologists soon were excavating the extensive remains of a rich and complex ancient Neolithic settlement.

The Lake Dwellers, as these people quickly were dubbed, were thought to have lived on pile-supported platforms built out over the water; evidence of their presence soon came from dozens of sites in Switzerland and northern Italy, and exploring these half-submerged villages became an important subbranch of European archaeology. The old theory of settlements actually located in the lakes has given way, however, to the idea that the villages had been built on low-lying swampy ground along the shore, at a time when lake levels were much lower than they are today; a subsequent rise in the lake drowned the shoreline villages and kept them hidden until the unusual conditions of 1854 revealed them.

An expedition sponsored by the Bern Historical Museum in 1957, under the leadership of a young archaeologist named Hansjürgen Müller-Beck, has shown that this was the case. Müller-Beck worked at a site on the south shore of the Swiss lake of Burgäschi, where several Neolithic villages had been founded early in the postglacial era of favorable climate, about six thousand years ago. When the settlers arrived, he wrote, "they found a broad and treeless strip of land that was ideal for culivation. The lake, of moderate size when it was formed in the last ice age, had been gradually retreating, leaving on its shores mollusk shells and the deposits of carbon and lime that form around the roots of water plants. The soil cover was still too light to permit trees to take root and grow, but it was quite heavy enough for the demands of primitive agriculture."

Though the beach area was perfect for farming, thanks to the fertile deposits of mud and minerals left behind by the retreating lake, it was not so suitable as a place to live. The weak, soggy soil could not support the weight of houses built in a conventional manner. As a foundation the settlers laid down a floor of rubble, branches, and earth, which they pounded firm; then they made this floor secure by driving thousands of wooden piles through it and through the swampy ground below, into the gravel bedrock underlying the boglike beach.

But ever warmer, wetter weather brought copious runoffs into the lake, and it began to expand again, causing troubles for the settlers at its shores. "The floors sank in the middle as the earth beneath them gave way," according to Müller-Beck. "For a while they could be leveled by the addition of new layers of rubble, branches, and loam. . . . But eventually more drastic action became necessary and the entire settlement had to be moved a few feet back from the lake, onto drier land." The archaeologist found the successive sets of piles that marked these moves back from the shore; but eventually the settlement was abandoned altogether, after about a century of occupation.

About 3000 B.C. the rise in mean temperature and precipitation, which had continued for at least two thousand years, began to flatten out, and the mild Atlantic phase of Europe's climate started to give way to a colder period of erratic weather known as the Sub-boreal. The changing pollen spectrum tells us of shifts in the forest population, with pine and beech replacing oak and elm. Now the climate grew much more dry, with severe winters and, probably, hot summers—the typical continental climate replacing the oceanic climate that had prevailed for millennia. C. E. P. Brooks, the advocate of geological disturbance as the main cause of climatic change, felt that this was due to a general uplifting of western Europe some five thousand years ago. "The southern part of the British

Isles, which had remained slightly elevated since the last glacial period," he wrote, "had now emerged to a height of nearly 90 feet above its present level; the area of Ireland had increased appreciably and part of the North Sea was land. The geographical changes were not great, but they were sufficient to turn the scale in the direction of a continental climate in the British Isles. . . . At the same time the low level of northern Norway, and possibly the persistence of warm conditions in the Arctic basin, more and more attracted depressions to the northernmost track, so that the British Isles especially, and to a lesser extent Holland, Germany, southern Scandinavia and Russia, came more persistently under the influence of anti-cyclonic conditions." The rainfall in these countries diminished appreciably; and forests emerged where there had been swamps and bogs during the Atlantic phase, the climatic optimum.

In Sub-boreal Ireland, for example, the bogs dried so thoroughly that they could be inhabited. In 1883 a two-story log house was uncovered in Drumkelin Bog, County Donegal; it was 12 feet square, 9 feet high, and a roadway of oak cords led to it across the bog. The swamp deposits were 14 feet thick beneath the floor of the house, and 26 feet thick above it; but the house had been built on what was, at the time, dry land.

This phase was brief. About 1800 B.C., when Europe was passing into that time of progress known as the Bronze Age, the climate worsened, bringing storms, floods, and advances of the Alpine glaciers. In western Europe the cold, rainy weather caused widespread replacement of forests by bogs, which at first had the effect of creating new trade routes through what had formerly been impenetrably dense woodlands. But as the swampy conditions intensified it became difficult to keep those routes open, even though wooden roadways were laid over the increasingly squishy countryside. Whatever shift of the cyclone belts caused this deterioration of the climate in Europe produced an opposite deterioration in central Asia, where a prolonged drought commenced in the second millennium B.C. As the climate dried and available pasture diminished, the horse nomads of the Asian steppes were impelled to seek better territory elsewhere, and the highly developed nations of the Near East were subjected to repeated invasions. Mesopotamia suffered severely, as we have already seen, from the onslaught of mountaineers coming by way of Iran. A related group, speaking a language of the Indo-European or Aryan family, crossed the Caucasus into Asia Minor to found the Hittite empire, while another Aryan group penetrated India from 1500 B.C. on, displacing the troubled civilization of the Indus Valley people.

Within Europe, this time of storms may have sent nomad barbarians spilling out of Austria and Hungary into Greece about 1300 B.C. The Greek world was then dominated by the island of Crete, where a powerful seafaring people known as the Minoans had arisen in the course of the generally northwestward movement of civilization's center away from Egypt and Mesopotamia. The events of this era are too much a matter of controversy now for detailed discussion; but it is at least likely that climatic forces were pushing barbarians down into the Minoan realm at just about the same time that Crete was shattered by a terrible earthquake. Certainly by 1300 B.C. the Minoans were in eclipse and the new people, who called themselves the Achaeans, were in command. These were the Homeric Greeks, the race of Agamemnon and Menelaus and Achilles, who within another century would be invading Asia Minor to destroy the great city of Troy.

The cold, rainy period lasted for about thirteen centuries, with the peak of the bad weather coming between 900 and 450 B.C., a period designated as the Sub-Atlantic phase. This is shown not only by the pollen charts but by such sites as Biskupin in Poland, where in 1933 a change in the level of a lake revealed the roofs of submerged houses. Excavation of the waterlogged shoreline uncovered a village of more than a hundred timber houses dating from about 700 B.C. The original settlement had consisted of six acres of log cabins built in parallel streets atop a timber platform on an island in the lake. A thick rampart of wood-faced earth had been erected around the town; and the excavators found indications that rising lake levels had forced the villagers to rebuild their rampart twice, each time higher and smaller in diameter than its predecessor, as the water nibbled at the edges of the island. The great increase in rainfall finally sent water over the topmost rampart and into the town; a foot-thick layer of timber was put down above the old floors to raise the entire level of the village, but even that was futile, and by 500 B.C. Biskupin was abandoned. The lake broke through the neglected rampart; weeds and rushes grew in the village streets; decaying vegetation became thick layers of peat that covered and preserved the wooden structures until their accidental discovery by archaeologists.

The stormy weather that brought doom to Biskupin may have inspired the Scandinavian legend of the Fimbulwinter, the awful time of privation and cold that in Norse saga was destined to usher in the Twilight of the Gods and the end of civilization. The *Edda* of Snorri Sturluson, written in Iceland early in the thirteenth century and based on oral traditions, tells how "in that time snow shall drive from all quarters; frosts shall be great then, and winds sharp; there shall be no virtue in the sun. Those winters shall proceed three in succession, and no summer between; but first shall come three other winters, such that all over the world there shall be mighty battles. . . . Then shall happen what seems great tidings: the wolf shall swallow the sun; and this shall seem to men a great harm. Then the other wolf shall seize the moon, and he also shall work great ruin; the stars shall vanish from the heavens. Then shall come to pass these tidings also: all the earth shall tremble so, and the crags, that trees shall be torn up from the earth, and the crags fall to ruin; and all fetters and bonds shall be broken and rent." Snorri wrote near the close of a prolonged period of warm, dry weather that had lasted many centuries; his Fimbulwinter could not have been some remembered echo of the last ice age, as has sometimes been suggested, but it might well have evolved from a tale, handed down across the generations, of the fierce winters that gripped Scandinavia sixteen centuries before his time.

One of the most glittering epochs in human history may also have been a product of the storms of the Sub-Atlantic: the golden age of Athenian Greece. The era of the Homeric

Achaeans had come to a violent end about 1000 B.C. when a new wave of barbarian invaders from the north, the Dorians, conquered the great cities of Achaean Greece. Homer himself was a poet of the Dorian conquerors, singing of the legendary heroes of Achaean times. But it was centuries before the Dorians could reach the cultural heights attained by their predecessors in Greece; and the brilliant achievements of the Greeks after 600 B.C. have been associated with the coming of more turbulent weather.

This, of course, is the Ellsworth Huntington hypothesis. When he first stated it in his *Civilization and Climate* of 1915 he put his idea forth frankly as a guess, suggesting that in the time of Socrates Greece might have had somewhat cooler summers and winters than at present, a relative humidity perhaps 20 percent higher, and rainfall that exceeded the present amount by at least 50 percent, along with more frequent cyclonic storms and a general increase in the changeability of the temperature and precipitation from day to day. This, he said, would have provided the stimulus for the remarkable vigor of mind and body characteristic of the greatest days of Athens.

Huntington had nothing on which to base this supposition, other than scattered descriptions by Greek and Roman geographers of dense forests in areas of Greece that now are covered only by scrubby underbrush. But pollen analysis and other empirical methods have confirmed that Greece had indeed had a much more stormy climate between 800 and 300 B.C., with the peak of turbulence coming between 600 and 400 B.C., and thus coinciding exactly with the noblest centuries of Greek civilization, while a return to warmer and drier conditions after 300 B.C. coincided with the engulfment of Hellenic culture by the Romans. Huntington did not press the naïve claim that storms alone had made Greece great; they were, he said, only part of "a series of circumstances which favored a great outburst of genius. This series starts with the selective migrations of the Achaeans, Ionians, and Dorians, which presumably eliminated weaklings and purged the immigrant population of many persons who lacked intelligence, initiative, and determination. Then came the development of an aristocracy in almost every Greek state. . . . Such an aristocratic group was especially strong and exclusive in Athens, where genius flowered most fully. Next we have climatic conditions such that for two centuries or more there was a general improvement economically and presumably in diet and health. Finally, Greece, especially Athens, was greatly stimulated by cultural conditions which led to the mastery of the sea and the growth of trade." Similarly, he believed that the decline of Greece could be traced to other factors besides the decline in storminess after 300 B.C.—such as the fratricidal convulsion of the war between Athens and Sparta. But the change in the weather not only made the environment less stimulating in Huntington's sense of the word; it also diminished the flow of rivers and led to the formation of isolated pools in which mosquitoes could breed, resulting in debilitating epidemics of malaria.

Whether we can in fact credit the rise and fall of Greece even in part to climatic shifts is a matter for strenuous scholarly debate. But when we take the long view of the dynamic postglacial era, it is hard to escape the suspicion that some relationship between climate and civilization does exist. We see Europe emerging from the ice age and western Asia from its pluvial age between fifteen and ten thousand years ago; as the world grows drier and warmer, agriculture and domestication of animals appear in the fertile crescent of the Near East and spread first to Egypt and Mesopotamia, where great civilizations are founded, then to India, and, more slowly, into Europe. There comes a warm, wet age some seven thousand years ago, a time of cooler and less rainy weather two thousand years later, and then a period of growing chill and storminess in the final two millennia before the Christian era, which begins with a return to warmth and dryness. Thus it was a time of great change for mankind, of farmers and cities, of evolving technology, of rising and toppling civilizations, of vast migrations of nomads. And behind each of these twists and turns of the human story we can identify some shift in the pattern of temperature and rainfall that we call climate.

7

Irrigators and Nomads

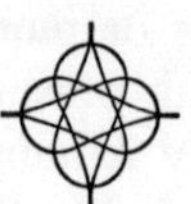

IN RECONSTRUCTING ANCIENT CLIMATES, IT CAN BE DANGEROUS to draw conclusions about one area based on what is known of the climate of another; and it is often equally risky to let oneself be guided by logic rather than by paleoclimatic evidence. The case of the Palestinian desert is an example in point.

The southern half of the State of Israel is a desert, desolate and parched and ruggedly beautiful: the Negev, which begins less than two hours' drive south of Tel Aviv and runs down to the Red Sea port of Eilat. The rainfall at the upper end of the Negev is about eight inches a year, most of it coming in a few heavy cloudbursts; near Eilat the precipitation is an inch a year or less, making this one of the world's most forbidding desert areas. Just as arid is the desert to the east in Jordan; and farther north, another desert stretches from inland Syria to the Euphrates.

In biblical times all this region was heavily populated. Everywhere in the Negev can be found the villages and fortresses of the Judaean kingdom, from the time of King Solomon at the end of the tenth century B.C. down to the early sixth century B.C., when the Hebrews were conquered by the Babylonians. King Solomon's mining town of Ezion-geber was situated in the terrifying dryness near Eilat; it has been excavated and is a popular tourist attraction today. Mud-brick villages five thousand years old have been excavated near Beersheba, in the northern Negev; settlements of the time of Abraham, about four thousand years ago, have been found in many parts of the desert. In Jordan, east and south of the Dead Sea, there are hundreds of ruined towns and cities, some of them minor outposts, some of them as impressive as Jerash (Gerasa), with its Roman theaters and half-mile-long colonnaded street, or stunning Petra, the "rose-red city half as old as time." Another string of ruins runs southward for hundreds of miles of what is now uninhabited territory in the Syrian desert.

The rainfall in all these wastelands is so scanty that it is difficult to see how they could ever have supported so many people; and the logical answer is that there must have been a major change in the precipitation pattern of the Near East in the last two thousand years. Thus H. C. Butler, in a 1920 issue of the *Geographical Review,* writes:

> The results of the explorations of the last twenty years have been most astonishing. . . . Practically all of the wide area lying between the coast range of the eastern Mediterranean and the Euphrates, appearing upon the maps as the Syrian Desert, an area embracing somewhat more than 20,000 square miles, was more thickly populated than any area of similar dimensions in England or the United States is today if one excludes the immediate vicinity of the large modern cities. . . . An enormous desert tract lying to the east of Palestine, stretching eastward and southward into the country which we know as Arabia, was also densely populated. . . . How far these settled regions extended in antiquity is still unknown, but the most distant explorations in these directions have failed to reach the end of ruins and other signs of former occupation. . . . It is perfectly apparent that large parts of Syria once had soil and forests and springs and rivers, while it has none of these now, and that it had a much larger and better distributed rainfall in ancient times than it has now.

Such dramatic and seemingly self-evident proof of a broad climatic shift attracted the attention of Ellsworth Huntington, who was ever alert for instances of man's dependence on environmental factors. Since his first books on the pulsatory hypothesis he had asserted that a great wave of desiccation had swept Asia and apparently much of the rest of the world in the early years of the Christian era, with disastrous consequences for settlements in marginal areas. He based this idea to some extent on archaeological evidence (sand-buried cities, abandoned desert roads, the shrunken shorelines of lakes) and also on chronicles, guesswork, and wishful thinking. To explain the death of the Palestinian and Syrian settlements Huntington invoked such material as Ptolemy's record of rainfall in Egypt in the second century A.D., which clearly showed greater precipitation then than now. "The ruins found in Palestine," Huntington wrote, "make it clear that in the early years of our era cyclonic disturbances followed more southerly paths than now, thus giving greater rainfall and greater variability of weather to North Africa and western Asia." The sharp variation in climatic zones in that region today lends some substance to this view. Alexandria is only a hundred miles north of Cairo, but its average rainfall is eight times as great. In Israel, a country about the size of New Jersey, the northern districts get about 42 inches of rain a year—as much as New York City—while in the southern Negev, only 200 miles away, the mean precipitation is less than in the most arid desert zone of the American Southwest. It would take only a small shift in the belt of storms to bring about great changes in climate here.

Unfortunately, Huntington had no data available on the climate of the biblical Near East, other than what he could draw by inference from the presence of such an abundance of ruined cities. It was necessary for him to turn as far afield as California and Ireland for support. In 1911 and 1912 he had measured the thickness of the annual growth rings of the stumps of some 450 Sequoia trees which had been cut in California. The ring count showed that the trees were from 250 to 3,250 years of age, with the majority 1,000 years old or more, 79 over 2,000, and 3 over 3,000. From variations in the width of these rings Huntington constructed a rainfall chart which he regarded as fairly accurate for the past 2,000 years and approximate for 1,000 years more. It showed California precipitation levels at their maximum prior to 100 B.C., falling off steadily to a low level at about 400 A.D. and remaining generally low for about 1,000 years, with minor increases in rainfall in 600 and 900, a major increase in 1,000, and severe droughts in 650, 725, 775, and 1150. Because it was a historical fact that many of the abandoned cities of the Near East had ceased to be inhabited between A.D. 400 and 700, Huntington drew the tempting but risky conclusion that the drop in rainfall indicated by the growth rings of California redwood trees had been a worldwide phenomenon.

The evidence from Ireland came from Roman geographers. About A.D. 43, at the time of the Roman conquest of Britain, Pomponius Mela wrote that the Irish climate was too cool and wet for growing grain, and spoke of the luxuriance of the grass. Solinus, about A.D. 218, also referred to the lush pastures, and added that there were no bees in Ireland, presumably because the summers were cold and stormy. These stray comments indicate that Ireland then was still in the Sub-Atlantic phase of climate that had lashed much of Europe with tempests since about 900 B.C.

But rainfall was already diminishing in California when Solinus wrote. Huntington observes that "Cormac mac Airt, the 'first real personality' in Irish history, began to rule in A.D. 227, when indications of the approach of a dry climatic phase are widespread from California to Central Asia. At Tara, his capital, where extensive ruins can still be seen, he is said to have founded schools of military science, law, and literature. The progress thus started reached its climax about A.D. 650 to 700." The laws decreed at Tara in the seventh century A.D. include minute regulations concerning the keeping of bees—showing, according to Huntington, a basic change in Ireland's climate toward the drier since Roman times.

But did the advent of beekeeping in Ireland have any connection with the decline of the desert settlements of the Near East? Many climatologists agreed with Huntington that it did, and until the 1930's it was customary to assume that the climate of the Negev and surrounding desert regions must have been far more favorable several thousand years ago. That belief has been shattered now. Archaeologists have shown that those desert settlements were able to exist not by virtue of a kindly climate but through human determination to triumph over an adverse environment; and in recent years Israeli pioneers, making use of techniques developed by their ancient predecessors, have demonstrated that the desert can be made to bloom without benefit of a change in climate.

The biblical scholar and archaeologist Nelson Glueck, now President of Hebrew Union College in Cincinnati, was the main force in overthrowing the Huntington view of Palestine's climatic oscillations. Glueck, ordained as a rabbi in 1923 at the age of 23, shifted his interests to archaeology after spending three years as a student at the American School of Oriental Research in Jerusalem, beginning in 1927. After that preliminary taste of the antiquities of the Holy Land, he returned in 1932 to begin years of research in the desert. It was a time of tension and danger as Jews and Arabs engaged in the first battles for possession of Palestine, but Glueck went unarmed into the bleak lands beyond the Jordan, won the friendship of Bedouin tribes, and was never molested. "That a Jew should wander by himself in Transjordan," he said, "was so unheard of that no one thought to ask."

Working in fearful places whipped by sandstorms and baked by intolerable heat, Glueck discovered hundreds of sites—more than a thousand in Transjordan and five hundred in the Negev—ranging in time from the Stone Age through the biblical era to the Byzantine period of the fifth and sixth centuries A.D., when human occupation of most of the desert outposts came to an end. Instead of carrying out an intensive excavation at any one site, Glueck deliberately remained a "surface man," preferring to survey a great many sites in the attempt to identify them by local tradition, biblical clues, and accessible artifacts. In this way he developed a reasoned view of the history of a comparatively large area through a lengthy span of time.

Glueck's conclusion, first made known in his 1940 book, *The Other Side of the Jordan*, and amplified in such later works as the 1959 *Rivers in the Desert,* is that the supposed climatic deterioration never took place at all. "I could show you," he wrote, "a thousand or more sites of antiquity in Transjordan which existed during and after the time the land was supposed no longer to be able to sustain them because of radical, pronounced and permanent climatic changes. The settlements on them flourished in spite of currently popular theories of a steady diminution of rainfall that made permanent, sedentary, agricultural occupation progressively impossible." Not that Glueck denies *all* climatic shifts in his chosen area. As he notes, the fossil bones of rhinoceroses, hippopotami, and elephants have been found all over Palestine, indicating that tropical conditions prevailed a hundred thousand years ago. "The land was raw and damp and hot. Then a series of radical changes followed . . . until a dry, warm climate developed at the beginning of the . . . Natufian period, about the eighth millennium B.C. By then the original types of animals had vanished, and deer and gazelles became abundant." But, he insists, "The climate has remained much the same to this very day!"

This argument runs all through Glueck's work. At times when civilizations thrived in the Negev, it was through skill and resourcefulness, not through an increase in rainfall; when those civilizations collapsed, their fall should "also not be attributed to the catchall excuse of climatic change," but must be blamed on "the horrifying tendency of man, wearily repeated throughout the centuries, to take his neighbor's goods or country, or to 'scorch' the land for his own protection and his enemies' hurt. . . . . It certainly makes understandable why scores of cities have been reduced to piles of faceless rubble, rich countrysides transformed almost overnight into wildernesses, and why dark ages have followed times of cultural enlightenment."

Glueck's view that there has been no substantial climatic change in the Near East since Natufian times is an extreme one, and not shared by all archaeologists. As we saw in the discussion of events in Egypt, Mesopotamia, and the Sahara, many authorities feel there is good reason to believe that steady or accelerating desiccation was experienced in that entire part of the world for thousands of years after 7000 B.C. Glueck, however, offers as evidence to the contrary the presence in 6,000-year-old sites in the Negev of the burned shells of a certain mollusk known to be highly sensitive to humidity. That mollusk is still found in the arid wastes around Beersheba; and its continued existence in the desert is proof that the Negev was no less arid in the days of Abraham and Isaac.

Though Glueck's views on that remote epoch remain the subject of debate, there now is general agreement that the alleged desiccation of the early Christian era, postulated by Huntington and others, never occurred. As the American authority on soil and water conservation, Walter C. Lowdermilk, put it in 1960, "Harsh as these [present] conditions are, there has been no significant deterioration in climate [in Palestine] since Roman times. The same plants still thrive in protected places, and springs recorded in the Bible still bubble from the ground. The 'desert' that took over the once-flourishing land was the work of man, not nature."

As his grand example of persistence and ingenuity in the face of a hostile environment, Glueck gives the Nabataeans, a desert people who came out of the barren southern reaches of Arabia early in the fourth century B.C., seized the wastelands of Palestine from the Edomites and Moabites who had occupied them since before the days of Moses, and founded a powerful commercial kingdom. At the height of their greatness—between the second century B.C. and the second century A.D.—Nabataean influence extended from Arabia to Syria, and westward into the fierce desert of Sinai almost to the borders of Egypt. Though originally pastoralist nomads, the Nabataeans after their eruption from Arabia became farmers, merchants, architects, and perhaps the cleverest hydraulic engineers of the ancient world. From their capital city of Petra they exercised a stranglehold control over the commerce of the entire Near East. Their principal cities—Avdat, Shivta, Eiseiba, Kurnub, and others—were situated in places that today are bleak desert outposts. They were, Nelson Glueck asserts, desert outposts even when the Nabataeans inhabited them. Yet in their day the desert blossomed with gardens and fields.

What was the secret of the Nabataeans?

They started from the premise that not even the desolate Negev and Sinai are completely waterless. As the Bedouins who roam the desert know, many wadis or ravines that seem cruelly dry have accessible groundwater. Genesis 26:19 tells how the servants of Isaac, digging in a ravine at Gerar, north of Beersheba, "found there a well of springing water." A similar story is found in II Kings 3, in which the kings of Judah, Israel, and Edom go into the wilderness to punish the rebellious king of Moab, and suffer greatly from lack of water until a minstrel offers oracular advice: "Thus saith the Lord, Make this valley full of ditches. For thus saith the Lord, Ye shall not see wind, neither shall ye see rain; yet that valley shall be filled with water, that ye may drink, both ye, and your cattle, and your beasts."

Not by wells alone did the Nabataeans build their kingdom. It rains, even in the worst of the Negev: eight inches or more per year in the north, two inches or less in the south. The rain is not spread out evenly through the twelve months, but comes in sudden violent downpours in the winter that bring magical, almost incredible transformations to the desert. "The grass and flowers fairly spring up after the first shower or storm," says Glueck, "and the grim desert becomes a colorful garden overnight. . . . Flocks of birds suddenly make their appearance then, to sing and to swoop about in happy flight, and bands of gazelles and ibexes graze and cavort through the lush green. Camels and goats and sheep and their young wax fat. They drink their fill at pools of water collected in hollows, making it unnecessary for months on end to find other supplies for them. Springs flow more strongly, wells rise to their highest levels and the underground water is replenished in the wadi beds, there to remain long after the flowers have faded and the grass has withered and gone."

But the impact of the rains is shortlived, and the water itself is uselessly dissipated. A Negev rainstorm produces flash floods in which the water rushes over the bare, practically impermeable soil without sinking in, gathering in force and stripping away the topsoil of hillsides as it races down the wadis. Uncontrolled, these swift torrents of muddy water do no good, and can bring vast devastation. The great accomplishment of the Nabataeans was to harness the flash floods and to hoard the water they brought, so that a few hours of rainfall a year could nourish the fields for season after season.

The core of Nabataean water technology was the use of terraces and retaining walls to slow and trap the soil-laden water cutting through the wadis. Their work began in the tributary ravines that fed water into the main wadi of a broad valley. High on the slopes they constructed a series of stone shelves that compelled the water of flash floods to descend gradually, step by step, releasing some of the load of suspended soil at each stage of the descent. In time the shelves became earth-covered terraces on which crops could be grown; the accumulation of soil also improved the absorption of flood water in the upper levels of the system and minimized the dangers of erosion below.

In the main wadi the Nabataeans also built water traps, but in somewhat more complex fashion. They erected stone walls in the deepest part of the ravine, its center; these divided the valley floor into a series of level plots, and served as dams that diverted flood water to higher plots along the sides of the wadi. In a heavy rainstorm all the walled plots became little ponds, and the water was distributed gradually and evenly over the entire valley floor, plot by plot. Where a wadi was unusually deep, cut to a V-shape by powerful erosion, higher dams were used, and stone conduits upstream acted to carry off excess water to adjoining plots. The one thing the Nabataeans did not do was to construct massive dams that would back up large storage reservoirs; the water loss through evaporation would have been too great, and they relied instead on their ingenious methods for quickly spreading rain runoff over the largest possible area. To collect supplies of drinking water they used conduits leading to underground cisterns where the sun could make no inroads on the reserve.

The system worked. Making maximum use of a minimal water supply, the Nabataeans grew wheat, barley, grapes, figs, dates, and a variety of vegetables, and made themselves agriculturally self-sufficient. Hundreds of villages and a number of fairly large cities survived quite comfortably for centuries in desert regions. No drop of water was wasted; no difficulty was too great to be mastered; the skill of the Nabataean engineers was a match for any problem of topography. Through their terraces, dams, cisterns, conduits, catchments, and spillways they protected themselves against flash floods, halted erosion of potentially valuable hillside topsoil, and enabled themselves to maintain a secure grip on their harsh but strategically located territory.

The forbidding terrain of the Nabataeans' country was the main caravan route through which all the rich cargoes of the East were transported. Not only did it link the important trading centers of Syria and Arabia, but also the merchandise of Africa, India, and possibly even China found its way through their land, coming by sea up the Persian Gulf to the port of Gerrha, and overland via the desert to be reshipped at the great market city of Petra. At every stage of the journey, Nabataean hostelries offered hospitality (at a price) to the men of the caravans, Nabataean merchants reaped the rewards of middlemen, and Nabataean exporters acquired goods which they would send on by sea to the Mediterranean ports. To control such a valuable intersection of commerce was well worth the struggle to scratch a livelihood from the desert.

Prosperity breeds dangers, and the end began for the Nabataeans when Emperor Trajan of Rome captured Petra in A.D. 106. Roman legionaries occupied the desert cities, and the Nabataean kingdom was engulfed in the Roman province of Arabia. The Nabataeans kept going on the momentum of the past for some centuries, but their power was gone, and their wondrous hydraulic systems slowly deteriorated for lack of sufficient motivation for keeping them in good repair.

Under the Romans the caravan routes shifted; Petra declined to the status of a provincial town by the third century A.D., and prosperity came instead to Palmyra, a town on an oasis in the central desert of Syria, which lay on the new path of trade. Palmyra became the chief gateway for eastern commodities passing onward to the Mediterranean world, and its population grew with its importance, requiring new application of engineering skill to sustain it in its expansion.

Palmyra had the benefit of shrewd leaders and a fortunate location. But there seems little foundation for Huntington's assertion that the time of the city's greatness coincided with "the rainy phase of a long climatic cycle"; nor is there justification for C. E. B. Brooks's comment that the existence of great aqueducts, "built to carry from the hill-springs to the city large volumes of water which these springs no longer deliver" proves that there has been a decrease in rainfall. The Palmyrans, like the Nabataeans, were expert at making much from little. Their chief means of obtaining water was a system known in Persian as a *kariz* and in Arabic as a *qanat,* and invented in Iran or Armenia sometime prior to 700 B.C. This is a gently sloping tunnel dug in the deposits of sand and gravel lying near the foot of hills or mountains. Ordinarily, rainwater and the output of springs sinks into this loose gravel and never reappears; but the tunnel taps the underground water and conveys it down the slope to the city in the plain below the hills, where it runs into irrigation channels. A series of shafts along the route of the tunnel permit entry for maintenance and the tapping of water at intermediary points.

Such tunnels have been employed all over the arid Near East since the Assyrian King Sargon II learned of them while invading Armenia in 714 B.C. At Palmyra, though, when the city's growth made it impossible to depend any longer on the small stream and springs that fed the original oasis, an elaborate tunnel system was created that reached toward the mountains in several directions and gathered an abundant supply of water which, since it came to the city underground, was protected from evaporation loss. Ultimately such a system would be self-defeating, since it was bound to lower the water table to a point where the flow became a trickle, especially if the city and its *qanat* network continued to grow at a rapid pace. But Palmyra's rulers, buoyed by pride, ambition, and wealth too swiftly gained, committed the more immediate error of challenging Roman supremacy. Under the famous Queen

Zenobia the audacity of Palmyra brought the wrath of Rome upon the city: in A.D. 172 the troops of Emperor Aurelian destroyed this gem of the desert, and the tunnels fell into disrepair within a few generations.

The fall of Palmyra brought a final flourish of prosperity to the Negev, where the Nabataean water-gathering system was still intact. Rome soon split into an eastern and a western empire, and the Near East fell under the hegemony of the eastern rulers, whose capital was Constantinople in Byzantium. During the Byzantine period Christianity came to the desert lands, and at such reconstructed sites as Avdat and Shivta in the Negev today one can see Byzantine chapels beside the older Nabataean buildings. In the middle of the fifth century Petra was the seat of a bishop; but this renaissance was short-lived, and the glorious Nabataean capital sank into squalor and by the early seventh century was abandoned altogether. Later in that century a new wave of conquerors swept out of Arabia as the Nabataeans themselves had done a thousand years before: the invincible Moslems, spreading their newly proclaimed creed by the sword and bringing an end to the Byzantine era of the Near East. With the triumph of Islam the last of the Nabataeans vanished, swallowed up in the conquest; and the cunning irrigation works, too complex for the invaders to maintain, passed from use.

Thus the land became a desert incapable of supporting anything more than aimless nomads and hapless subsistence farmers. But, Nelson Glueck notes, the Nabataeans "succumbed to conquest by arms and not to uncontrollable forces of nature. The resulting diversion of trade to other regions and routes drained away their economic lifeblood, and not the drying up of their lands because of a sudden lack of water."

That this is so can be seen from the events in Palestine within the last century, when after twelve hundred years of Arab occupation the barren and dismal land began to come into the possession of Jewish refugees from Europe. The Zionist movement toward a national Jewish homeland brought the first of these immigrants into Palestine late in the nineteenth century. They found evidence of neglect everywhere: the ruins of Nabataean and Byzantine cities and highways, the traces of vanished forests on naked slopes, the shattered remnants of dams, aqueducts, and terraced irrigation works. Along the coast, where rainfall was relatively heavy, erosion-laden streams had created marshes, and sand dunes had marched inland from the shore to smother thousands of acres of farmland.

The immigrants purchased "worthless" coastal land, drained the marshes, pushed back the dunes, and reclaimed areas that had not been farmed for a millennium. But the real redevelopment of Palestine had to wait until after the war of liberation that created the State of Israel in 1948. Given a land of less than eight thousand square miles, of which more than half was desert, the Israelis launched a reclamation program on a scale not seen since Nabataean times. Archaeologists joined forces with engineers, studying the ancient methods so that they could be adapted for modern use. The old terraces in the wadis of the desert were restored; irrigation channels that followed routes two thousand years old were constructed; cisterns of antiquity returned to use in the hillsides of the Negev. Within a decade, thousands of acres of the Negev were yielding crops, and each year some 25,000 additional acres come under cultivation. Of course, the Israelis have access to such things as pumps, sprinklers, and tractors, not available to the Nabataeans, but the basic point is unaltered by this: man is not necessarily the helpless victim of his environment. In our time we have seen the Israelis make the Negev bloom, though there has been no change whatever in the climate that prevails there; and two thousand years ago the Nabateans worked the same miracle, likewise without the aid of the providential rains Ellsworth Huntington postulated for them. Climate is not the only determining factor in the story of man.

Another region for which a desiccation theory has been proposed and debated is central Asia, that broad and dry and largely empty expanse of land bounded by the Himalayas on the south, the forests of Siberia on the north, Manchuria on the east, and the Caspian Sea on the west. Several great mountain ranges cross this region, and there are a few lakes and rivers;

but mainly it is a long stretch of arid steppe, at best suited for grazing, in its worst places a forlorn desert. Mongolia's Gobi Desert leads to the Takla-makan Desert of Sinkiang; and beyond the T'ien Shan Mountains are the deserts of Kyzyl Kum and Kara Kum. Throughout most of history this has been a land of nomads, driving their herds from pasture to pasture; but there are oases in the bleakness, where cities with magical names have long met the needs of weary travelers: Samarkand, Khotan, Tashkent, Ferghana, Kashgar.

The history of the central Asian steppe has been one of conflict between the nomads and the settled agriculturalists. Periodically the central Asian nomads spilled out of their steppe homeland into the Near East and India; in the thirteenth century the Mongol war machine set in motion by Genghis Khan struck deep into Europe. Most often it was China, though, lying south of the steppe country, which felt the brunt of these nomad excursions. Repeatedly the Chinese were invaded, and often conquered; Chinese annals tell of twenty centuries of attack by tribes variously termed the Jung, the Ti, the Hsiung-nu, the Hsien-pi, the T'o-pa, the Khitan, the Jurchen. "Cathay," the medieval name for China, is really *Khitai,* derived from the name of the Khitan barbarians who conquered China in the tenth century. Kublai Khan belonged to a dynasty of nomad conquerors from Mongolia; and the dynasty that ruled China for nearly three hundred years until its overthrow in 1912 was a line of former barbarians from Manchuria.

These barbarians all were of the same basic racial stock as the Chinese, though they spoke languages unrelated to those of China. The real difference lay in their way of life. The barbarians were pastoralists, depending on livestock for meat and milk; the Chinese were agriculturalists, raisers of wheat and millet in the north, rice in the south, and, of course, were rooted to their land, in contrast to the necessarily nomadic ways of the pastoralists.

The gulf between Chinese and barbarian was a natural geographic one. China proper is fertile and well watered, ideal for cultivation once problems of flood control and irrigation were mastered. But beyond lie three differing but inhospitable zones where agriculture is impossible. In the west is the Tibetan plateau, a high frozen desert suited only for a nomadic economy of shepherds driving herds of yak and goats from one patch of alpine grass to the next. The plateau gives way to the high steppe of Sinkiang and Mongolia, which is arid grassland along the Chinese border, bleak desert farther north. Here, too, the economy must be based on sheep, horses, camels, and cattle. The animals convert grass into meat and milk. Skins and furs yield food and clothing and shelter; animal dung provides fuel. Wells and oases are few. When rain is sparse, the pastures cease to support the grazing animals, and life is hard. Wheat must come from the south, from China, obtained through trade or, in bad times, through raiding.

The third frontier zone of the north is Manchuria, in the east. The geography here is less brutal; there are grassy steppes, watered plains, and, in the north, thick forests. But agriculture of the Chinese type could not flourish there until recently; it was a land of shepherds in the steppe and hunters in the forest. Only in the present century has the Manchurian steppe been turned into farmland.

China began to consolidate into an urban civilization about 1500 B.C. under the domination of the Shang Dynasty, a warrior caste whose origins are still a mystery. As China expanded under the rule of the Shang and their successors, the Chou, the aboriginal peasantry apparently was forced into ever more marginal land until it took up the pastoral life in the steppes. In time these displaced tribes began to force their way back into more congenial territory, with the first recorded invasion coming in 771 B.C. when the Jung barbarians sacked the capital of the Chou. To protect their boundaries, the individual Chinese states began to erect lengthy walls, a project that culminated in the construction of the Great Wall of China.

The Great Wall was the work of Ch'in Shih Huang Ti, the despotic emperor who in 221 B.C. was the first ruler to weld China's fractious states into a single realm. Linking the separate walls into a single wall running for more than fifteen hundred miles along the top of his empire was more of a public works project than a military-defense enterprise; Ch'in Shih Huang Ti's program of agrarian reform had set free from the land large numbers of men who were not landowners or heads of families, and this floating population of unemployed men could not be used for a standing army, for there were no feudal kingdoms left to conquer in China. The emperor conscripted most of these men to build the wall that is his most enduring monument. The standard explanation of the decision to build the wall is that Ch'in Shih Huang Ti felt "threatened" by the northern barbarians, but in fact the nomads seem to have been weak and divided at the time, posing no real threat to the stability of the empire. The old nomad tribes such as the Jung had broken up, and in their place were such tribes as the Hu and the Hsiung-nu, quite probably of the same stock. They spoke languages of the group called Turkic, and lived by herding livestock.

The Great Wall served as a cultural barrier, a line drawn across the geographical divide between grassy steppe and fertile farmland. It was never very useful for keeping really determined invaders out, but it provided a way of preventing China's farming population from drifting off into nomadism. Thus the wall marked China's outer limit of desirable expansion.

Ch'in Shih Huang Ti's dynasty did not survive his death in 210 B.C. by more than four years; but the wall remained, a great collar shackling China, spanning 1,850 miles including all bends and twists. It ran from Shanhaikuan on the Yellow Sea to Kia-yü-kuan far in the west; in places it was 24 feet high and wide enough for eight men to march along its top; watchtowers placed every few hundred yards served as warning stations in times of barbarian invasion.

The invasions came frequently; China rarely knew more than a few years at a time of freedom from nomad pressure, and all too often the barbarians burst through the Great Wall to establish dynasties of their own, some of which lasted for centuries. Thus much of northern China was under barbarian rule from A.D. 386 to 589, from 907 to 1368, and from 1644 to 1912; on several occasions one nomad dynasty succeeded another, as in the period from the tenth to the fourteenth centuries when China was ruled successively by the Khitan, Jurchen, and Mongols. These cycles alternated with periods of native Chinese supremacy under such dynasties as the T'ang, the Sung, and the Ming.

Though to the citizen of Peking it must have seemed as if every year brought the fierce horsemen of the north down upon the settled lands, the invasions followed a definite rhythm, which the environmental determinists have linked to the fluctuations of climate in central Asia. In the third volume of his *A Study of History* (1934) Arnold Toynbee provided a chart of the migrations of nomads from the deserts and steppes of Asia and Africa into the surrounding agricultural lands, in which he correlated outward migrations with periods of diminishing rainfall and aridity, and a return to the steppes with increased rainfall. In this way he ascribes the Mongol upsurge led by Genghis Khan to a "paroxysm" of aridity in central Asia in the thirteenth century, followed at the beginning of the fourteenth century by a "physiographical recoil towards humidity" which "likewise corresponds in date with the rapid ebb of the Mongols." Toynbee makes allowance for the possibility that the particular nomads attacking a settled country may not always have been forced into migration by aridity in their own pastures. A case in point is the Yuëh-chih, a tribe of western Mongolia which was pushed even farther westward, over the mountains of the Pamirs, by the restlessness of their nomadic eastern neighbors, the Hsiung-nu. This took place about 150 B.C.; later the Hsiung-nu themselves came west, first into Asiatic Russia and then, in the fourth century A.D., bursting into Europe as the terrifying Huns who helped bring about the final collapse of Rome.

Toynbee's views of the "push" of climate and the "pull" of settled lands were based largely on the work of Ellsworth Huntington. Huntington had explored central Asia in 1903 as part of an expedition led by Raphael Pumpelly; he found the ruins of deserted cities, the ghostly shorelines of vanished lakes, and the moraines of ancient glaciers, and emerged from the experience with the nucleus of his theory of climatic pulsations.

On a second expedition in 1905 he collected additional evidence of desiccation, and two years later published *The Pulse of Asia,* the book on which his popular reputation was founded. Huntington considered a series of six lake basins—Gyoljuk, the Caspian, Seistan, Turfan, Lop Nor, and Kashmir, spanning a region 1,600 miles long from north to south and more than 3,000 from east to west. "All this great area," he wrote, "seems to have been subject to the same great waves of climatic change.

"In the ancient days when the Oxus River entered the Scythian Gulf of the expanded Caspian Sea, and Lake Gyoljuk discharged permanently to the Tigris, the lake of Seistan had not been converted into dry land. . . . Kashmir was so cold and snowy that agriculture was impossible. . . . In the Lop basin the rivers were full of water; Lop Nor was the 'Great Salt Lake'; the desert was comparatively small and the zone of vegetation extensive; and on all sides there was a density of population and a degree of prosperity far beyond those of today. And in the Turfan basin the same was probably true.

"A great change took place throughout the six basins during the early centuries of the Christian era. The lakes of Gyoljuk, Seistan, the Caspian, Lop Nor and presumably Turfan were greatly reduced in size. In the case of the first three, parts of the old lake-beds were used as sites for villages. Except in Kashmir, the change of climate appears to have brought disaster. . . .

"Again there came a change [about A.D. 700]. The process of desiccation gave place to a slight but important tendency toward increased rainfall and lower temperature. Kashmir became colder and more snowy, and hence more isolated; the rivers of Lop and Turfan gained greater volume; and the lakes of Lop, the Caspian and Turfan expanded once more. The habitability of the arid regions began to increase; migrations came to an end; and central Asia was prosperous for a time. Finally [about 1350] a latest and slightest change took place in the other direction, and we seem today to be in the midst of an epoch of comparative equilibrium, with no marked tendency towards climatic change in either direction."

In forming these ideas Huntington used the information he had gathered on his own expeditions, the results of certain archaeological work we will discuss below, and such evidence as historical records supplied. For example, he based his figures for fluctuations in the level of the Caspian Sea on the presence of the ruins of submerged buildings and sea walls within the modern-day lake; on the geological evidence of ancient shorelines high above the current level; on the writings of such ancient geographers as Strabo; and on a survey conducted at the orders of Alexander the Great. In the Armenian lake of Gyoljuk were the stone houses of a village built about the year 500—twenty to thirty feet under water. In the east, he found matching proofs of his theory at the oasis towns beyond the end of the Great Wall.

Huntington claimed to have found a 600-year cycle of nomadic "eruptions" that could be keyed to periods of desiccation, and Toynbee followed him in this rhythmical view of history. Huntington's cycle began about 2000 B.C. with the invasion of Mesopotamia; the next period of disturbance, between 1500 and 1300 B.C., sent the Aryans into India and the Achaeans into Greece; from 1000 to 600 B.C., the Dorians took Greece, the Scythian and Cimmerian nomads came out of central Asia into Russia, and the Medes overran Persia, while China suffered at the hands of the Jung. Shortly after 200 B.C. the Hsiung-nu of what is now Mongolia began to move outward, forcing their Yuëh-chih neighbors into a migration of their own, and by a domino effect causing trouble as far west as Italy. Five or six centuries later (the periodicity is not always exact) another time of troubles began: civilized kingdoms in India were crushed by barbarians about A.D. 250, the Goths entered Athens and threatened Rome, and China split into three kingdoms, all of which were under the rule of nomad dynasties by the middle of the fourth century. The Hsiung-nu, or Huns, poured into eastern Europe about A.D. 375, sending Gothic refugees spilling westward into Rome, which they proceeded to conquer.

Toynbee cites the outpouring of the Arabs under Mohammed, which began in the middle of the seventh century, as the next phase of climate-inspired migration. Six centuries later, as though on schedule, came perhaps the most terrifying and successful of all these "eruptions," the expansion of the Mongols under Genghis Khan, which resulted in the swift formation of a Mongol empire that spanned nearly all of Asia. Finally Toynbee offers various minor migrations of the nineteenth century—such as the outward movements of certain Arabian tribes toward Syria and Iraq, and of a Saharan tribe into Nigeria—as the most recent fulfillment of the cyclical concept.

Certainly there were great nomadic movements in approximately every sixth century since 2000 B.C., and we can choose the Achaeans, the Dorians, the Hsiung-nu, the Arabs, and the Mongols as our star exhibits. But the concept is weakened by the need to assume that each 600-year cycle includes 300 years of increasing aridity and 300 years of a return to better conditions, which means that it can be argued that nomads should go on the rampage about half the time; such a theory can be used to prove almost anything. Nor do all of the star exhibits coincide precisely with known periods of adverse climate. Toynbee has various explanations for the time lags, as does Huntington, who made a valiant effort to correlate every nomad outburst with the information from the growth rings of his California redwoods, and found that the outbursts did not always match the times of greatest aridity. (Whereas a period of terrible drought in California about A.D. 1490 was unaccompanied by nomad migrations.) Toynbee's assumptions, as the geographer Owen Lattimore pointed out in a 1934 critique of the historian's work, are "reasonable enough in themselves," but "make it possible to account for almost any migration in history, since the lack of any immediate and obvious climatic explanation can always be attributed to the time lag between aridity in one place and the appearance of nomad invaders at some quite distant point, a good many years later. Such assumptions are tempting and dangerous. Our knowledge of the details of many nomadic movements in the past is not sufficiently exact. By piling one assumption on another it is possible to tabulate the history of successive migrations in a manner that looks astonishingly accurate and convincing. It is well to remember therefore that the results which look so solid are based largely not only on a chain of speculative causes and assumed effects, but often on original details which are much too fragmentary to carry so solid a superstructure."

The details that carry the superstructure of Huntington's pulsatory hypothesis deal largely with supposed desiccation in central Asia over a thousand-year period ending about A.D. 700. In particular, he dealt with the withering of civilization in the narrow oasis-dotted panhandle beyond the western end of the Great Wall of China. To the Chinese, the lonely, haunted land beyond the wall's end at Kia-yü-kuan was known as K'ou Wai, "Outside the Passes." The sky-piercing fangs of Tibet's mountains lie to the south, the lifeless wastes of the Gobi and Taklamakan deserts to the north; but in ancient times the route between was the famed caravan track called the Old Silk Road. In the time of the Han Dynasty, which succeeded the dynasty of the wall-builder Shih Huang Ti, China reached out along this road to make contact with the western world.

Under the expansionist Emperor Wu Ti, who ruled for fifty-four years beginning in 140 B.C., China sent first scouts, then ambassadors, and in the end armies of conquest into the panhandle of oases. It was one of the few foreign adventures in China's history, and one of the most successful. The oasis cities, nourished by the water of melting snows running down from the Pamirs into the Tarim Basin, had much that Wu Ti coveted—splendid horses, works of art, exotic delicacies of all sorts—and also offered him a way to increase the power of his empire by opening contact with the kingdoms of the west. Chinese troops first cleared the Hsiung-nu nomads back from the line of the Great Wall, pushing them deep into Mongolia; then they marched west of the wall to conquer the oases.

The greatest resistance came at Ferghana in what is now the Uzbek S.S.R. An exhausted Chinese army crossed the towering Pamirs in 104 B.C. and met heavy defeat there; a second army, better prepared, laid siege to the city two years later. The Han Dynasty historian Ssŭ-ma Ch'ien wrote that in Ferghana "there were no wells, and the people had to obtain water from a river outside. Experts in hydraulic engineering were therefore despatched to divert the course of the river so as to deprive the city of water." As the water supply dwindled the people of the besieged city assassinated their king and surrendered. Now China had full command over the road to the west; and about 100 B.C. the Emperor Wu Ti took a characteristically Chinese measure to assert that command: he extended the Great Wall beyond its century-old terminus at Kia-yü-kuan. The new section reached some three hundred miles farther, ending near the city of Tun-huang. Beyond Tun-huang some isolated watchtowers were built, but apparently there was no attempt to continue the wall itself into the Tarim Basin.

The garrisons patrolling the new wall would protect the Chinese caravans making their way into foreign lands. The new western terminus of the Great Wall, Tun-huang, was the key strategic outpost of the caravan route. This city, founded in 111 B.C., was situated at an oasis in the western province of Kansu, along the narrow panhandle that runs between the mountains of Tibet and the desert of Mongolia. It was the last town of China proper, and was strongly fortified, since it controlled the access routes to central Asia. Here began the Old Silk Road. Actually there were two silk roads leading out of Tun-huang: a northern one across the desert and the foothills of the T'ien Shan range, and a southern one that rimmed the Tsaidam Plateau of Tibet. (A third route, beginning just west of Tun-huang at Yü-men, the "Jade Gate," ran across arid country to Loulan, a city near the lake of Lop Nor; but worsening desert conditions forced the abandonment of this route after a time.)

All the routes met again at Kashgar, more than a thousand miles from Tun-huang, and there diverged again. One led into Ferghana and on to Samarkand and Antioch in Merv (not the well-known Syrian city); another road out of Kashgar passed through Bactria, to the south. These roads now entered Parthia, a kingdom in eastern Iran which had recently come to power and was challenging the authority of Rome itself. Parthia impressed the Chinese, who described it as a huge country producing rice, wheat, and grapes, where silver coins circulated, and where "they make signs on leather from side to side by way of literary record." The Chinese brought silk and other goods to Parthia, and their ambassadors returned with Parthian conjurers, the eggs of "great birds," and other novelties.

The silk route ended in Parthia so far as China was concerned. The Parthians preferred to serve as middlemen rather than letting merchants of other lands pass through their domain. Under Parthian auspices, then, goods continued along the Old Silk Road from Hecatompylos and Ecbatana to the twin cities of Seleucia and Ctesiphon on the Tigris just below modern Baghdad, and from there to Syria and the rest of the Near East, where they could be transshipped as far as Rome.

There was no economic need for the Chinese to export silk. The precious fabric was largely of diplomatic value, going westward as gifts to rulers of the newly reached lands. (The secret of making silk was something that the Chinese kept to themselves as long as possible.) In Parthia and in Rome silk garments were eagerly sought, becoming something of a craze in the time of Julius Caesar. The Chinese emperors received in return such gifts as gold, jade (contrary to common belief, China has always been forced to import jade from the west; it is not found in her territory), fine horses, exotic delicacies like raisins, and slaves who were skilled in the arts and in the crafts. But these were matters between rulers. The real value of the silk trade to China was not in the relatively slight luxury flow out of the west, but in the general prosperity and security that resulted from regular travel through the Kansu panhandle. What had been a sparsely populated region subject to nomad raids became wealthy and populous, and the hundreds of thousands of colonists who streamed into the frontier areas to take advantage of the new channels of trade formed a powerful bulwark against the Hsiung-nu.

The garrisons along the extended Great Wall played an important part in maintaining this prosperity. The wall was kept in good repair and the Hsiung-nu were steadily kept back for nearly a century after the conquest of Ferghana. But Wu Ti's successors gradually steered China into internal confusion, which resulted in the temporary overthrow of the Han Dynasty about the time of Christ. Order was restored, eventually, and the garrisons returned to Tun-huang; after a spectacular cultural and political renaissance in the later Han period, though, a new period of anarchy commenced about A.D. 150, leading to the ultimate collapse of the dynasty seventy years later and general anarchy in China. The Kansu outposts were again abandoned, the descendants of barbarians took over the management of the silk route, and the extended Great Wall was allowed to fall into disrepair.

After a while China seemed to forget that the wall had ever reached beyond Kia-yü-kuan. Maps of the wall once again showed it ending at the original terminal city, and desert sand swept in to engulf Wu Ti's 300-mile extension and the towns that had grown up along and beyond it. Though the region enjoyed a rebirth under the magnificent T'ang Dynasty of the seventh and eighth centuries, whole cities remained buried by sand until their rediscovery by European explorers a few generations ago.

The rediscovery began with the work of the Swedish geographer Sven Hedin, whose reconnaissance of central Asia started in 1893. From Kashgar, now one of China's westernmost cities near its border with the Soviet Union, Hedin explored the desolate uplands of the Pamirs, and in 1895 set out across the Takla-makan Desert, on a crossing so terrible that he, his men, and his camels nearly perished from thirst in the dunes. By January, 1896, he was at the ancient oasis town of Khotan, where he was irresistibly drawn by two T'ang Dynasty legends to search for buried cities in the desert.

One of these tales, dating from the year 632, told of a lost town called Ho-lao-lo-kia northwest of Khotan. Once this town had boasted a famous statue of Buddha, 20 feet high, made of sandalwood and glowing with an inner light. But when a sage came to Ho-lao-lo-kia to worship at the image, the inhabitants treated him harshly, burying him to his neck in the ground and leaving him to starve. A pious man rescued him; and as the sage took his leave he said, "Within seven days, Ho-lao-lo-kia shall be buried by sand from heaven, and thou alone shalt be saved." The rescuer of the sage warned the townsfolk, but they would not listen, and at last he took refuge alone in a cave. On the seventh day came a rain of sand, burying the town and suffocating everyone in it; the pious one emerged from his cave and fled to another city, and the wondrous image of Buddha followed him, flying through the air.

A Chinese travel account of the same period says of the desert regions north of Khotan, "There is neither water nor vegetation, but a hot wind often rises, which takes away the breath of man, horse, and beast, and not seldom is the cause of sickness. You hear almost always shrill whistlings, or loud shouts; and when you try to discover whence they come, you are terrified at finding nothing. It very often happens that men get lost, for that place is the abode of evil spirits. After four hundred *li* [133 miles], you come to the ancient kingdom of Tu-ho-lo. It is a long time since that country was changed into a desert. All its towns lie in ruins and are overgrown with wild plants."

Men of Khotan also told Hedin stories of sand-buried cities in the desert; he hired two as guides, and with four other native companions set out, following the Keriya River to its end in the sands. The dunes were 35 to 40 feet high; in some places, where they were lower, gaunt dry sand-smothered trees, dead for ages, jutted into view. The guides led him to the ruins of an ancient city, as they had promised; they called it Dandan-uilik, "The Ivory Houses." Hedin wrote, "Most of the houses were buried in the sand. But here and there, posts and wooden walls stuck out of the dunes; and on one of the walls, which was possibly three feet high, we discovered several figures, artistically executed in plaster. They represented Buddha and Buddhistic deities, some standing, some seated on lotus-leaves, all robed in ample draperies, their heads encircled by flaming aureoles. All these finds, and many other relics, were wrapped up carefully, and packed in my boxes; and the fullest possible notes on the ancient city, its location, sand-covered canals, dead-poplar avenues, and dried-up apricot orchards were entered in my diary. I was not equipped to make a thorough excavation; and, besides, I was not an archaeologist. The scientific research I willingly left to the specialists." From measurements of the rate at which the dunes moved during sandstorms, Hedin calculated that it had taken about two thousand years for the desert to extend from the region of the buried city to its present southern border.

On a later expedition, Hedin explored the eastern end of the Tarim Basin, once the site of a great lake of which nothing remains but the nearly dry, salt-encrusted Lop Nor. In March, 1900, he discovered another ancient city that had been exposed by wind erosion; some hasty work with a spade turned up a few Chinese coins, iron axes, and wooden carvings. Hedin returned to the site the following March for a more extensive examination, and found nineteen houses made of wood and clay-covered wicker. "In three places," he wrote, "the door-frames still remained upright. One door actually stood wide open, just as it must have been left by the last inhabitant of this ancient city, more than fifteen hundred years ago."

Excavation yielded scraps of blankets, pieces of red cloth, brown human hair, boot-soles, fragments of skeletons of domestic animals, pieces of rope, an earring, coins, potsherds, and other odds and ends. What Hedin wanted was some written document to identify his lost city. "The days went by," he wrote. "Dawn found us already at work. We made excavations in every house. At last there remained only one house, of sun-dried clay, in the shape of a stable, with three cribs opening outward. Mollah found a slip of paper, with Chinese ideographs, in the crib on the extreme right. . . . The paper lay two feet deep under sand and dust. We dug deeper and sifted the sand and dust between our fingers. One piece of paper after another was brought to light, 36 in all, every one of which bore writing. We also discovered 121 small wooden staffs, covered with inscriptions." Examination of these documents a few years later by German scholars showed that Hedin had found the city of Loulan, once a way station on the Old Silk Road. Many of the inscriptions bore dates; most had been written about A.D. 270, but one, which was a century older, was the earliest known example of handwriting on paper ever discovered. The cache included letters of condolence, military reports, warehouse inventories, and postal data; the topics discussed are such things as nomad raids, the punishment of tax evaders, the organization of caravans, and the procurement of army supplies.

From his investigations Hedin was able to declare that Loulan had had warehouses, an inn, a hospital, a post office, a temple, private dwellings, and huts for the poor. References to imports in the translated documents, particularly that of Chinese silk for local use, indicate a large population. "In the better houses," Hedin wrote, "hard earthen floors were covered with reed mats, on which lay the precious woven rugs. Large clay jugs, with water for the household, stood in the yards. Bowls and dishes decorated with Indo-Persian lion-heads were in use; also, glass from Syria, the nearest country in those days which understood the manufacture of glass."

The Han Dynasty had fallen in A.D. 220, China had been partitioned by three potent warlords, and chaos was descending. The records of a frontier outpost such as Loulan tell of the growing internal disturbances, which left the Silk Road towns without support. Hedin found accounts of revolts, military expeditions, battles, and the loss of territory to the barbarians; by the early part of the fourth century it was clear that continued occupation of Loulan was impossible. "But the authorities never flinched in their duty to the state, in spite of the ominous cloud that hung over the town. Everyone did his part," Hedin declared. "When the drums outside the walls sounded the call to arms, and the fires burned on the towers, these officials remained steadfast in their places, finishing their reports as if nothing unusual had happened. They sent New Year's greetings and letters of condolence to their friends, not allowing themselves to be disturbed by the impending danger. We read with admiration and emotion of the strength of character and the courage with which these Chinese did their duty. . . ." But the city fell, and the desert sands moved in to cover it.

By his own admission Hedin was no archaeologist, and he hoped that some expert would take over the task of uncovering the buried cities of the Tarim Basin. That man was already at hand, making his first expedition to the region in 1900, the same year Hedin found Loulan. He was the Hungarian-born

Mark Aurel Stein (1862–1943), who had gone to England as a young man to study, accepted a post in the Indian Service, and by 1900 was Inspector of Schools in the Punjab. Excited by news of Hedin's 1896 finds near Khotan, Stein obtained a year's leave of absence from his post, and with a few porters and an expert Indian surveyor set out to investigate the desert of Takla-makan, starting from Khotan in October, 1900.

The Tarim Basin that he was entering was grim country. "By far the greater part of this basin," Stein wrote, "is filled by the dune-covered Takla-makan and the wastes of hard salt crust or wind-eroded clay of the Lop desert which stretch almost unbroken for a total length of over 800 miles from west to east. In them the absence of moisture bans not only human existence but practically also all animal and plant life." Only at scattered oases was permanent occupation possible, thanks to intensive irrigation.

Stein's first call was at the buried city of Dandan-uilik, which Hedin had visited briefly five years before. The temperature in the desert never rose above freezing, and in the night went down below zero; Stein camped in a flimsy tent, warmed only by a tiny stove, and depended for his water on a well dug through the sand. Here, he wrote, spread over several square miles, "there rose from among the low dunes the remains of buildings, modest in size, but of manifest antiquity. Where the sand had blown away, the walls constructed of wattle and plaster were exposed to view, broken down to within a few feet of the ground. Elsewhere the walls could be made out only by rows of wooden posts emerging above the drift sand. All structural remains left exposed showed signs of having been searched by 'treasure-seekers.' The damage done by their operations was often only too evident."

With thirty laborers Stein uncovered a great deal of Dandan-uilik, discovering Buddhist shrines and images, household goods, coins, wooden tablets, and manuscripts. The coins were T'ang Dynasty copper pieces dating from the period A.D. 713–741, indicating the probable time of the town's abandonment. This was confirmed by manuscripts on small sheets of thin paper, relating to loans, deeds, requisition orders, and the like, which could be dated to the eighth century; the most recent of these bore the date 790. "From their very character and the condition in which they were found, scattered amidst rubbish in ground-floor rooms used as quarters or kitchens," Stein wrote, "it is quite safe to conclude that [the documents] were penned during the closing years of the occupation of the site and left behind when it was finally abandoned."

In January, 1901, Stein moved his operations to a mound near the sandy bed of the dying Niya River. This river flows northward from the Kunlun Mountains and loses itself in the Takla-makan Desert east of Khotan. Most of the year its flow is barely sufficient to irrigate a small oasis town, though at the time of the spring thaw on the mountains it is much greater. But in the past it reached 80 miles beyond the oasis, to a point 30 miles beyond the present limits of the spring floods; and there Stein spent sixteen days uncovering the ruins of another city that contained a rich hoard of documents. From the information on these documents he was able to identify the town as Chadota, and to show that it had been abandoned at the close of the third century A.D. Nearby, at a place where the Endere River once had flowed, Stein wrested from the sand a small Buddhist shrine containing important Tibetan manuscripts. A Chinese inscription scratched into the temple wall gave a date corresponding to A.D. 719, and there was other evidence of occupation into the late eighth century. This was curious, Stein wrote, for "Hsüan-tsang, the great Chinese pilgrim who had passed by the same route from Niya to Charchan about A.D. 645, found no inhabited place on his ten days' desert march. But he distinctly mentions in a position exactly corresponding to the Endere site ruins of abandoned settlements. . . ." Stein concluded that the unsettled conditions in the third century after the fall of the Han Dynasty had forced the abandonment of the Endere site, but that it had been reoccupied in T'ang Dynasty times shortly after Hsüan-tsang's visit. He later found third-century documents which confirmed this guess, and thereby provided Ellsworth Huntington with ammunition for his hypothesis of climatic pulsations.

Eventually Stein amassed twelve huge boxes of archaeological treasures, which he saw safely to England and delivered to the British Museum in July, 1901. His discoveries won him immediate fame, and after he had spent several years analyzing his findings and publishing reports on them, he returned to central Asia under British Museum auspices for further work. Setting out from Khotan in July, 1906, Stein worked at a number of sites, some newly uncovered, others first touched in his 1901 expedition. All proved to be rich mines of antiquities. He worked once more at the Niya River site in October, removing the contents of buried Chadota dwellings untouched in sixteen hundred years. "Though nothing of intrinsic value had been left behind by the last dwellers of this modest Pompeii," he wrote, "there was sufficient evidence of the ease in which they had lived in the large number of individual rooms provided with fireplaces, comfortable sitting-platforms, wooden cupboards, etc. Remains of fenced gardens and of avenues of poplars or fruit-trees could be traced almost invariably near these houses. Where dunes had afforded protection, the gaunt, bleached trunks in these orchards, chiefly mulberry trees, still rose as high as ten to twelve feet." All about lay the wide vistas of the desert, an expanse of yellow dunes like the open sea, "with nothing to break their wavy monotony but the bleached trunks of trees or rows of splintered posts marking houses which rose here and there above the sandy crest. They often curiously suggested the picture of a wreck reduced to the merest ribs of its timber."

He continued eastward to the edge of the lake of Lop Nor, where he worked at the site of the abandoned city of Loulan, and uncovered Chinese manuscripts on paper and silk, halting his work when the water supply failed. After a rest, Stein set out in a northeasterly direction on February 21, 1907, through the dreary wasteland of the dried-up inland sea. His goal was Tun-huang, the Han Dynasty's western terminus of the Great Wall. In March Stein began to encounter isolated watchtowers in the desert, well preserved and sturdily constructed. Closer to Tun-huang he came upon the remains of the Han extension of the Great Wall, in some places almost six feet high, in others ground down by erosion to a height of inches. After reprovisioning and collecting workmen in Tun-huang—"a dozen opium-smoking coolies, all the labor that could be raised"—he returned to the desert and followed the wall for sixteen miles practically without a break. Here it was eight feet thick and over seven feet high. In the refuse heaps of the watch-towers Stein discovered a number of slips of wood inscribed with Chinese characters, many of the slips bearing dates. "Our excitement was great when my Chinese secretary showed that all these dates belonged to the first century A.D.," Stein wrote. "It thus became certain . . . that I had in my hands the oldest written Chinese documents so far recovered." The documents were mainly military: records of supplies, troop movements, and so forth. Bronze arrowheads lay near the wall and towers, and in the dryness Stein was able even to find the track worn into the coarse gravel soil by the patrols that had tramped it for centuries. When he had completed his season's work along this ruined wall, Stein returned to Tun-huang, where he achieved his most famous coup by gaining possession of a cache of Buddhist manuscripts dating from the eighth through eleventh centuries A.D.

Han Dynasty annals declared that in 102 and 101 B.C., "military posts were established from place to place from Tun-huang westwards to the Salt Marsh." That Stein had found the Han wall was demonstrated by his discovery of documents dated with the Chinese equivalents of 94, 96, and 100 B.C. Others bore dates corresponding to 68 B.C., to 56 B.C., and to A.D. 75, but there were none later, indicating that the extension of the Great Wall had probably been abandoned before A.D. 100. A third Stein expedition in 1913 and 1914 saw him following the line of the ancient wall for more than 250 miles; but there was nothing to indicate that the watchtowers had been occupied after the later Han days. Emperor Wu Ti's dream of westward expansion had ended in drifting sand.

But what had blighted the towns and cities of Kansu and the Tarim Basin?

To Ellsworth Huntington, who had been through this territory between 1903 and 1906, the answer was climatic change. Periodic pulsations bringing alternating times of moisture and desiccation had permitted the original Han expansion in 100 B.C. and had turned the western outposts to deserts 250 years later, he said. By the end of the third century A.D. the aridity had compelled the abandonment of nearly all the Tarim Basin towns; but Tun-huang, east of the basin, had flourished again in the fifth century, when the astonishing statue-filled grottoes known as the Caves of the Thousand Buddhas were begun; two centuries later, under the T'ang Dynasty, a benevolent climate permitted development of the western region almost to its status under the Han, and such ruined sites as the one by the Endere River were reoccupied. But new desiccation turned the oases to sand, and once more the area died in the eighth century. And so on.

Huntington used some of Stein's data to confirm these theories. In his 1903 book, *Sand-buried Ruins of Khotan,* Stein had said of the Niya River site of Chadota, "It is certain that this now sand-buried settlement was abandoned to the desert at the close of the third century A.D. The extreme dryness of the climate has allowed all these relics to survive in wonderful preservation, e.g., the trunks of dead trees still rising above the sand in arbors and orchards near the deserted habitations. . . . Certain it is that no amount of engineering skill could now make the waters of the Niya River reach the point near the southern end of the dead settlement where a fallen footbridge, lying across a dry bed, proves them to have flowed once. There is thus afforded indisputable proof of a great shrinkage in the volume of the river since the third century A.D."

Stein himself, though he admitted that the Tarim Basin had been the scene of considerable desiccation, was not at all sure of the validity of Huntington's ideas. He doubted that there had been fluctuations in the amount of rainfall, suggesting that "the climatic conditions of the periods immediately preceding abandonment must have been practically as arid as they have been since and are now." The advantage held by the earlier settlers, he said, was the presence of glaciers on the surrounding mountain ranges, which fed the Tarim rivers with spring runoff. On these rivers the irrigation of the basin depended, rather than on rainfall; and as the glaciers diminished, the rivers grew more feeble, leaving towns that once had been well supplied with water now stranded miles from any source.

The shrinkage of the glaciers, Stein argued, "can well be accounted for by assuming . . . that those glaciers comprise great reserves of ice which have been left behind by the last glacial period and have been since undergoing slow but more or less continuous reduction through milder climatic conditions. This process of using up what might be called 'fossil ice' would suffice to explain shrinkage in the sources of irrigation during historical times without the climate of the basin as a whole having undergone any appreciable change."

Apart from this, Stein felt that the real villain in the Tarim was not desiccation or glacial shrinkage but political instability. At Dandan-uilik, for example, the time of abandonment coincided almost exactly with the T'ang Dynasty's loss of control over the Tarim region in A.D. 791. Nomads now swarmed through the area, and continued maintenance of the irrigation works on which the community depended became impossible. Similarly the fall of the Han Dynasty five centuries earlier had spelled doom for the Tarim settlements existing then. It was evident at some sites that abandonment had been forced by armed attack; the encroachment of the desert had come later, with sand moving in to cover a city whose inhabitants were no longer on hand to take the necessary protective steps. "The progress of general desiccation cannot by itself supply an adequate explanation of all such changes in the extent of cultivated areas," Stein said. He was able to cite districts which had been reclaimed from the desert in the twentieth century, though there had been no change in rainfall. Revisiting in 1906 a place that had been covered by sand on his 1901 visit, Stein saw "how cultivation was now gradually being extended over ground abandoned for centuries to the desert. In the fertile loess soil to which new cuts carried ample water, the poplars, willows, and Jigda trees usually planted along the edges of fields were shooting up rapidly. Hence it was easy to note at a glance the new conquests made each year from the desert sands. . . . And I wondered whether, in spite of slowly progressing desiccation, the time was not near when, under the pressure of increased population and a growing need of land, the oasis might victoriously recover most of this desolate waste. . . ."

Warfare and pestilence, maladministration, lack of security—these, not the creeping sands, had driven man out of the Tarim. In happier times, the intensive application of irrigation techniques had made the desert habitable. Huntington, who outlived his friend Stein by four years, clung to the idea of rainfall fluctuations to the end. Probably the truth lies somewhere between their positions: climatic pulsations have occurred in central Asia, making agriculture more difficult at some times than at others; but even in the worst of times the irrigators would have been able to hold their own against the desert, if only a stable government had protected them against the nomad raiders who, themselves pushed from their pastures by drought, threatened and ultimately destroyed the settlements of the oases.

8

The Little Ice Age

FEW MAJOR CLIMATIC SHIFTS ARE SO WELL DOCUMENTED AS the deterioration of the climate of Europe in medieval times. The chronicles of monks, the records of royal surveyors, and the evidence of archaeology all show in detail how a mild and equable environment turned bitterly cold.

The Christian era had begun with a time of storms and chill; but by about A.D. 300 the summers were becoming warm and dry, and the winters less harsh. Thus Julius Caesar, in 55 B.C., said of Britain that "the greater part of the people never sow their lands, but live on flesh and milk and go clad in skins," as though the climate were too cold and wet for agriculture. By the time of the historian Tacitus, who wrote of Britain about A.D. 98, matters had improved somewhat there: "With the exception of the olive and vine and plants which usually grow in warmer climates the soil will yield . . . all ordinary products." And the Roman Emperor Probus, who ruled from A.D. 276 to 282, issued an edict that suggests that grapevines could now flourish there, for it gave formal imperial permission for Britons to cultivate vineyards and make wine.

The spread of vineyards in England seems a reliable index to the general warming of the European climate between A.D. 400 and 1200. The Venerable Bede (673–735) observes that in his day the vine was raised "in some places." Among the laws of Alfred the Great, who ruled from 871 to 899, is one that says, "If anyone does damage to the vines of his neighbor . . . let him make good whatever is claimed." Vineyards are mentioned in the annals of several succeeding Anglo-Saxon kings, while William the Conqueror's Domesday Book survey of 1085 lists 38 vineyards in England other than those belonging to the crown; one of these is said to yield twenty casks of wine in a good year. The vineyards flourished in northern regions where today springtime frost is the general rule. In the twelfth century the wines of Gloucestershire still could be compared in quality with those of France.

Europe's weather reached a peak of benevolence between A.D. 800 and 1000. During this amiable epoch the mean temperature seems to have been five or six degrees higher than it is at present, both on land and sea. One effect of this was a great reduction in oceanic ice in the Arctic, along with a corresponding drop in the frequency and vehemence of storms at sea. Though C. E. B. Brooks's suggestion that the Arctic ice pack melted entirely at this time is not widely followed, it does appear as though only the far northern regions were afflicted with permanent ice. Icebergs and drifting floes were rare south of 70°N. in the ninth and tenth centuries, and apparently were altogether unknown in the eleventh and twelfth. This left the sea open for European expansion; the time of warmth was the time of the remarkable exploits of the Viking sea-rovers, which led to the Norse colonization of Iceland, Greenland, and even the northern shores of the North American mainland.

Men had rarely visited these frosty regions. Perhaps the first was the Greek mathematician, astronomer, and geographer, Pytheas, born about 360 B.C. in the colony of Massilia, now Marseilles. Pytheas served as navigator on an expedition sent out by Massilian merchants to search for a sea route toward the sources of those valuable commodities, tin and amber. He led the ship through the Strait of Gibraltar and up the Portuguese coast toward Brittany, then across to Kent and the tin mines of Cornwall. Continuing northward up the British coast, Pytheas got at least as far as Scotland, where, according to the

Roman naturalist Pliny, he observed tides running "eighty cubits high." The explorer's track now becomes somewhat uncertain. He may have journeyed still farther north, into the sub-Arctic regions, or he may have been content simply to question the inhabitants of Scotland about what lay beyond. Evidently he did reach a latitude of 61°N., if no more. Here, at the northernmost of the Shetland Islands, he heard about a land called Thule, six days' sail to the north. Thule was the northern termination of the world, beyond which no man could go.

Pliny says that one day's sail past Thule lies "the frozen sea." Strabo quoted Pytheas as referring to "the congealed sea." Whether he saw it with his own eyes or relied on the word of others, it seems clear that the Arctic waters were filled with ice in the fourth century B.C.

Strabo also provided this strange passage: "He [Pytheas] had also undertaken investigations concerning Thule and those regions, in which there was no longer any distinction of land or sea or air, but a mixture of the three like sea-lung, in which he says that land and sea and everything floats; the sea-lung binds everything together, and can neither be traversed on foot nor by boat. The substance resembling lung he has seen himself, as he says; the rest he relates according to what he has heard."

It is an odd term, this "sea-lung." What did Pytheas mean by it? Some commentators have suggested jellyfish, or some mysterious pulpy mass in the sea. Fridjtof Nansen of Norway, himself a great explorer as well as a scholar, offered a more plausible explanation: "What Pytheas himself saw may have been the ice-sludge in the sea which is formed over a great extent along the edge of drift ice, when this has been ground to a pulp by the action of waves. The expression 'can neither be traversed on foot nor by boat' is exactly applicable to this ice-sludge. If we add to this the thick fog, which is often found near drift ice, then the description that the air is also involved in the mixture, and that land and sea and everything is merged in it, will appear very graphic."

Nansen felt that Pytheas' Thule was Norway, and that

Pytheas had indeed been there, as proved by his accurate description of drift ice as "sea-lung." Another modern explorer, Vilhjalmur Stefansson, also accepted Nansen's explanation of sea-lung, but felt that Thule lay not northeast of England but northwest, and had been Iceland, a conceivable six-day journey away. Stefansson argued with some plausibility that Pytheas "learned about Thule in Britain, that he went to Thule, that he reported what he saw there, and that he proceeded a day's sail further north," turning back when stopped by "the congealed sea."

Certainly Iceland is what the Irish geographer Dicuil referred to in his account of a voyage to Thule that took place a thousand years after that of Pytheas—at a time when the northern sea was considerably more favorable for shipping. Writing in A.D. 825, Dicuil said, "Thirty years ago I spoke with some pious men who had visited the island of Thule from February to August. They said that the summer nights there were strangely light. The sun went down, but it was as if it had only hidden behind a hill. It did not get dark; you could go right on working, even pick lice off your shirt. Higher up in the mountains, the sun perhaps also shone in the night. According to these pious men, the open sea lay all around Thule, but north of the island, a day's journey away, they came upon icebergs."

These "pious men" of Dicuil, who had taken advantage of the almost ice-free sea to reach unknown Iceland, were Irish hermits. This was a time of bold Irish voyages in the name of the Lord; Celtic missionaries traveled vast distances, reaching even to Africa and perhaps North America. A twelfth-century Icelandic historian, Are Frode, offered this confirmation of Dicuil's report: "In those days there were Christian men here whom the Norsemen called *papar.* These men later moved away because they did not want to live with the heathen. They left behind Irish books, bells, and croziers, from which we may deduce that they came from Ireland."

The Norsemen reached Iceland in the century after the Irish. In their slim, elegant boats the Vikings swept out from Scandinavia, first striking terror in western Europe, then ranging into the unknown westward seas. A Norse saga tells of the discovery of Iceland by the Viking Floke Vilgerdsson in the 860's. The sight of glaciers on the mountains led him to name the place Iceland; but a young man named Thorolf, who was in his party, returned to Norway to say that "in the land they had discovered, butter dripped from every blade of grass." A few years later, a man called Ingolf explored the island, finding a place where geysers spouted. He named it Reykjavik, or "Warm Springs." But the real Norse settlement of Iceland did not begin for another decade or so, until the bloody reign of Harald Fairhair of Norway. Coming to the throne at the age of ten in 860, Harald began six years later to eliminate the dozens of petty rival kings in his land, and by 872 had made himself the first ruler of a unified Norway. He proceeded next to tax the landholdings of the nobility, which he did with such vigor and ruthlessness that many of his opponents fled to Iceland, where they could live as free men in the old style. These forced migrations continued all through Harald's reign of more than seventy years; and by the time of his death in 933 Iceland had a population of nearly twenty thousand.

Though it lies north of the 63rd parallel, on the same latitude as Baffin Island and northern Alaska, Iceland today has a relatively agreeable climate, thanks to the Gulf Stream. Reykjavik, the capital, has winter temperatures no more severe than those of New York City, which is at 40°47′ N. In the summer, though, Iceland's mean temperature is only 52° F. in its warmest region, the southwest; the climate is too cold for growing most crops, though some agriculture has become possible under the generally milder conditions experienced in the twentieth century.

Those who fled the wrath of Harald Fairhair to Iceland found it a more hospitable land than it is today, particularly on the south and west coasts, where exposure to the Gulf Stream is greatest. Farms were numerous; there was ample pasture for the herds; population grew rapidly, and even the north and east shores, washed by the frigid polar currents, were settled. The coast was clear of ice, making easy contact feasible between Iceland and Norway.

The next step outward was taken by a turbulent Norseman named Erik the Red, who was born about 950. Forced to flee Norway at the age of twenty after committing murder, Erik lived for some years in Iceland, but quarreled with his neighbors and slew several of them. About 980 he was brought for trial before the Icelandic *thing*, or parliament, which banished him for three years. Erik chose to spend his time seeking certain small islands rumored to lie west of Iceland, and set out with scanty equipment and few provisions in an open Viking ship.

What he found was no small island, but the largest one in the world. The *Landnámabók*, a saga written at the beginning of the fourteenth century, says that "Erik came from the sea to land at the middle glacier—from thence he went south along the coast to see if the land was habitable." That was Greenland's eastern coast, today blocked by drift ice for the greater part of the year. Though northern Greenland, where Erik made his first landfall, was icy even then, things looked more inviting the farther south he went. He rounded the island's southernmost point—Cape Farewell today—and spent his first winter of exile on a small isle close to shore. In the spring he continued to the fjord area known today as Julianehaab, where he saw groves of dwarf willow and birch, bushes laden with berries, and plentiful pasturage for cattle and sheep. It would be a good site for a settlement, he decided. Later he went on to the east and found a second place that could be colonized along the shore.

After spending his three years of banishment in a leisurely reconnaissance of the newly discovered land, Erik returned to Iceland to tell his story. According to one of the old sagas, he called the new territory Greenland, "and said that having a good name would entice men to go thither." Quickly he organized an expedition of 25 ships to settle Greenland. They sailed in 986, carrying some 500 to 700 settlers, along with horses, cattle, goats, sheep, and household goods. Only 14 of the ships reached their destination; the others were driven back or destroyed by storm, but the sagas make no mention of drift ice blocking the route from Iceland, nor were Viking ships capable of sailing through a really icy sea. The way must have been clear.

Two colonies sprang up in Greenland at the sites chosen by Erik the Red. The one near Julianehaab was called *Österbygden,* "the Eastern Settlement," though it was actually on Greenland's western coast; still farther to the west was *Vesterbygden,* "the Western Settlement." Life was never easy in these small villages, which occupied narrow strips along coastal fjords, with towering glacier-covered mountains just a short distance inland. Even during that time of mild weather Greenland was almost wholly in the grip of ice. But farming of sorts was possible along the western shore; Österbygden grew until it had about two hundred farms, and Vesterbygden perhaps half as many. The population may have reached three thousand within a generation after Erik the Red planted his first colonies. The brave, determined settlers made the best of their surroundings; and what the farms could not supply, hunting did, for the land was rich in bear, reindeer, birds, and hares, and the sea yielded fish, seals, and whales. Regular voyages from the mother country of Iceland and from the older mother country of Norway kept the Greenland pioneers stocked with the goods they were unable to produce themselves.

During these flourishing early years of the Greenland colonies, word came of land still farther to the west. A fourteenth-century tale, perhaps apocryphal, relates how a young man named Bjarne Herjulfsson, whose father had migrated to Greenland with Erik the Red in 986, set out alone to go to him, went astray in the sea, and sighted a land far more pleasant than Greenland could ever be, with low-lying hills and green forests. He sailed its coast, realized he had come to the wrong place, and made his way back to Greenland, having been the first European, perhaps, to sight Baffin Island in North America.

The tale is also told of Leif, the son of Erik the Red, who in 999 sailed directly from Greenland to Norway, where he found that King Olaf Trygvasson had imposed the Christian faith on all Norsemen. The king commanded Leif Eriksson to transport a priest of the new gospel to Greenland; but Leif was carried off course in his return voyage, and came to strange lands in the west, first a rocky plateau that he named *Helluland*, "Land of Flat Stones," and then a wooded region that he called *Markland*, "Woodland," and finally a third land to the south, which he named *Vinland*, which means either "Land of Vines" or "Land of Grass," depending on which etymology you choose to accept. Leif Eriksson's Vinland was a lovely place of large trees, grassy fields, and rivers thick with salmon. When he came back to Greenland to tell of it, men dubbed him "Leif the Lucky," and in the next twenty years several parties of colonists set out from Greenland to make their homes in Vinland.

The identities of the places discovered by Leif Eriksson have long been controversial, but Helluland has generally been considered to have been Baffin Island, Markland the coast of Labrador, and Vinland Newfoundland. The long debate over whether the Norse voyages to North America ever took place at all was ended, apparently for good, by the discovery in 1961 of an indisputable Viking settlement at L'Anse au Meadow, Newfoundland; carbon-14 readings on charcoal found in the pit of a smithy gave dates in the early eleventh century.

The outposts in Iceland and Greenland, and those in Vinland as well, thrived all through the eleventh and twelfth centuries. But a transformation of Europe's climate began about A.D. 1200. A marked instability developed, bringing drought and flood, great heat and great cold. A Scottish chronicle of 1239 declares that in that year "no rain fell and the wines were so strong that no one could drink them without water"—while in 1257 the winter was so cold in England that many fig trees were killed. A trend toward colder and more stormy weather set in. Ellsworth Huntington regarded this breakup of the prevailing pattern of mild climate as the prologue to the great political and intellectual ferment that swept Europe in the thirteenth and fourteenth centuries; he cites peasant uprisings, the decline of serfdom, the rise of religious heresies, and the birth of middle-class parliamentary representation as examples of the stimulative effect of the suddenly uncertain weather. However much truth there is in this, it is beyond question that the vineyards of the northern countries were wiped out by the change in climate, and that the settlers in the lands discovered by the Norsemen entered into a time of grave hardship.

For the first time drift ice hindered free navigation between Iceland and Greenland. The *Kungaspegel*, or *King's Mirror*, an anonymous Icelandic work written about 1250, warned navigators that the old sailing route around the southern end of Greenland was now unsafe because of ice, and a more southwesterly route had to be used. Yet the Greenland colonists were still holding their own against all difficulties. The *King's Mirror* tells us:

> In Greenland, as you probably know, everything that comes from other lands is dear; for the country lies so distant from other lands that men seldom visit it. And everything they require to assist the country, they must buy from elsewhere, both iron and tar and likewise everything for building houses. But these things are brought thence in exchange for goods: buckskin and ox-hides, and sealskin and walrus-rope and walrus ivory. But since you asked whether there was any raising of crops or not, I believe that country is little assisted thereby. Nevertheless there are men—and they are those who are known as the noblest and richest—who make essay to sow; but nevertheless the great multitude in that country does not know what bread is, and never even saw bread. . . .
>
> Few are the people in that land, for little of it is thawed so much as to be habitable. . . . But when you ask what they live on in that country, since they have no grain, then you must know that men live on more things than bread alone. Thus it is said that there is good pasture and great and good homesteads on Greenland; for people there have much cattle and sheep, and there is much making of butter and cheese. The people live much on this, and also on flesh of all kinds of game, the flesh of reindeer, whale, seal, and bear; on this they maintain themselves in that country.

In 1250, then, Greenland was already isolated—"men seldom visit it," says the *King's Mirror*—but life was still tolerable there. The fourteenth century, however, brought climatic catastropies and upheavals in renewed measure to all of Europe. The chroniclers of many lands report startling events. The Kattegat, the strait between Denmark and Sweden, had never frozen over within the memory of man; but it did so in 1296,

1306, 1323, and 1408, and in those years horses and sleighs could cross safely from one country to the other. The Skaggerrak, between Sweden and Norway, also froze several times, and packs of wolves scampered over the ice. In the coldest year, 1323, the entire Baltic was a vast ice field, and there was brisk traffic across it between Sweden and Germany. The snowy winters were followed by torrential spring floods, inundating low-lying areas of England and the Netherlands. Cool, rainy summers harmed the crops and gave England the three worst famines in her history in 1315, 1316, and 1321, while all through the century food was scarce and prices high. In fifty-five years of the century there were severe summer floods in Europe as a result of these rainstorms; but in other years there were extraordinary droughts, most particularly in 1357, when the Danube nearly dried up and the Rhine could be forded at Cologne.

The impact of these disturbances was greatest where life at best had been marginal, as in Greenland. Now the northern seas were increasingly blocked by ice. About the year 1050 the Norwegian King Harald Hardraade had made a voyage of Arctic exploration that may have taken him as far north as Spitsbergen or Novaya Zemlya before he was seriously inconvenienced by ice; and during the eleventh and twelfth centuries men from Iceland, Greenland, and Norway had pursued seals, walrus, and whales far into those high latitudes. The spread of drift ice ended those ventures by 1250, with consequent effects on the food supplies of the Norsemen; and within another few generations even the regular sailing routes were blocked. Trading ships known as *knarren* had been traveling between Greenland and Norway since the time of Erik the Red, but by 1294 the only contact between Scandinavia and the island outpost was a single *knarr* owned by the King of Norway, which made one round trip every few years. Communication dwindled to almost nothing. A letter from a Norwegian bishop to a bishop in Greenland, written in 1308, takes it for granted that the Greenlanders have not yet heard of the death of King Erik of Norway in 1299. In 1327 Greenland still thrived sufficiently to be able to ship 250 walrus tusks to Norway as a tithe for the Church; and in 1346 another fully laden *knarr* reached Norway from Greenland. But it evidently was not until 1355 that the next ship sailed to the colony, and it did not return until 1363. The *knarr* sent out from Norway in 1366 was wrecked at sea; a ship the following year succeeded in getting through the ice, bringing Greenland her new bishop; the records state that at that time the Greenlanders had been without a bishop for nineteen years.

Contact grew ever less frequent; cut off from their only source of manufactured goods, blocked by drift ice from reaching their old fishing grounds, almost forgotten by the outside world, the Greenlanders were forced back on their own skimpy resources. The last visitors to the Greenland colonies were three Icelanders who were driven off course in 1406 while sailing from Norway to Iceland; they stayed in Greenland for four years, perhaps because they were compelled to wait that long for favorable conditions for a voyage. After their departure in 1410, there is no further notice of contact between Greenland and the rest of the world.

In 1492 the plight of Greenland came to the notice of the newly elected Pope Alexander VI, who had been the notorious Rodrigo Borgia. A Benedictine monk named Mathias applied to the Pope to be Bishop of Greenland, and announced his willingness to go there as a missionary. Pope Alexander replied:

"As we are informed, the church at Gade [Gardar] lies at the world's end in the land of Greenland, where the people, for want of bread, wine, and oil, live on dried fish and milk; and therefore, as well by reason of the extreme rarity of the voyages that have taken place to the said land, for which the severe freezing of the waters is alleged as the cause, it is believed that for eighty years no ship has landed there; and if such voyages should take place, it is thought that in any case it could only be in the month of August, when the same ice is dissolved; and for this reason it is said that for eighty years or thereabouts no bishop or priest has resided at that church. Therefore . . . to provide them with a fitting shepherd . . ." the Pope appointed Mathias to the bishopric and exhorted him to go to Greenland at once.

It does not appear that Bishop Mathias ever took up his responsibilities in Greenland. By 1516 Greenland had been so thoroughly forgotten that it came as a surprise to Erik Walchendorf, the new Archbishop of Trondheim in Norway, that his archdiocese included a place called Greenland that had paid no taxes to the Church in over a century. Walchendorf suggested an expedition to rediscover the lost colony, and volunteered to lead it himself; but the plan came to nothing. In 1540, an Icelander found his way to Greenland, and saw signs of habitation in the interior of a fjord, but did not make contact with the people. He observed a man lying dead on the ground with a knife in his hand, no attempt having been made to bury him. Beginning in 1568 King Frederik of Norway and Denmark sent five successive expeditions to Greenland, but the route itself was now unknown, and the explorers sailed northwest instead of west. They were stopped by the Arctic ice without a glimpse of the great island. Not until the eighteenth century was Greenland reached, and by then there was no one alive in any of the old Norse settlements.

Why had the Greenland colonies perished?

Eskimo invasion is one explanation. Eskimos are generally not a belligerent people, and such authorities on the Arctic as Fridtjof Nansen have expressed doubt that they were capable of attacking the Norsemen. But there is a great deal of evidence to indicate that in the middle of the fourteenth century an Eskimo migration began—perhaps induced by the general climatic deterioration—which brought the dwellers of the ice world into conflict with the Norsemen living on Greenland's western coast. Icelandic accounts say that Eskimo attacks forced the abandonment of Vesterbygden in 1342. (One chronicle maintains that the settlers fled to Vinland at this time; but this is doubtful, as is the continued existence of the settlements in North America after the twelfth century.) Eskimo attacks next descended on Österbygden, where in 1379, according to an Icelandic account, eighteen Norsemen were slain and many taken prisoner. Finally, a letter from Pope Nicholas V to the two bishops of Iceland, written in 1448, is often cited to show that about thirty years earlier a devastating

Eskimo onslaught left Österbygden all but depopulated: "The barbarians . . . so destroyed the . . . sacred edifices with fire and sword that only nine parish churches were left in the whole island, and these are said to be the most remote, which they could not reach on account of the steep mountains." The Pope declared that the invaders had "carried the miserable inhabitants of both sexes as prisoners to their own country, especially those whom they regarded as strong and capable of bearing constant burdens of slavery. . . . But since . . . in the course of time most of them have returned from the said imprisonment to their own homes, and have here and there repaired the ruins of their dwellings. . . ."

Eskimos, however, have never attacked "with fire and sword," nor have they been known to take slaves; and it seems likely that the Eskimo raids of the fourteenth century, if they took place at all, were only one contributing factor to the doom of the Greenlanders. The increasing harshness of the climate may have been a more terrible foe. In 1921, a Danish archaeological expedition led by Dr. Poul Nörlund excavated the Norse settlement at Herjulfsnes, near the site of vanished Österbygden. The graves of the cemetery were in permafrost—ground that never thaws out—and, from the nearly perfect state of preservation of the coffins, clothing, and bodies, it was clear that the hard freeze had been unbroken almost since the time of interment. Yet the ground had not been permafrost when the graves had been dug; even today, in permafrost regions, no attempt is made to dig graves in frozen ground. So the climate must have been growing colder at about the time of the burials, in the early fifteenth century. The oldest burials were deepest; as the permafrost zone moved upward it became necessary to dig graves closer to the surface, until at last no graves could be dug at all, nor life sustained in the colony. The final proof of the shift in climate is the network of tree roots in which many of the coffins were enmeshed; the roots could not have penetrated into the permafrost that later engulfed the earth there.

The bodies found in the coffins, clad in the woolen robes and pointed caps of the fifteenth century, revealed the terrible condition of life in the last days of the Greenland colonies. The people were deformed, twisted, dwarfed; their skeletons show evidence of rickets, tuberculosis, tooth decay, malnutrition; lives were short and dismal. A delicately built woman not yet thirty years old was only 4 feet 6 inches tall, with a crooked back; another woman, 5 feet 2 inches, was the tallest, but she, too, was a hunchback, and her narrow pelvis could never have tolerated a childbirth. The hardy seed of the Vikings had come down to this miserable remnant of starved sufferers, to whom extinction could only have been a mercy.

A Swedish oceanographer, Otto Pettersson, produced in 1912 a book called *Climatic Variations in Historic and Prehistoric Time,* in which he offered a theory of the medieval climatic severity that still has many advocates. Pettersson, who died in 1941, spent most of his ninety-three years on the shores of the Baltic, and over a lengthy period carried out measurements of the oceanic tides of the Atlantic that each day send salt water surging in and out of that inland sea. The height of the tides, he found, varies not only throughout the day but in cycles of many years; and the tidal cycles have a profound effect on climate.

As Pettersson expressed it, the power of the tides is governed by the relative positions of the sun, moon, and earth. Once every eighteen hundred years, approximately, those three bodies come into such a configuration that the tides grow exceptionally great. The effect of this tidal upheaval is to send unusual quantities of warm Atlantic water welling into the Arctic Sea at deep levels; thawing causes thousands of square miles of the Arctic ice pack to break up and drift south via the Labrador Current into the Atlantic. This chilling of the ocean in low latitudes disrupts the entire global pattern of circulation, so intricately balanced; the winds take up new courses, cyclonic storms increase as low-pressure belts shift, oceanic currents are deflected so that the mild Gulf Stream no longer bathes the shores of Greenland, Iceland, and northern Europe. A time of savage cold and brutal storms, of floods and catastrophes, shakes Europe.

Pettersson calculated that tidal peaks had come in 3500 B.C., in 2100 B.C., in 350 B.C., and in A.D. 1434. It is not easy to match the earliest two of these peaks to what is known of European climate from other sources; in 3500 B.C. Europe was still enjoying the mildness of the climatic optimum, and though a stormy epoch eventually came, it arrived in 1800 B.C. and not in Pettersson's predicted 2100. But there is strong evidence for a time of storms between 600 and 400 B.C., which perhaps was connected with Pettersson's postulated tidal peak in 350; when Pytheas made his northward voyage Europe may well have been undergoing climatic reversals, since, as we have seen, accounts of Pytheas' travels indicate the presence of drift ice in northern waters. Floods, barbarian migrations, and other catastrophes also marked this period of disruption. And A.D. 1434, Pettersson's most recent tidal peak, certainly coincides with a period of widespread foul weather.

The weather had been growing worse since the early thirteenth century; by the fifteenth, it had brought the downfall of the Greenland settlers; and the trouble was just beginning, for Europe was entering a time of adverse climate sometimes termed "the little ice age." This amply documented chilly era persisted almost to the second half of the nineteenth century. The glaciers of Europe's mountains reached their most extensive positions in ten thousand years; the polar pack ice on the North Atlantic made sea travel hazardous and at times almost impossible; famines were common, and northern land had to be abandoned to the encroaching cold.

In Iceland, where villages had survived the change of climate that had undone Greenland, the distress was particularly severe, especially in the eighteenth century. An Icelandic parish record offers such cheerless entries as these:

"1709. *Breithamörk* (farm). Half King's ownership, half owned by the farmer. Derelict . . . a little woodland, now surrounded by glacier. . . ."

"*Fjall* (farm). Owned by the Church. Derelict. Lies northeast of Breithamörk. Fourteen years ago had farmhouse and buildings, all now come under the glacier. . . ."

A different annal gives the date of the abandonment of the

farm Breithamörk as 1698: "There was some grass visible then, but since the glacier has covered all except the hillock on which the farmhouse at Breithamörk stood and that is surrounded by ice so that it is no use even for sheep." That hillock too was eventually covered by the ice.

The British naturalist Joseph Banks, who visited Iceland in 1772, wrote of "so violent a cold in 1753 and 1754, that horses and sheep dropped down dead on account of it, as well as for want of food, horses were observed to feed upon dead cattle, and the sheep eat of each others' wool. In the year 1755, towards the end of . . . May, in one night the ice was one inch and five lines thick. In . . . 1756, on the 26th of June, snow fell to the depth of a yard, and continued falling through . . . July and August. In the year following it froze very hard towards the end of May and the beginning of June in the south part of the island, which occasioned great scarcity of grass, insomuch that the inhabitants had little or no fodder the ensuing winter for their cattle; these frosts are generally followed by a famine. . . ." Famine, indeed, carried off ten thousand Icelanders between 1753 and 1759, one fourth of the population.

Nor was Iceland the only place that suffered. The entire Northern Hemisphere was gripped by cold, with only brief reversions to the previous mildness. In North America, the worst year appears to have been 1816, known in New England as "the year without a summer," or "Eighteen Hundred and Froze-to-Death." There was snow in June, frost in July; thousands of farmers were forced to migrate to points west in search of a livelihood. The Mediterranean region had exceptionally severe winters; glaciers expanded in mountainous regions everywhere; accumulations of snow formed on the high peaks of Ethiopia, where snow now is never seen.

A true ice age of the Pleistocene sort takes thousands of years to make itself known; the "little ice age" that convulsed Europe between the fifteenth and nineteenth centuries came on too suddenly to have been anything more than a passing inconvenience. By 1850—just at the time when the first theories of glaciation were being worked out—the climate relented.

The swing to warmer weather only gradually became evident; there were always oldsters who claimed that winters nowadays weren't a patch on those of their childhood, but the backing and filling that accompanies any climatic change blurred the evolving pattern so that it was not discerned in any systematic way until generations after the shift had occurred. One of the first manifestations was a warming of northern waters that permitted a sudden and dramatic expansion of fisheries. Cod made its first appearance in many parts of Greenland in the first decade of this century, began to move northward, and grew more abundant; over forty years the average Greenland catch increased from 500 tons a year to 15,000. A million square kilometers of drift ice melted in the Russian sector of the Arctic Sea, with 100,000 square kilometers vanishing in the two years beginning May, 1927. Glaciers shrank, particularly in Alaska, where one glacier receded more than six miles in a dozen years. The melting of snowfields in Norway revealed artifacts sixteen centuries old; elsewhere in Scandinavia, land that had not been accessible for hundreds of years returned to cultivation. Greenland once more was green, at least along some of its coastline, and its interior glaciers retreated somewhat. The warming trend continued almost without an interruption until the 1940's; and then, just as climatologists were growing perturbed over the prospects of global tropicalization, a return to cooler conditions evidently began, and is still in force. But there is no indication, at present, that the grim "little ice age" is about to resume.

9

Climatic Shifts in the New World

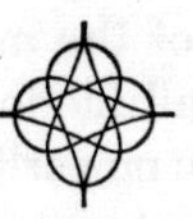

VERY LITTLE HAS BEEN SAID, IN THE PRECEDING CHAPTERS, about the effects of environmental changes on human life in the Americas. The omission was deliberate. It is not that the New World has been blessed by an unchanging climate, for the glacial and postglacial upheavals in the Western Hemisphere were as drastic and as potent as those elsewhere; but throughout most of the epochs that we have been examining, there simply was no human life in the Americas on which those environmental changes could have had an impact. Man was a latecomer to the New World.

During the million-plus years of the Pleistocene glaciations, Europe and North America experienced parallel sequences of cold. Corresponding to the European glacial stages usually known by the shorthand designations of Günz, Mindel, Riss, and Würm are the similar and roughly contemporary North American stages termed Nebraskan, Kansan, Illinoian, and Wisconsian. (The last of these is sometimes given a substage, the Iowan.) But while Europe was the scene of the push and pull of many human cultures as the temperatures rose and fell, the Americas were free of men during nearly all of this time. In Europe the Abbevilleans and Acheulians, Clactonians and Mousterians, and other Pleistocene groups played out their varying fortunes, but beyond the great ocean lay lands where huge beasts roamed, unmolested for hundreds of thousands of years by that most ferocious beast of all.

The time of man's arrival in the New World has long been one of the most controversial questions of prehistoric studies, but all factions in the dispute agree that it could have taken place no earlier than the Wisconsian glaciation—that is, within the last seventy thousand years, and probably within the latter half of that period. By then the modern form of *Homo sapiens* had appeared, and it was as *Homo sapiens* that man came to the Western Hemisphere. Thus the whole story of human evolution had already been told when the first men reached the Americas. There were never any American pithecanthropoids, no American branch of the Neanderthals, no Yankee australopithecines.

The evidence for this is negative, but impressive in its negativeness. No one has ever found a fossil human of a pre-*sapiens* type in the Western Hemisphere. Nor have any fossil apes been found. No higher primates inhabited the Americas at all, so far as we know, except for the tailed monkeys of South America—until that relatively recent immigrant, *Homo sapiens.*

There is almost no debate at all over the route that that immigrant took. Only in one place does the New World impinge on the Old: in Alaska, where the 56-mile-wide waterway of the Bering Strait divides North America from Asia. It is difficult to imagine primitive man spanning the Atlantic or the Pacific to reach the Americas, but not at all hard to see how, even with his extremely limited skills, he could have crossed the Bering Strait. The strait is broken by two islands, the Diomedes, so that the longest stretch of open water is only 23 miles. That would be no real challenge even for men paddling in the crudest of canoes. And in winter Bering Strait freezes over. A bridge of ice is formed, over which men can—and do—cross from Asia to North America.

If the first men entered Alaska during the last glacial period, they need not have troubled to build canoes or to clamber over ice. They could have walked across the Bering Strait on dry land. So much water was locked up by the world's glaciers during the fourth ice age that sea levels were more than 250 feet lower than they are today. The floors of the English Channel and the southern half of the North Sea were exposed; the straits separating Ceylon from India and New Guinea from Australia dried up; the continental shelf of eastern North America was above water, so that mastodons and other animals grazed in places now forty miles out to sea; and the Bering Strait, which at its deepest point is only 180 feet deep, held no water. North of the strait for some 400 miles runs the Chuckchi Sea, less than 250 feet deep. At the peak of the Wisconsian ice age the bottom of this shallow sea was a nearly flat plain, the Bering-Chuckchi Platform, comprising a land bridge 600 miles wide between the two continents. There was free access for migrating animals of all kinds, since there were no glaciers on either side, only a cold, bleak tundra. Bands of straggling hunters could easily have filtered into North America out of eastern Asia. The flow may have been only a trickle at first, a hundred people a year or less, with long periods when no one made the crossing at all. Those who came found routes open to them, leading into the heart of a virgin continent. For several thousand years during the glacial period, an ice-free corridor existed just east of the Rockies, from the Arctic down into the northern United States. Later, another pathway was available through the Alberta-Saskatchewan plains; a different route led from the northern coastal lowlands to the Mackenzie River, and then south along its valley, which was never glaciated.

One substantial and extremely vigorous school of American prehistorians found it impossible to accept the idea that man had come to the New World during the last glacial period. The leader of this group was the brilliant, fiery, and dogmatic Aleš Hrdlička of the Smithsonian Institution, who served for decades as the spokesman for those who believed that man was an extremely recent arrival here. Hrdlička's first major work, the 1907 monograph *Skeletal Remains Suggesting or Attributed to Early Man in North America*, was a useful corrective for much nineteenth-century pseudoscience; applying strict and austere methods, Hrdlička was able to demolish certain purported examples of extremely ancient human fossils found in the New World. But in succeeding years he went after every alleged find of primitive men in the Americas; his papers bristled with phrases like "not in the least primitive," "essentially modern," or "not to be distinguished from the modern Indian," and he rejected with sweeping condemnation all suggestions that man had reached the Americas much before the time of Christ.

Hrdlička's work was valuable, for it cleared away a great deal of error, confusion, and downright fraud. But as he grew older his opinions hardened into prejudices, which he proclaimed so vehemently that it was considered not quite respectable for any scientist to hold an opposing theory; it could also be professionally dangerous to attempt to contradict the revered Hrdlička. Not until the Folsom finds of 1926 and 1927 was any solid proof offered that man's antiquity in the New World was considerably greater than Hrdlička would admit.

J. D. Figgins of the Colorado Museum of Natural History, carrying on archaeological excavations near the town of Folsom, New Mexico, uncovered a stone artifact of unusual form in 1926. What Figgins found was a "point"—a neutral term used by archaeologists to designate worked stone objects of ambiguous function, which may have been employed as arrowheads, the tips of spears or darts, or as cutting tools. The Folsom point was about two inches long and made of a pinkish-brown stone called chert. Down the center of each face a single long narrow groove, or fluting, had been carved. The outer edges of the point had been very delicately worked. It was an attractive artifact, obviously the product of a skilled craftsman. What made it most remarkable was that Figgins found it embedded in clay surrounding a bone from the skeleton of an extinct form of bison. Everyone—even Hrdlička—agreed that that species of bison had been extinct for at least eight thousand years. Figgins thought that his point proved that man had been present in New Mexico and hunting that bison in the distant past.

His report received a cool response. Most authorities declared that the point was "intrusive"—that is, that it was fairly recent, and had worked its way downward from its own level to the much older bison level. Perhaps, they suggested, a burrowing rodent had buried it in the older strata.

Figgins went back to Folsom in 1927. Once again, he found a fluted point associated with bison bones. But this time the point lay *between the ribs* of the bison.

Halting work at once, Figgins sent telegrams to every important prehistorian in the country, inviting them to inspect the site before he proceeded with the excavation. Figgins was a fairly obscure archaeologist, and only three authorities responded; but they, fortunately, were of the highest rank. They supervised Figgins' excavation and testified that the 1927 Folsom point was indeed no intrusion. A human being, not a squirrel, had driven that point into the fossilized bison bone; and it had been done thousands of years ago.

Over three seasons, nineteen Folsom points were found at the site, as well as the skeletons of twenty-three bisons. There was every reason to think that ancient American hunters had slain and consumed those bison. Significantly, the tail bones of each animal were missing, indicating that the huntsmen had skinned their prey. Since then, Folsom points have been found all over North America—from Alaska to Georgia, in fact. No one now questions the fact that the makers of the Folsom points were hunters who wandered the North American continent a hundred centuries ago.

Nor was the Folsom culture the oldest in the Americas. Since 1927, points of many kinds have come to light that antecede Folsom—the Sandia, Clovis, Yuma, and Gypsum Cave points, to name just a few, each representing a distinctive and characteristic point-making industry. Carbon-14 dating and other modern methods are helping to provide some idea of the age of these points. The points themselves cannot be dated by carbon 14, which works only with organic material; but analysis of material found with the points shows that the Sandia points were fashioned more than 20,000 years ago and that Folsom man flourished between 12,000 and 10,000 years ago. Isolated carbon-14 readings from sites in California and Texas have given dates of 27,000, 38,000, and 40,000 years.

These findings have been repeatedly challenged, but an increasing number of American archaeologists now accepts unhesitatingly the idea that man has inhabited the Western Hemisphere for a minimum of 30,000 years, and perhaps arrived ten or twenty thousand years before that.

In the spring of 1959, a discovery in Mexico lent substance to those high radiocarbon dates. Dr. Juan Armenta Camacho, working at a site southeast of Puebla, Mexico, found four fragments of mammoth or mastodon bone on which can be seen the outlines of bison, tapir, or mastodons, engraved when the bone was fresh. Dr. Armenta cautiously has expressed the opinion that the mastodon or mammoth whose bones served as the "canvas" for the prehistoric artist may have died as long as 30,000 years ago. And on Santa Rosa Island off the California coast, the remains of dwarf mammoths have been found, their bones charred and separated as though they had been butchered for a prehistoric barbecue. The carbon-14 date for these charred bones is about 27,000 B.C.

These various early American hunting cultures are collectively grouped as the Paleo-Indians, but we know very little about their physical appearance, or whether they were directly ancestral to the American Indians of historic times. With one or two possible exceptions, we have never found any of their skeletal remains. The population of North America in Folsom times was never greater than a few tens of thousands at any one time, and finding the remains of these huntsmen is very much a needle-in-the-haystack proposition. Furthermore, it is likely that Folsom man simply exposed his dead to the elements, which would almost guarantee the total nonsurvival of Folsom fossils. "Under such circumstances," one anthropologist has written, "it would be the merest chance to come across a skeleton of Folsom man anywhere in the enormous area of our Great Plains country. It would be even more remarkable to recognize him as such, unless he had a Folsom point in his hand or was holding an elephant by the tail." Such few Paleo-Indian skulls as have been found indicate that the earliest Americans may have been an extremely primitive form of *Homo sapiens,* with long, narrow heads, protruding faces and jaws, receding chins, and bulging brows; the skulls of recent Indians are generally round and wide.

The Paleo-Indians left no dwellings for archaeologists to find, no works of art, no signs of their presence save the points of their weapons and the charred bones of the animals they killed and cooked. They were nomads, drifting where the big game went, killing and roasting and eating, then moving on. Perhaps they varied their diet by gathering wild berries and roots, but they had no fields, no farms, no villages. The continent they entered, twenty or thirty or forty thousand years ago, was quite different from modern North America. Glaciers still blanketed much of the north and were retreating only a little, baring a few hundred yards of tundra, possibly, each year. South of the glacier line the climate was predominantly cool and rainy, even in regions that are desert today. Giant mammals now extinct roved the forests and plains: the ground sloth and the great bison, the saber-toothed tiger and the dire wolf, the mammoth and the mastodon.

A single site—Sandia Cave in New Mexico—provided a vivid glimpse of that other North America, with its greatly different climate, when it was first excavated in 1936 by a group led by Frank C. Hibben of the University of New Mexico. On the top level of the cave floor Hibben found a layer of Pueblo Indian artifacts—broken pottery, fragments of baskets and sandals—all quite recent and not at all extraordinary. Below this level the archaeologists came to a deposit of travertine, a kind of limestone formed by water dripping from the cave roof. This layer, which was six inches thick in places, could have been laid down only at a time when New Mexico's climate was far rainier than it is today. Breaking through the travertine, Hibben and his co-workers found another stratum of human occupancy sealed beneath it. This new layer contained the shattered bones of bison, mammoth, camel, ground sloth, and other long-extinct species. With them were Folsom points, so that an age of some ten thousand years could be assigned to the level. Clearing away the Folsom layer, the archaeologists uncovered a deposit of yellow ocher, a substance produced by fir and spruce trees under conditions of cold and moistness. The layer ranged in thickness from two inches to two feet, indicating a lengthy period of deposit. Beneath the ocher there lay still another stratum of human occupation, containing, once again, bones of mammoth, camel, and bison. The bones had been cracked open for their marrow. Ash-filled fireplaces indicated the sites of ancient barbecue pits. The tools of prehistoric man lay scattered about: flint knives, scrapers, and projectile points larger and more crudely made than the Folsom points. These were the first Sandia points to be discovered, and carbon-14 dating of associated matter has shown them to be about twenty thousand years old.

The presence of Paleo-Indians in New Mexico at such an early date indicates that the migration into the New World must have begun at least several thousand years earlier. It was not a purposeful migration in any sense, probably, but merely extended gradual roaming, as the nomadic hunters followed the game on which they preyed. The animals probably kept close to rivers, and so did the men who pursued them. One group of wanderers came down east of the Rockies and spread out, in little hunting bands, over the western United States. Some of them reached cool and rainy New Mexico and one day held a feast in Sandia Cave, leaving their weapon points behind to announce their presence eventually to Dr. Frank Hibben. Others kept on going, on into Mexico, then through Central America, and down South America's western coast clear to Patagonia. By 8000 B.C. the task of covering the 11,000 miles between Bering Strait and the Strait of Magellan was done; that is the carbon-14 date from Fell's Cave, Chile, almost at the southern tip of South America, where long-headed human skulls and charred animal bones were found.

The early Americans were restless. They built no communities. They paused from time to time in their wanderings, but never long enough to leave a permanent impress at any one place. Their projectile points, widely scattered, mark their presence in many parts of the United States. While one thrust of migrants was moving southward through the Rocky Mountain region into Latin America, another band was heading eastward in slow stages. Possibly as early as 11,000 B.C. there were huntsmen east of the Mississippi, living in the newly thawed Great Lakes region. They moved on into the eastern woodlands. Fluted points similar to the Folsom points have been found in Vermont, Pennsylvania, Michigan, Ohio, and Massachusetts.

The climate was changing gradually but steadily throughout the time of the Paleo-Indians. In the north, an ice sheet gave way to a tundra on which spruce and birch sprouted, then pine, then the deciduous trees of a milder climate. In the south, where pluvial rather than glacial conditions had been experienced, a growing aridity set in, becoming extreme some eight or ten thousand years ago. The effects on the Paleo-Indians were calamitous. Moist regions became deserts, cold woodlands became forests; and the giant mammals, unable to adapt, migrated in search of the climate they preferred, and, eventually finding it nowhere, died out.

The hunting tribes may well have died out, too. Certainly the traces of Paleo-Indian life can no longer be found in the American Southwest after about eight thousand years ago, and a new culture appears, one that did not depend on the killing of big beasts. Man in North America passed from the big-game-hunting stage to the food-gathering stage, depending for his food supply upon the collecting of seeds, berries, and roots, and the hunting of small game such as rabbits, prairie dogs, and doves. It is not possible at present to determine whether this new culture of foragers and food gatherers evolved out of the Paleo-Indian culture or if the Paleo-Indians simply vanished after the extinction of the big game, to be replaced by an entirely new group of migrants out of Asia.

The first evidence of the existence of the food-gathering culture was unearthed near the town of Cochise, Arizona, in 1926. The Cochise people may have begun their way of life about ten thousand years ago; certainly they were occupying their territory within two thousand years after that, since the Cochise site has a carbon-14 date of 6240 B.C. The Cochise people were not farmers yet, but they did make one significant invention. Archaeologists have found grinding-stones and pestles at the Cochise sites, indicating that they milled the roots and seeds they collected, and thus were taking the first steps toward controlling their environment—for certain types of seeds are edible only when milled.

The earliest Cochise people of southern Arizona lived in a fairly moist environment. We know this because archaeologists have discovered charcoal made from hickory at their sites, and hickory grows only in a land where rainfall is plentiful. Much of their region was covered by a vast pluvial lake, now gone, called Lake Cochise by prehistorians. But as the climate became more dry and the lake dwindled, new food sources were needed; the milling of seeds was the first Cochise response to the increase in aridity, and later came the discovery of corn.

Corn is an extraordinary vegetable, capable of resisting almost every extreme of climate and producing a generous yield of nutritious food. It grows under near-desert conditions and in the rain-flooded fields of India. It thrives as far north as Canada and Russia, as far south as the tropics. It grows below sea level in eastern Europe and at heights of 12,000 feet in the Peruvian Andes. There are hundreds of different varieties of corn, adapted to many types of growing conditions.

In the Americas, the cultivation of corn probably began in Peru or Mexico, seven or eight thousand years ago. It was to the Indian cultures of the New World what wheat and barley were to the Old World: the foundation of all progress. The bounty of corn freed many people for tasks other than food gathering, since a relative handful of farmers could produce enough corn to feed many people. That left hands and minds unencumbered to invent new ways of doing things. The wonderful arithmetic of the corn yield led the way to a breathtakingly rapid expansion of Indian culture.

Indian corn, *Zea mays,* is not a wild plant. Its seeds, its kernels, are sheltered behinds tough husks, and without the help of man those seeds cannot reach the soil. Obviously, ancient American farmers had practiced a kind of artificial selection that created a highly edible kernel and a species unable to disperse its seed unaided. One of the long-standing puzzles of American archaeology was to find the ancestral wild grass that had been turned into Indian corn. Two candidates had been proposed, both grassy weeds that show definite kinship to modern corn. These were teosinte and *Tripsacum,* both found in a natural state in the Mexican and Central American highlands. During the 1940's, studies by Paul C. Mangelsdorf of Harvard University and other researchers showed that neither of these could be the ancestor of corn, for both had evolved relatively recently. Mangelsdorf suggested that the true ancestor of corn would turn out to be a kind of popcorn, with kernels encased in pods.

Archaeologists set about the search. In 1953, cores of earth brought up by drilling into the old lake beds on which Mexico City stands produced grains of corn pollen eighty thousand years old. This was the ancestral wild corn that had grown in Mexico thousands of years before the first human settlers reached the New World. The quest now turned to the desert area stretching from the American Southwest to southern Mexico. In 1948, corncobs about six thousand years old were found by Richard S. MacNeish of the University of Chicago in the arid state of Tamaulipas, in northeast Mexico. The following year MacNeish, now working under the auspices of the National Museum of Canada, returned to Tamaulipas to continue his search. Several years of work produced a good deal of early corn, a tiny-eared variety that was eaten raw, roasted, popped, and ground into meal. One Tamaulipas site yielded a carbon-14 date of 6544 B.C. ± 450 years, showing that agriculture was nearly as ancient in the Americas as in the Old World, since only a few extraordinary Old World sites such as Jericho had produced evidence of earlier cultivation. But MacNeish did not find wild corn there. He moved on to the Valley of Tehuacán, where in 1960 he discovered three unusually primitive-looking corncobs whose carbon-14 dates were five hundred years older than those of any corn yet found in the New World. A major archaeological effort followed; in four seasons from 1961 to 1964 MacNeish and his collaborators excavated twenty-eight separate levels of occupation in a single cave, covering a span of almost twelve thousand years. In the course of this work he turned up tiny corncobs "no bigger than the filter tip of a cigarette . . . under a magnifying lens one could see that they were indeed miniature ears of corn, with sockets that had once contained kernels enclosed in pods. These cobs proved to be some seven thousand years old. Mangelsdorf is convinced that this must be wild corn—the original parent from which modern corn is descended."

The idea of cultivating corn spread quickly, and one of the earliest places where such agriculture was practiced was New Mexico. At Bat Cave, in the western part of the state, archaeologists in 1948 found small corncobs buried in a layer of debris that also included weapon points in the Cochise style. Carbon-14 analysis gave an age of nearly six thousand years. The Bat Cave corncobs were extremely primitive, each ear only a few inches long and huskless, but they indicate that the Cochise folk had learned the secrets of agriculture at an early date.

The rate of progress accelerates once a steady food supply is assured. The Cochise people, becoming more efficient farmers all the time despite the ever-increasing aridity of their environment, began to develop a fairly advanced agricultural society—the first of its kind in the United States. By about 1000 B.C. they occupied much of southern Arizona and New Mexico, living in small villages near their fields. They learned the arts of basketry, using the tough fibers of such desert plants as the yucca. They made sandals and mats and nets, and dug shallow pits for houses, roofing them over with twigs and small branches. About 300 B.C. they added the immensely important craft of making pottery, learning it, probably, from the Indians of Mexico. So many changes now entered Cochise society that archaeologists do not use the term "Cochise" to describe it after this point; instead they consider the Cochise to have divided into two daughter cultures, which they call the Hohokam and the Mogollon. (The Mogollon were named after the Mogollon Mountains of southeastern Arizona and New Mexico, which themselves were named for an eighteenth-century Spanish governor, Don Juan de Mogollon. "Hohokam" is the term used by the modern Pima Indians of Arizona for the early inhabitants of their region, and means "ancient people," or "those who have gone away."

Environment provided a considerable challenge for these

two groups. The Mogollon country is high and dry; the hills are covered with the scrubby underbrush common to arid mountainsides. The Mogollon raised their crops in the valleys, made their homes in sunken pits, and built fairly extensive villages. For a thousand years or more they tilled their harsh land, until finally they were peacefully absorbed by other Indian groups migrating from the north.

The Hohokam lived in even less promising country to the west, in the Arizona desert. Mesquite and cactus were the typical vegetation of their area. The rainfall seldom amounted to more than ten inches during the year, and in the summer the temperature was over 100° F. much of the time. Yet the Hohokam raised corn, squash, beans, and later cotton, in this desert. In the early phase of their culture—from the time of Christ to about A.D. 500—they depended on what is called "floodwater irrigation" for their crops; that is, they lived near streams and rivers that tended to overflow their banks during the rainy part of the year, and planted their crops in the flood-moistened land. This gave them only a short growing season, and in a dry year there might be no flood at all, and thus no harvest.

In the sixth century A.D. the Hohokam began to build their first irrigation channels. By conveying water through canals from the biggest rivers of their fields, they avoided a dependence on the uncertain mercies of the rainy season. Work was slow, since the only digging tools these farmers of the desert had were crude wooden shovels and stone scrapers. But within two centuries the Hohokam managed to gouge out an impressive system of canals, and they went on enlarging them for hundreds of years thereafter.

It must have been an enormous community effort. Such great projects could only have been achieved after careful planning, and with the wholehearted cooperation of thousands of people. The existence of the Hohokam canals indicates a well-organized society with strong leaders.

The canals were about five feet wide and five feet deep at first, and as much as ten miles long. Through generations of patient toil under the sizzling desert sun, the Hohokam enlarged the canals to meet their growing needs. Some later canals were ten feet deep and thirty feet wide, and ran for vast distances. One system of canals in the Salt River Valley of Arizona totals 150 miles. Since the rivers carried great quantities of silt, it was necessary to work constantly on canal maintenance, forever clearing the channels of accumulated silt. Some of the Hohokam canals have been cleaned out in the twentieth century and incorporated into modern irrigation systems.

The Hohokam civilization was rich and complex. There is evidence that contact with the highly advanced civilizations of Mexico was frequent and regular, judging by the presence of such things as huge ball-courts in the Mayan style at every Hohokam village. The Hohokam were not only clever engineers but skilled workers in stone, who fashioned excellent stone axes, grinding tools, and even jars and bowls. Their handsome jewelry was highly prized by surrounding tribes, for it has been found at many sites far from Hohokam territory. The Hohokam jewelers achieved wonderful effects, making mosaics of turquoise and shell in geometric or animal-figure designs. About 1100 they discovered the technique of etching—perhaps the first people in the world to do so, since etching did not develop in Europe until the fifteenth century. The Hohokam used a mild acid, possibly made by fermenting the juice of a type of cactus, to eat designs into the backs of lustrous, iridescent abalone and olivella shells. These shells they obtained over three trade routes leading from California across the desert regions into Arizona. Hohokam traders also were middlemen for goods from Mexico, such as copper bells and cotton textiles, which they took to the Indians of northern Arizona and New Mexico. In return, the Hohokam received the northerners' products: baskets, pottery, mineral paints, and ornaments of the highly valued blue-green stone called turquoise.

The northerners were just beginning to develop a significant culture of their own. Their heartland was the high plateau known as the Four Corners country, where Arizona, New Mexico, Colorado, and Utah come together at right angles. It is a spectacularly beautiful region of prairies, mountains, deep gorges, eroded terraces, and steeply rising mesas. Cliffs of bright red sandstone sparkle in the hard, clear sunlight. It is dry country, but not nearly so dry as the desert land where the Hohokam once lived, and not nearly so hot. Even at the height of summer the daytime temperatures are comfortable; at night there can be a sharp chill even in July, because of the altitude, much of the area being more than ten thousand feet above sea level. Where the land is high, it is covered with a forest of stumpy piñon pines and gnarled junipers; in the lowlands, gray-green sagebrush spreads over mile after mile, dotted with clumps of yucca and beargrass.

Here the great Pueblo Indian culture of the American Southwest began. An ingenious, stubborn band of farmers came to dwell here, and left their mark. They started by living in caves and shallow pits, and eventually built the grandest cities of the United States. Archaeologists often call these unusual folk, forebears of the Indians of the twenty-five surviving pueblos of the twentieth century, the Anasazi. It is a word from the language of the Navaho, late arrivals in the Southwest, and means "the Old Ones"—the builders of the great ruins of the Four Corners country. The main divisions of the Anasazi civilization are recognized: the early stage, called the Basketmaker phase, and the later or Pueblo phase.

The Basketmakers came to the Four Corners country about two thousand years ago. We know very little about their earlier life. Possibly they were desert dwellers from Utah or Nevada; perhaps they drifted up from the Cochise country in the south. They wandered into the Four Corners region in small groups, a few families at a time. There they found what seemed to them like a friendly environment. They had just enough water to permit them to raise their corn and squash, and along the steep canyon walls there were shallow caves in which they could take shelter.

Their culture had simple beginnings. They could farm, more or less; they had heard how the people to the south planted seeds and watered the ground and made crops grow, and they imitated them, clumsily at first. Small cornfields provided enough food for survival. The caves that were their homes were hardly more than niches, open to the sun and the wind.

Where no caves were handy, they built crude brush shelters. They did not yet have the use of pottery, but they made excellent watertight baskets from yucca fibers.

In time they abandoned the caves, moved to open ground, and began to build small villages. By about A.D. 500 they were living in pit-houses, round or oval, two to five feet deep and nine to thirty feet across, covered with sturdy roofs of mud-plastered timber and reeds. They learned the craft of pottery from the Hohokam or the Mogollon; they grew new varieties of corn, with bigger ears than the earlier kinds, and added such high-protein foods as beans to their crops. Their culture grew more complex in many ways. About A.D. 700 the most enterprising of the Anasazi villages experimented with a new kind of dwelling, entirely aboveground, with upright walls and flat roofs. Within two centuries, these rectangular houses were being built in rows up to fourteen units long. These were structures of poles and mud at first, then of stones embedded in mud, and ultimately of neatly squared slabs of sandstone set in adobe mortar. It became possible to add a second story on top of the first. Villages took the form of double-tiered rooms, arranged either in a crescent or a straight row.

The pace of progress quickened among the Anasazi. It had taken hundreds of years to make the move from cave shelters to pit-houses, and another three centuries had gone by before aboveground dwellings became common. Now the villages grew larger, the architecture more sturdy. New concepts evolved as Anasazi culture spread. The heart of the civilization was still the Four Corners country. There were three main centers of Anasazi life there: the Mesa Verde area of southwestern Colorado, the Chaco Canyon district in northwestern New Mexico, and, in northeastern Arizona, the vicinity of the modern town of Kayenta. In these places, similar but independent cultural groups were making rapid strides. Less advanced groups who shared some of the Anasazi traits could be found in such outlying areas as Utah, southeastern Nevada, and the Big Bend country of Texas.

In this time of expansion corn remained the basic food. The ears could be stored like stacked logs after the harvest, and the dried kernels ground into meal as needed during the months that followed. Beans and squash were still the important secondary crops. The invention of the stone hoe made cultivation easier and produced a bigger yield of food. Anasazi hunters, armed with bows and arrows, brought back bear, elk, buffalo, wolf, mountain sheep, and other game.

The villages—which we know by the Spanish term, "pueblos"—underwent radical transformation. The basic unit was still the rectangular room built of stone slabs mortared with mud and roofed with poles and brush, but now these units were added together to form great compounds, some with hundreds of rooms. This was the most impressive achievement of Anasazi civilization. At Chaco Canyon, at Mesa Verde, and at hundreds of other sites throughout the Four Corners area, towering pueblos were constructed, enlarged, modified, repaired—and ultimately abandoned.

We can set extremely exact dates for the construction of these huge "apartment houses," thanks to a method known as dendrochronology, or tree-ring dating—probably the most precise system of archaeological dating yet devised. It was developed by an astronomer, not an archaeologist: Dr. Andrew E. Douglass, who died in 1962 at the age of ninety-four. At the beginning of this century Douglass was studying sunspots at Arizona's Lowell Observatory. Seeking some correlation between the eleven-year cycle of sunspot frequency and weather on earth, Douglass was hampered by the absence of reliable weather records prior to the eighteenth century. What had the weather been like five hundred or a thousand years ago, when no one had kept weather charts? As he rode through a forest of tall ponderosa pines near Flagstaff, Arizona, he thought of the growth rings of trees. He knew that each year a tree adds a new layer of wood over its entire living surface. Seen in cross-section, the annual growth pattern appears as a series of ever-expanding rings. In a wet year the ring is broad; in a year of drought it is narrow, since a tree grows less if it lacks nourishment.

Beginning in 1904, Douglass began to analyze cross-sections of ponderosa pine from the Flagstaff area. The trees averaged

348 years old, according to a count of rings. He measured the width of each ring and found that the outer sequences of wide and narrow rings corresponded with local rainfall records. Moreover, the same patterns could be found in every tree. He identified sequences that became familiar to him as he examined more trees: perhaps three wide rings followed by two narrow ones, a wide, two more narrows, two wides, three narrows—a year-by-year record of drought and rainfall. His sunspot theory was confirmed: years with greater-than-usual sunspot activity had produced wide growth rings, indicating heavy precipitation, while the years of low sunspot activity had evidently been years of drought.

By 1915 Douglass had pushed back his analysis of tree-ring patterns far beyond the earliest records of rainfall or sunspots. The patterns still held true. By collecting specimens from the giant sequoia trees of inland California, he was able to extend his observations back three thousand years, following the eleven-year sunspot cycle into the far past.

Though his basic interest was astronomical, Douglass found himself becoming deeply involved in Southwestern archaeology. Since the oldest living pines in the Southwest were only about 640 years old, he turned to the Pueblo Indian ruins, hoping to extend his record of tree-ring patterns by examining ancient logs and timbers that had been used as building materials. From his sections of living trees, he had plotted a tree-ring graph that showed him the relative width of rings for the years from 1300 to 1916. He could compare a section from any living pine of Arizona or New Mexico with his master chart and discover when that tree had begun growing. Thus he could confidently point to certain rings on his chart and declare that the Southwest had experienced droughts in 1379 or 1672, for example.

In 1916 the American Museum of Natural History allowed Douglass to examine some sections of pine logs from Pueblo Bonito in Chaco Canyon and from the ancient ruined pueblo near Aztec, New Mexico. Three years later he visited the ruin at Aztec and took fifty samples from house beams. These enabled him to develop a new chart covering some two hundred years. None of the ring patterns on this chart corresponded to those on his chart of 600-year-old living trees. That told him that the logs at Pueblo Bonito had been cut some time before 1300. But how much earlier?

Douglass called this prehistoric chart his "floating chronology." His hope now was to tie it to his living-tree chronology; if he could join the two, he would not only have gained much information about ancient weather and sunspot patterns, but would provide a startlingly accurate tool for the dating of the pueblo ruins.

Archaeologists provided extensive cooperation. Douglass received more specimens from Pueblo Bonito, and thereby added 150 years to the floating chronology. From the Mesa Verde ruins came other samples that provided an entirely new set of ring patterns, matching neither the Pueblo Bonito chart nor the modern chronology. Douglass suspected that the Mesa Verde rings went somewhere between, in the mysterious gap, but at the moment they simply gave him a second floating chronology.

In 1928 timbers from a ruin in Arizona supplied a pattern that matched the latest rings of the Pueblo Bonito chronology and the earliest ones of the Mesa Verde chronology, joining the 350 years of the first to the 180 years of the second. The new floating chronology now covered more than 580 years in continuous prehistoric sequence. In the same year a National Geographic Society expedition visited the Hopi Indian villages of Arizona, which had been continuously inhabited since the fourteenth century. Douglass went along, and after lengthy efforts at persuasion won permission to drill sample cores in the oldest-looking ceiling beams. In an abandoned house in the village of Oraibi he found a sample that gave a clear series of rings fitting into his modern chronology and carrying it back forty years, to A.D. 1260. The log had been cut about 1370, Douglass found.

Even now, however, the modern chronology could not be linked to the prehistoric floating one. Douglass suspected that the gap was unlikely to be large. The Oraibi sample indicated that there had been a great drought late in the thirteenth century. The Mesa Verde samples revealed the thin rings of drought at their late ends. Douglass now followed a trail of archaeological clues to solve his problem. The Hopi, it was clear, had come to Oraibi at the beginning of the fourteenth century, just after the time of drought. Where had they lived previously? If the site could be found, a beam might be discovered that joined the chronologies.

Pottery led him to his answer. A comparison of pottery types showed that the Hopi migration route had passed through Arizona, and in 1929, at the small Arizona town of Showlow, Douglass drew from an ancient pueblo his missing rings. The pueblo had been destroyed by fire centuries ago, but Douglass had developed techniques for reading the tree-rings even on a bit of charred, blackened wood. One fragile, bady burned log seemed to hold the key. Douglass gave it a field label, numbering it Beam HH39, and took it to a nearby house for study. At once he recognized the now familiar rings of the fourteenth century at the outer end of the beam. He followed inward—1380, 1350, 1300. Now he came to the time of the great drought. He wrote a few months later, "Here were the very small rings that told of the hardships the tree had endured in 1299 and 1295. As we studied the rings further toward the center, 1288, 1286, 1283, and 1280 each told the same story we had found in other beams of lean years and hard living."

The drought rings continued back to 1275. Beyond them were many more rings, corresponding to the Oraibi beam. That one ended in 1260, but HH39 went on and on—1254, 1251, 1247. "Finally," Douglass wrote, "came the one at the very core, and from its central ring we learned that this charred old stick began its life as a promising upright pine, A.D. 1237, just ten years after the Sixth Crusade moved eastward to compel the Saracens to restore Jerusalem."

Late that night, under a sputtering gasoline torch, Douglass labored to link his chronologies. Beam HH39 had carried the modern chronology back twenty-three additional years, from 1260 to 1237. He turned now to the floating chronology. Its 551st ring matched perfectly with that of the ring for the year 1251 in Beam HH39. The gap no longer existed. Douglass now knew that his floating chronology began in A.D. 700, and that its final worn and defective rings actually overlapped with the earliest rings of his Oraibi beam.

Everything fell into place. His oldest Pueblo Bonito timber had been cut in 919, from a tree 219 years old. An important section of Pueblo Bonito had been built in 1067, and the pueblo still had been occupied in 1127. The ruins at Kayenta, Aztec, Mesa Verde, and elsewhere could be assigned precise and accurate dates. His discovery was a landmark in archaeology.

Dr. Andrew Douglass continued to study the tree rings for the rest of his long life. At the time of his death he had lived to see the tree-ring chronology extended back to A.D. 11. His students have successfully developed tree-ring calendars in Alaska, Turkey, and other parts of the world, but that for the American Southwest is the lengthiest and most satisfactory.

The tree rings tell a detailed story of the rise and fall of the great pueblos, and of the environmental forces that buffeted the diligent farmers who built them. In New Mexico's Chaco Canyon, for example, sprawling buildings occupy a somber desert. Between the irregular red sandstone walls of the canyon lies a broad, parched plain, more than a mile wide, sandy and forlorn. Tough, scraggly desert plants live here: sagebrush, saltbush, greasewood, rabbit brush. No trees are in sight. Tiny ground-squirrels scurry across the sand. Yet nine centuries ago this valley swarmed with busy men and women. In what is now a barren waste of sand and rock, bitterly cold in winter and fiercely hot in summer, more than a dozen great pueblos were built. A visitor in the year 1050 would have seen a lively vista: men at work in green fields of corn, women squatting before their houses and artfully shaping vessels of clay, naked children chasing one another through the broad plazas, pet dogs barking and pet turkeys gobbling. Chaco Canyon throbbed with life.

Then everything changed. The clouds no longer dropped life-giving rain. The stream that was the source of life for the Chaco folk went dry. The fields of corn shriveled. The villagers moved away. Under the merciless eye of the sun the stone buildings crumbled and collapsed and were covered with drifting heaps of hot sand. Chaco Canyon became a land of the dead, bone-dry, fit only for lizards and sagebrush.

The toppled pueblos remain as a sign of vanished greatness. Today five of the dozen most important Chaco ruins have been excavated completely or in part. The rest remain as time has left them: shapeless mounds overgrown with weeds, out of which jut leaning stone walls. Pueblo Bonito is the grandest—a breathtaking sight, even in its present ruined state. It is D-shaped, with the curving belly of the D close to the cliff wall, and the backbar looking south across the canyon. That straight south-facing wall is 518 feet long. Behind it lies a great open plaza, and beyond was the main section of the pueblo, terrace after terrace of rooms that rose in ancient times to a height of five stories. The entire pueblo covered three acres and contained some eight hundred rooms. It housed as many as twelve hundred people. For centuries Pueblo Bonito was the largest apartment house in the world; it was not surpassed until the building of the Spanish Flats in New York City in 1882. (The Spanish Flats are gone, demolished to make way for still bigger buildings. Pueblo Bonito remains.)

The oldest section of Pueblo Bonito dates from about A.D. 900. The masonry of the pueblo is of several styles, showing successive expansions; the earliest work is quite crude, but later sections are elegantly constructed, and archaeologists believe they represent the work of a distinctly different group of Anasazi who took over the existing pueblo. Tree-ring dates show that construction ended at Pueblo Bonito in 1130. A migration from the pueblo began; many upper rooms were abandoned and allowed to collapse; stubborn hangers-on inhabited the lower sections for another twenty or thirty years, and then they, too, were forced to leave.

Attacks by savage nomads probably helped to spur this migration, but the main reason for the abandonment of Pueblo Bonito seems to have been environmental. The canyon was growing dry and barren. From 1090 to 1101, the tree-rings tell us, there was one year of drought after another at Chaco. The crops withered. And the Anasazi had themselves changed the environment of Chaco Canyon for the worse. When they had arrived, thick stands of pine and fir grew in the canyon; but they had felled thousands of trees for the roof beams of Pueblo Bonito and the other huge settlements. The timber found in the pueblos showed no scars indicating that it had been cut a great distance away and hauled to Chaco Canyon. It was local wood.

When all the trees of the canyon were gone, no root systems remained to slow the rush of flood waters in the wet years. Now the spring floods came sluicing through the canyons, scouring away the fertile topsoil and exposing the bare rock below. The floods moved so swiftly through the now treeless valley that a deep arroyo, or gully, was cut. It became the only channel for the water that once had swirled over the entire canyon floor to bring life to the fields. The shrubs and grass beyond the edges of the arroyo died of thirst, and, with that ground cover gone, the flood runoff became even more violent. In dry years, no moisture; in wet years, savage floods ripping down the arroyo. Harried by nomads, bewildered by the rapid transformation of their fertile valley into a desert, the Pueblo Bonito folk moved on to other parts of the Four Corners region. Perhaps a dozen families still remained in the great pueblo by 1150, paralyzed by fear, victims of the marauders who entered Bonito again and again and escaped with corn, slaves, even the jewels that adorned the bodies of the dead.

The other pueblos of Chaco, some of them nearly as majestic as Bonito, were being abandoned too. At the height of the canyon's glory, late in the eleventh century, all these pueblos were simultaneously inhabited, giving the valley a total population of thousands. But by the middle of the twelfth century all were virtually deserted.

While the exodus from Chaco was going on, one band of Anasazi seems to have moved *into* the canyon. They came from the north, from the Mesa Verde country, and built a pueblo west of Bonito, known today by the Navaho name of Kin Kletso. It is totally unlike the other Chaco pueblos, which are large and sprawling, centering around big open plazas. There is no plaza at Kin Kletso; the building is small, compact, forbidding-looking. It has yielded tree-ring dates as late as

1178, almost half a century later than those of the neighboring pueblos. We can picture these latecomers building their town as a fortress against the nomad raiders, and settling down every night after hauling up their ladders to grant no access to the doorless walls of the ground floor. But a time came when these people had to leave Chaco too, and when they were gone, the valley fell silent.

One of the places the Chaco people went was Aztec, some sixty miles to the northeast. It is poorly named, for there never were Aztecs here; the name, born of ignorance in the nineteenth century, simply persisted until it became permanent. Aztec was built quickly, between 1110 and 1124; it is a well-planned village, three stories tall in some places, whose masonry is of the high quality associated with the latter-day work at Chaco Canyon. But the builders stayed at Aztec less than a generation; about 1130 they moved on to parts unknown. There could have been no shortage of water at Aztec, as at Chaco, so perhaps nomad raiders were to blame for the evacuation. For a full century Aztec stood abandoned, until about 1225 wanderers from the Mesa Verde area of the north moved in, rebuilt the pueblo in their own style, and occupied it until about 1300.

The record of the tree-rings shows a severe drought in the Southwest that lasted from 1276 to 1299, and this quarter century of little rain must have played its part in pushing the occupants of Aztec toward new territory. Drought alone would not have been enough to force the Anasazi from Aztec, but there were other hardships. Fire broke out in the east wing of the pueblo and destroyed many rooms. Those who were left homeless evidently preferred to migrate rather than to rebuild. The troublesome nomads assailed the village. When the people left, it was a quick departure. They sealed all doors and windows as though they planned to return someday, and wished to protect the things they were leaving behind. But no one returned until explorers found the ruins in 1859.

The great drought of the late thirteenth century had severe effects also on the major Anasazi center of Mesa Verde in the heart of the Four Corners country. This region had been occupied since Basketmaker days, and the entire sequence of Anasazi dwelling types can be seen there, from primitive pit-houses to large pueblos. While the giant buildings of Chaco Canyon were being constructed, these northern folk were erecting smaller apartment houses in somewhat the same style. And after Chaco had been abandoned, the northerners began to construct pueblos of a new type, which cannot match those of Chaco for size, but which have such otherworldly grace and splendor that they have become the most famous of Anasazi dwellings. These are the cliff-houses of Mesa Verde: castles in the sky, airy villages nestling in shallow niches high above the canyons.

Until about 1200 the Mesa Verde people lived atop their flat plateaus. Evidently under pressure of enemy attack, though, they took a drastic defensive step by moving to great high vaults in the sides of cliffs, protected by huge stone overhangs but open to the sun. These caves were not deep—it might be no more than sixty or seventy feet from the rim of a cave to the back wall—but they were so high and broad that an entire pueblo could be built in one.

So the strange and wonderful cliff-houses were built. Some were big enough to house hundreds of people; others had no more than three or four rooms. In every cranny of the Mesa Verde cliffs the new houses rose, always in hard-to-reach places whose trails needed only a few warriors to guard them. But the cliff-houses of Mesa Verde were inhabited only a short while. In one brief furious century of building, scores of the lofty, romantic dwellings were constructed, and then were abandoned. By 1300, hardly anyone remained. The Four Corners country, ancestral home of the Anasazi, was left behind, and the Old Ones headed south and east and west to new lands, new homes—some to Arizona to found the Hopi villages, others into New Mexico to settle along the valley of the Rio Grande.

Why did they leave?

Drought is one answer. The tree-ring tale is grim: almost no rain at all from 1276 to 1299. Lean harvests, springs running dry, trees withering in the canyons, and always the mocking smile of the cloudless blue sky. An entire generation was born and came to adulthood without knowing a real downpour. Farming became a grueling battle against dryness. Water had to be rationed; women now walked for miles to bring water from the nearest spring. Animals fled to greener pastures, cutting the game supply. Even the wild nuts and berries were hard to find. The men danced and chanted, begging the gods to send rain, and no rain came.

But the people of Mesa Verde had known drought before, and it had not driven them from their homes. The tree rings tell of dry spells lasting five years or more about 1170, 1218, and 1237. Why did the Anasazi leave now? Was this drought so much more terrible than those of the past?

Perhaps wandering warlike tribes were invading Mesa Verde also. The cliff-houses themselves were safe from attack, but nomads rampaging on the mesa-tops could cut the Anasazi off from their fields and springs. Archaeologists have found little evidence of actual warfare in the Mesa Verda area; but possibly the combination of drought and frequent raids convinced family after family that the gods had withdrawn their blessing from Mesa Verde, and that it was time to seek new homes. For a full generation the outward flow continued. Finally there was no one left; and the Anasazi in their new homes never reached the levels of expansion of the past, but were content to live in small villages of simple adobe houses.

Drought, which harassed and menaced the Anasazi, has never ceased to be a problem in the western United States. A vast inland area, far from any sea, depends on the uncertain mercies of the winds for its rainfall; and when the winds blow dry instead of wet, terrible hardships result.

The hardships have been compounded by man's insensitive use of his land, which increases and intensifies the effects of drought. Indiscriminate cultivation that stripped the prairie land of grass and exposed loose topsoil to wind erosion in time of drought added a dread phrase to America's vocabulary in the 1930's—"dust bowl." In that dark decade, and several times since, the wind has sent black blizzards howling over the plains.

In the middle of the nineteenth century America pushed westward from the Mississippi, evicted the Indian huntsmen of the plains, and set up homesteads from the Dakotas south to Texas. Thousands of square miles of grass-covered prairie felt the plow for the first time; and fields of wheat sprang to life where nothing useful had grown before. It was a grand and profitable accomplishment to turn the great open spaces into farmland. But the soil was thin and sandy, the weather was rarely anything but dry, and the winds were fierce.

It took a while for the full effects of land misuse to make themselves felt. Dust storms were already common in Kansas in the 1870's, but agriculture continued to expand. Such events as a plague of grasshoppers in 1892 and droughts in 1894 and 1895 checked the advance, but only temporarily. A decade of good weather brought thousands of new settlers to the plains; the sod was broken up, the grass banished. Then the dust storms began.

Over the parched earth raced the wind, picking up the topsoil and carrying it hundreds of miles, depositing it in great drifts of "black snow." Despite the dust, the farmers continued, for now World War I was bringing an enormous demand for wheat. In the flush of postwar prosperity, even more land came under the plow; and by now the best land was gone, so the new farmers worked in marginal soils of doubtful fertility. Not even the crash of 1929 slowed the expansion seriously; people still had to eat, and the effective new farm machines ripped up millions of acres in record time. Production boomed; the price of wheat fell; the farmer, to make ends meet, reached yet farther into the prairie.

In 1933 came a summer of drought. Laconic entries in the United States Weather Bureau's *Weekly Weather and Crop Bulletin* sketch the woes that followed:

"July 25, 1933: Corn needing rain badly and some greatly damaged."

"August 1, 1933: Pastures poor or dried up, cattle being

shipped out in some localities. Stock water scarce in many places."

"June 26, 1934: Needing rain badly in all parts."

"July 17, 1934: Corn stunted and burned until almost ruined. Pastures too poor to support livestock."

"August 7, 1934: Conditions worst ever known in many places. Corn not sufficient growth even for fodder in many western counties."

"November 27, 1934: Wheat fields bare in nearly all of western third."

"February 27, 1935: Severe dust storms."

Those entries refer to western Kansas, but conditions were no better elsewhere on the plains. The dust storms, at first localized, engulfed whole states.

The first sign of what was to come appeared in the Dakotas on November 12, 1933. That Sunday morning a strange wind began to blow, rushing over the surface of the dry plains and scooping topsoil up by the ton as it sped eastward. Churchgoers setting out for services stared in disbelief as the morning turned dark as night, and a choking, blinding, stinging wave of dust swept down upon them. "A wall of black appeared in the northwest," wrote Richard Cropp, a South Dakota historian. "Then it was on us. Tumbleweeds flew along like bowling balls. The air turned pitch black. Dust seemed to be everywhere."

People fled, but there was no place to hide. The dust invaded houses, cupboards, closets. Stuffing cloth around door and window frames hardly seemed to help; suffocating clouds of dust were everywhere. The drivers of automobiles, unable to see, halted their cars and huddled miserably inside. Static knocked out telephone lines; cattle were asphyxiated in the fields; when street lights came on, they provided only a faint, ghostly green glow in the darkness. The dust storm raged in the Dakotas for four hours, causing property damage in the millions of dollars. Finally the fury passed on, and the stunned residents emerged to begin the gigantic cleanup job. There was only one death in the Dakotas—a farmer killed by flying debris—but later in the day a young man in Illinois, blinded by the black pall, was killed when he stumbled into the path of a moving car. Still farther east in Chicago, the Century of Progress world's fair, scheduled to close that night, had its final festivities ruined by the dust, which sent thousands of fairgoers streaming from the midway to seek shelter, and turned the climactic display of fireworks into a dim fizzle. There was a rain of dust in Philadelphia the next night; and when an ordinary rainstorm also began, the dust came down as mud in a quantity estimated at three tons of dirt per square mile. A thin layer of grime coated much of the eastern coast afterward.

In the spring of 1934 new dust storms made the first one seem mild. Strong westerly winds picked up some 350 million tons of topsoil and distributed it over thousands of square miles from Texas to North Dakota. New York, Baltimore, and Philadelphia watched the sun disappear as though eclipsed by the airborne dust. In Washington, dust sifted into the White House and landed on the desk of President Franklin D. Roosevelt. Ships 350 miles out to sea received a dusty fallout.

The drought continued all through 1934 into 1935, and still the wind skinned away the parched soil and hurled it eastward. On the plains the farmers made dark jokes about their plight; they told of a parachutist who spent six hours shoveling his way back to the ground, and of a farmer who fainted when hit in the face by a raindrop. "It took two buckets of sand in the face to revive him," the jokesters said. But the dust storms were no joke. The dust-bowl region covered millions of acres. Livestock and crops were destroyed; some villages were buried to depths of five or six feet; farm machinery was ruined. There were 40 major dust storms in 1935, 68 in 1936, 72 in 1937. President Roosevelt ordered millions of dollars spent on drought relief; but not even the New Deal could hold back the terrible winds that knifed over the plains.

H. H. Finnell, a Department of Agriculture soil-conservation specialist, wrote, "Farmers groped through the dust for an explanation of the unprecedented scourge. The things that were blamed for it ranged all the way from plows to drought, from people to sunspots, from gas wells to sin. The suggested remedies were of an equally fantastic variety. They included such ideas as coating the soil surface with plaster of Paris, junking all one-way disk plows, depopulating the plains, damming a pond on every farm, mulching the land with crushed limestone, planting mulberry trees, irrigating all the cultivated land from wells!"

The farmers of the dust bowl could no longer remain to see if such projects would work. Six million acres of farmland had been put out of cultivation altogether by wind erosion, and 100 million additional acres could produce little more than the next season's seed. In a nation already in the grip of a financial crisis, the farmers were hardest hit. Thousands of farm families headed west to such dust-free states as Washington, Oregon, and Idaho. The population of the five plains states in the heart of the dust bowl—the Dakotas, Nebraska, Kansas, and Oklahoma—fell by a quarter of a million in the 1930's. Deserted farmhouses and nearly empty villages dotted the dust-swept prairies.

Government conservation experts, meanwhile, were studying the causes of the catastrophe. The drought alone was not to blame, they found; even in a good year there had never been very much rainfall in the dust-bowl states. The trouble had begun during the great expansion of cultivation into marginal areas. Land with thin, sandy soil, which never should have been farmed at all, had been converted from pasturage to fields; and when the grass that had held the soil in place was plowed away, the winds were free to do their work of destruction.

Millions of acres of poor land were purchased by the government, retired from cultivation, and reseeded with grass. Federal experts supervised the emergency planting of trees for windbreaks and of such crops as sorghum to hold the soil in place. Farmers were taught to leave a protective stubble of stalks and straw on their fields as cover. Contour farming was introduced to conserve water that might otherwise run off; irrigation ponds were built; the technique of strip cropping (plowing only alternate rows for planting) was established. Though rainfall continued to be subnormal, the dust storms diminished. In 1938 there were 61, 11 fewer than the year before; in 1939 there were 30; in 1940, a year of good rainfall, there were just 17. The end of the cycle came in 1945, when only one dust storm raked the plains.

But this success bred a false confidence, and the lessons of the past went unlearned. Hardly had the dust bowl of the Depression years been conquered than World War II produced new pressures for an increase in farm yield. Once again, millions of acres of submarginal land came under cultivation. The farmers of the five dust bowl states now knew how to avoid wind erosion, but in Western Texas and eastern New Mexico, Colorado, and Wyoming, crops were planted in blithe disregard of safety. There, in regions that got less than seventeen or eighteen inches of rain a year, it had previously been unprofitable even to attempt to farm; but the demand created by the war saw cotton and wheat planted in shallow clay and silty soils. And by 1947 the dust storms were beginning again. They blew yellow now, not black, for what was being carried aloft was not the rich, loamy earth of the plains but the thin soil of the arid western lands. Three dust storms in Texas and New Mexico in 1947 sounded the alarm; in 1948 there were 17 storms in the first five months alone, engulfing 3.5 million acres. Nearly all of the land affected had first been farmed in 1941 or later. In six years there had been a fourfold expansion of agriculture in the western states, but now it was time to pay the price. Once more the sky was darkened; once more good land was smothered by the eroded soil of poor land; once more it became necessary for government experts to stabilize and tend the blown-out fields.

The government, however, cannot legislate against folly. The exploitation of poor land, the destruction of soil cover, and the failure to heed the techniques of conservation continued into the 1950's. Individual farmers, recognizing the dangers of what they were doing, still hoped to squeeze one more crop and then just one more out of land that should not have been farmed at all. From 6 dust storms in 1950 the number increased to 11 in 1952, 41 in 1953, as drought years returned. H. H. Finnell, writing in 1954, declared, "The southern high plains as a whole have too high a productive potential to be abandoned as a farming region, but those who farm there will have to learn how. Nature will not be outraged with impunity. The people of the region are now talking about conservation legislation. They have done that before. Several states passed conservation laws and tested them successfully in the courts, but, when the pressure of natural emergency eased, so did the public conscience: the laws were repealed and land exploitation was resumed with the vicious result we see today. It is not law, nor incentive payments, nor more scientific information that we need. It is the will to conservation."

Today state and federal laws protect against the worst abuses of the dust-bowl era, but there is still no assurance that the skies will not go dark at midday once again. No major climatic shift brought about the disruption of thousands of lives and the loss of millions of dollars' worth of crops; it took only a few years of drought to demonstrate the hidden dangers in the great American agricultural expansion of the twentieth century.

What would be deemed a good year for rainfall in Nebraska would be considered a drought year in New York; and several successive years of below-average rainfall taught the nation's most populous area that it, too, is vulnerable to the whims of weather. It came as a rude shock to a complacent region when the water supply it had long taken for granted was suddenly threatened.

Los Angeles, which has nowhere near the amount of annual rainfall usually granted New York, made a virtue of necessity long ago in planning for its future expansion. Early in this century, while still relatively small, Los Angeles reached far upstate into the valley of the Owens River, developing an aqueduct system to meet the city's needs. By 1928, when the Owens Valley supply began to seem inadequate, Los Angeles and thirteen neighboring communities joined to form the Metropolitan Water District of Southern California and reached still farther, 392 miles away to the Colorado River. Subsequently the California city—now a giant—extended its aqueducts to the Feather River Canyon of the Sierra Nevada, 700 miles away, and expanded the Owens Valley water system. The result of all this costly construction has been to assure Los Angeles of a dependable water supply all the year round; even when two or three months go by without perceptible rain, a common event, lawns are watered, cars are washed, swimming pools are filled.

New York City, with the Hudson River at its front door and an average annual precipitation of about 45 inches, had long regarded a serious water shortage as something about as likely as an earthquake or the collision of a meteorite with the Empire State Building. Expansions of its water system into adjoining Westchester County were made slowly and only after some critical need had appeared. Not even a drought that lasted from 1929 to 1932 caused much apprehension; and when the rains failed again in the summer of 1949, the huge city was caught unprepared. Belatedly the city government urged residents to conserve water. The drought went on through 1950 and 1951, compelling the city to construct a million-gallon filtration plant near Poughkeepsie to pull water from the polluted Hudson, clean it, and inject it into the diminished reservoirs. But in 1952 the rains came again, and in a characteristic move the city dismantled the Poughkeepsie plant as though future droughts were inconceivable.

For nearly a decade New York enjoyed its customary bounty of rainfall. The emergency of 1949–50, though, had taught it to emulate the planning of Los Angeles, and so the city established a new water system that drew not on the Hudson but on the distant Delaware River. Delaware water was diverted to fill three immense reservoirs at Pepacton, Neversink, and Cannonsville, New York. This caused some uneasiness downriver, since the Delaware is the chief source of water for the Philadelphia region; and after prolonged legal maneuvers the Supreme Court ordered New York to join a Delaware River Basin Commission, made up of Pennsylvania, New Jersey, Delaware, and the United States Department of the Interior. The court ruled that New York must not divert so much water as to reduce the river flow below 1,525 cubic feet per second, which would cause salty tides from the Atlantic to move upstream and affect the water supply of the downriver cities. An official known as the rivermaster was appointed to keep watch over the activities of the various Delaware River states.

In September and October, 1961, rainfall in the Delaware Basin was less than 50 percent of normal. In only five of the next twenty-four months did precipitation reach average levels; in four of the twenty-four, precipitation was sharply below normal. By November, 1963, the cumulative deficiency was some twenty inches—nearly half of a normal year's rainfall.

The impact had been felt as early as the summer of 1962, when lawn watering in suburban regions caused a sharp drain on the reservoirs. Wells ran dry; streams shrank; rivers were sluggish. In New York City, where water consumption was running at better than 900 million gallons daily, little was done to conserve water in that first year of the drought. The city administration assumed that everything would return to normal in a few months. Some conservationists suggested that the residents of New York's apartment houses be given individual water meters, so that they would have some financial motivation for cutting down on usage; but it was considered both costly and politically unwise to change the existing system, whereby the landlords of apartment houses purchase water at a low flat rate and include the cost in rent, leading tenants to believe water is "free."

The unusually dry April of 1963 saw forest fires breaking out over a wide area. The drought now covered the entire Northeast, and by mid-June farmers were applying for federal crop-disaster assistance. With New York City making heavy diversions of water from the Delaware, salt began to creep upriver from the sea. The combined effect of the drought and New York's diversion was considerable: the Delaware's flow in October, 1963, was the least of any October in fifty years of record.

Under the terms of the court order, New York was releasing enough water from its reservoirs into the Delaware to keep the river flow at the stipulated minimum. Heavy rains in November, 1963, and January, 1964, aroused some hopes that the drought had been broken; but as spring came, rainfall dwindled. The Northeast was drier than ever, and but for the releasing of reservoir water, the flow of the Delaware that November would have been 27 percent less than the previous record low flow of 1915. Eventually things grew so critical that New York City halted its releasing of water altogether. This caused justifiable outrage in the downriver cities of the Delaware Basin, who saw no reason why the political timidities of New York City's mayor should be allowed to deprive them of their water supply. They pointed out that New Yorkers still were encouraged to squander water by getting it without metering, whereas their own residents had meters; they accused New York of failing to do anything about leaks in its water system, which were wasting an estimated 200 million gallons a day; and they protested the violation of the Delaware River agreement.

The flow of the Delaware now was 943 cubic feet a second lower than the court-decreed minimum. A salt front was advancing up the river at 3,000 feet a day. Farmers in southern New Jersey faced the threat of salt entering their fields. Industrial plants, unable to use the corrosive ocean water, were forced to buy water from private sources. Under severe pressure from the Delaware River Basin Commission, New York agreed to open its dams once more and let water into the river; but by then the reservoirs were so depleted that the releases did not bring the flow gauge up to minimum. Only the timely arrival of rain in the summer of 1965 stopped the advance of the Atlantic after the salt water had traveled ninety miles from the river's mouth. By then, the cumulative deficiency of rainfall since the beginning of the drought in late 1961 was thirty-eight inches—almost an entire year's supply.

The drought went on, with only occasional interruptions. In New York City, harsh conservation measures were finally put into effect. The city had already taken the quaint step of requesting restaurants not to serve water except on request, but now it instituted strict controls on watering of lawns and washing of cars, and made an effort to patch the leaks in its antiquated system of mains. The Hudson River pumping plant near Poughkeepsie was hastily rebuilt, and millions of gallons of questionable water were filtered and put into the reservoirs.

This proved to be necessary only for a short while. In 1967, the rain-delivering westerlies, which had unaccountably shifted their path so as to dump into the Atlantic the rain normally destined for the Northeast, returned to their accustomed routes. A cold, rainy spring was followed by an extraordinarily rainy summer. New York newspapers ceased running the disquieting graphs that showed the daily drop in reservoir levels; by mid-year the reservoirs were full and the region was beginning to shake off the effects of its ordeal of dryness. Whether the above-normal precipitation of 1967 represents a true breaking of the drought, or is only an interruption in a newly established pattern of aridity in the Northeast, is something that will not become apparent for several years. But the great northeastern drought—already only a fading memory for millions of people—served as an ominous reminder of our vulnerability. Despite our amazing technological advances, despite the power and richness of our society, we are still dependent on the forces of nature. The experience was humbling and instructive. Such ingenious peoples as the Nabataeans and the Hohokam Indians, accepting an environmental challenge far more drastic than anything that New York faced, applied their energies to the problem and triumphed over it. But amid all its plenty the mightiest city of the modern world nearly let itself run dry, for lack of proper planning and in the irresponsible assumption that heaven's rains are as immutable as sunrise and sunset.

10

Tomorrow's Climate

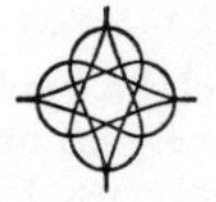

"EVERYBODY TALKS ABOUT THE WEATHER," MARK TWAIN IS supposed to have said, "but nobody does anything about it."

That was scarcely true in Mark Twain's time, and is even less the case today. For thousands of years people have been doing something about the weather, or trying to; the trouble is that very little that has been done has had any discernible effect. From primitive witch doctors to giant modern corporations and instrumentalities of the United States Government, weather-modification schemes of every conceivable kind have been tried. The results thus far have been indifferent.

The main concern of the weather changers has been rainmaking, for rain is essential to agriculture. Virtually every culture except those of the rainy tropics has had its rain ritual, and rainmaking has been deemed the responsibility of the tribe's most skilled holy men. Most accounts of life among the American Indians describe the conjuring up of rainfall, as in this description of the Mandan Indian rain ceremony written in 1845 by John Frost:

> It was in a time of great drought that I once arrived at the Mandan village on the upper Missouri. The young and the old were crying out that they should have no green corn. After a day or two the sky grew a little cloudy in the west, when the medicine men assembled together in great haste to make it

> rain. The tops of the wigwams were soon crowded. In the mystery lodge a fire was kindled, around which sat the rain-makers, burning sweet-smelling herbs, smoking the medicine pipe and calling on the Great Spirit to open the door of the skies to let out the rain. At last one of the rain-makers came out of the mystery lodge and stood on the top of it with a spear in his hand, which he brandished about in a commanding and threatening manner, lifting it up as though he were about to hurl it at the heavens. He talked loud of the power of his medicine, holding up his medicine bag in one hand and his spear in the other; but it was of no use, and he came down in disgrace. For several days the same ceremony continued, until a rain-maker, with a head-dress of the skins of birds, ascended the top of the mystery lodge, with a bow in his hand and a quiver at his back. He made a long speech, for the sky was growing dark, and it required no great knowledge of the weather to foretell rain. He shot arrows to the sunrise and sun-down points of the heavens, and also to the north and south, in honor of the Great Spirit, who could send rain from all parts of the sky. A fifth arrow he retained until it was almost certain that rain was at hand. Then, sending up the shaft from his bow with all his might, to make a hole in the dark cloud over his head, he cried aloud for the waters to pour down at his bidding and to drench him to the skin. He was brandishing his bow in one hand and his medicine in the other, when the rain came down in torrents.

This bit of transparent mummery, like most others of its kind, needs no scientific explanation; but somewhat more puzzling is the snake dance of the Hopi Indians, which is performed in late summer, when the corn stands tall and one last heavy downpour is needed to see the crops safely through the harvest time. The men of certain secret societies seclude themselves for days, pray, and go forth to gather desert snakes. The serpents are brought to the *kiva,* the sacred headquarters of the secret society; there may be as many as a hundred of them, tangling and twining on the kiva floor—gopher snakes, bull snakes, sidewinders, rattlers. Usually most of them are rattlers. On the proper day the men of the secret societies, their bodies painted, emerge from the kivas and enter the pueblo's plaza. They dance about it, carrying the deadly snakes. The dance goes on and on, until every snake has been danced with. Some of the dancers are bitten—for, though they hold the snakes behind the head in a position that keeps them from striking, now and then a snake twists free and sinks its fangs into the body of the man who holds it. A dancer may stagger in pain and seem to lose consciousness as he is bitten; but he recovers, regains his stride, and continues to dance. Some say that the snakes have had their venom sacs removed before the dance. Others claim that during their captivity in the kiva, the snakes are allowed to strike at small animals, exhausting their poison before the ceremony. Another theory is that the dancers condition themselves by taking small doses of venom regularly. The Hopi themselves provide no explanation, nor do they allow white men to examine the snakes. Many dancers have been bitten, but no dancer has been known to die from the bite.

When each snake has been carried around the plaza, a group of women makes a circle of cornmeal into which the serpents are thrust. Then a signal is given, and the dancers rush forward. Each gathers up as many snakes as he can hold. Off they run, down the trail that leads from the village to the desert. They carry the snakes to the four quarters of the compass and release them. "Elder brothers," they chant, "crawl down in your holes to the underworld and ask the rain gods to have mercy."

At sunset the men return to the pueblo. The snake dance is over. The skies open, and torrents of rain descend. The dance almost always brings rain, usually within a few hours after the last snakes have been released, a fact that perplexes skeptics each year. In those rare years when rain does not come immediately, it means that some dancer has failed to observe the right ritual, or that there is wickedness in the pueblo.

Indians who have become Christians have likewise sought the intervention of the Deity in meteorological matters. A nineteenth-century account published in the *New York Tribune* provides this list of decrees promulgated by the mayor of a drought-stricken Mexican town:

> "Considering that the Supreme Creator has not behaved well in this province, as in the whole of last year only one shower of rain fell; that in this summer, notwithstanding all the processions, prayers and praises, it has not rained at all, and

consequently the crops of Castañas, on which depend the prosperity of the whole department, are entirely ruined, it is decreed:

"Article 1. If within the peremptory period of eight days from the date of this decree rain does not fall abundantly, no one will go to mass or say prayers.

"Article 2. If the drought continues eight days more, the churches and chapels shall be burned, and missals, rosaries, and other objects of devotion will be destroyed.

"Article 3. If, finally, in a third period of eight days it shall not rain, all the priests, friars, nuns, and saints, male and female will be beheaded. And for the present permission is given for the commission of all sorts of sin, in order that the Supreme Creator may understand with whom he has to deal."

The most remarkable feature if this affair is the fact that four days after these resolutions were passed the heaviest rainfall known for years was precipitated on the burning community.

More scientific, though evidently less effective, was the approach toward rainmaking taken by the pioneering American meteorologist, James Pollard Espy (1785–1860). Espy, who helped to organize the United States Weather Bureau, was the first to suggest (in 1830) that there was a connection between convection—the rising of warm air—and the condensation of atmospheric vapor into rain. Though he was unable to explain the mechanism by which condensation took place, he suggested in his *Philosophy of Storms* in 1841 that rain might be induced by setting great fires to heat the air, and in 1845 offered this proposal in an open letter addressed "To the Friends of Science":

Let masses of timber to the amount of forty acres for every twenty miles be prepared and fired simultaneously every seven days in the summer, on the west of the United States, in a line of six or seven hundred miles long from north to south; then the following results seem highly probable, but not certain until the experiment is made: A rain of great length north and south will commence near or on the line of fires; this rain will travel eastward; it will not break up till it reaches far into the Atlantic ocean; it will rain only a short time in any one place; it will not rain again until the next seventh day; it will rain enough and not too much in any one place; it will not be attended with violent wind, neither on land nor on the Atlantic

> ocean; there will be no hail nor tornadoes at the time of the general rain nor intermediate; there will be no destructive floods, nor will the waters ever become very low; there will be no more oppressive heats nor injurious colds; the farmers and mariners will always know before the rains when they will commence and when they will terminate; all epidemic diseases originating from floods and subsequent droughts will cease; the proceeds of agriculture will be greatly increased, and the health and happiness of the citizens will be much promoted. These, I say, are the *probable*—not certain—results of the plan proposed—a plan which could be carried into operation for a sum which would not amount to half a cent a year to each individual in the United States. . . .

In case this plan should seem too grandiose a beginning, Espy also offered a trial scheme by which fires would be lit in four ten-acre lots every seven days in each of ten counties along the Alleghany Mountains in Pennsylvania, Maryland, and Virginia. However, it seems that even this lesser project never underwent a test.

A civil engineer named Edward Powers concluded from a study of military history that rainfall often occurs after great battles, and in 1871 published a small book called *War and the Weather, or the Artificial Production of Rain,* in which he argued that the detonation of explosives can stimulate precipitation. Most copies of Powers's book were destroyed in the Chicago fire of 1871, but he was able to win the support of the influential Senator Farwell, who in 1874 petitioned Congress for an appropriation to underwrite Powers' experiments. Not until 1890 did Senator Farwell squeeze some money from his fellow legislators; he obtained $2000 and then $7000 more, but the man chosen to carry out the study was not Powers but a certain R. G. Dyrenforth. Dyrenforth made his experiments in Texas and near Washington, D. C., in 1891. Setting off explosions on the ground and in airborne balloons, he created a great deal of noise and also, according to the report he filed with Congress in 1892, produced some rain. Dyrenforth declared "that when a moist cloud is present, which, if undisturbed, would pass away without precipitating its moisture, the jarring of the cloud by concussions will cause the particles of moisture in suspension to agglomerate and fall in greater or less quantity, according to the degree of moistness of the air in and beneath the cloud." He added that "storm conditions may be generated and rain be induced" even under unfavorable conditions for precipitation, but that in such cases there would be "a wasteful expenditure of both time and material."

On the strength of this, Congress appropriated another $10,-000, of which Dyrenforth spent $4,913.59 on additional experiments. But nothing further was heard of the success of his research.

Louis Gathman of Chicago also used explosive concussion in his method of making rain, described in his little book of 1891, *Rain Produced at Will.* Gathman obtained a patent on a process of chilling the atmosphere suddenly by spraying it with liquid carbonic acid. He asserted that he had caused a cloud "visible for miles" to form in a clear sky by firing an explosive shell loaded with carbonic acid to a height of six hundred feet, and that even better results might be obtained by carrying the shell "into the upper regions of the atmosphere" aboard a balloon, with the explosion caused "by an electric current controlled by persons upon the earth." Carbon dioxide, he wrote, "is liberated in the upper regions of the atmosphere and will, of course, instantly evaporate and spread out in a sheet of vapor of an extremely low temperature and produce a cloud. The surrounding atmosphere will be chilled by its proximity to the cold vapor and the moisture in the atmosphere will be condensed thereby. The condensation takes place in large quantities and with great rapidity, so that a cloud is formed that will precipitate a rainfall upon the earth." Gathman estimated that the work cost $30 to $90 per square mile, and claimed, "I can produce rain whenever necessary or at will." This boast was not confirmed by later results.

These early rain-makers, working in virtual ignorance of nature's own methods, were not much better off than the Indian medicine men. The present theory of the rainfall mechanism was not proposed until 1935, when the Swedish meteorologist Tor Bergeron published his startling idea that most rain begins as snow. His hypothesis was later expanded by a German physicist, Walter Findeisen, and as the Bergeron-Findeisen theory has won wide acceptance in the scientific world.

The theory attempts to explain what causes water vapor to condense and fall. Water, in the form of invisible vapor held in the atmosphere, hovers overhead in immense quantities, of which we are aware only when precipitation begins. A seventh of an inch of rain spread over 120 square miles brings a fall of a million tons of water, virtually all of it condensed from vapor during the rainstorm. This water is released when the atmosphere chills, for warm air has a much greater capacity than cold to hold vapor; this capacity is halved with each drop of 20° in temperature, which is why summers tend to be far more humid than winters. As air cools through rising, the water vapor it holds begins to coalesce into tiny droplets, too light to fall, which drift along in the form of clouds. And under certain circumstances the droplets come together until a million or more of them comprise a single raindrop, heavy enough for gravity to pull down to the ground.

What circumstances cause the droplets to form and then to collect into drops large enough to fall?

It was found that drifting foreign particles in the atmosphere attract water vapor and serve as condensation nuclei about which droplets can form. Salt crystals evaporated from ocean spray thrown into the air are among the most common condensation nuclei; dust particles and the pollutants given off by fires, automobile exhausts, or factories are other important classes of nuclei. Molecules of water in the clouds gather around nuclei and condense into droplets. Though the temperature at which this takes place is often less than 32° F., these minute droplets of pure water do not ordinarily freeze, but remain liquid in what is called a "supercooled" state; such droplets, it has been shown, can remain supercooled and liquid down to —40° F.

But a few ice crystals do form in the clouds, Bergeron observed, and these drift through the supercooled cloud with its billions of watery droplets. An ice crystal near a group of droplets will induce evaporation of the droplets; once more in vapor form, the water molecules leave their original condensation nucleus and rapidly condense on the ice crystal. It grows larger, expanding the zone of evaporation around it, and within a few minutes it is a snowflake heavy enough to begin its descent from the atmosphere. As it falls, the snowflake collides with more droplets and collects them also. If the temperature is above the freezing point as the snowflake nears the ground, the flake will melt and become a raindrop. If the air is cold all the way down, snow will result; and such intermediate forms as hail and sleet result from more complex atmospheric conditions on the way down.

The Bergeron-Findeisen theory of condensation of droplets around ice crystals did not explain the heavy precipitation in the tropics, where cloud temperatures are ordinarily well above freezing. A separate mechanism was needed here. In equatorial latitudes where the atmosphere is warm, convective currents are strong, causing an energetic churning of cloud droplets. Most of the droplets are large, since they have as their nuclei salt crystals from ocean evaporation, and salt crystals provide larger nuclei than dust or other foreign matter in the air. Collisions are frequent among these big droplets, and as they collide they coalesce until they reach raindrop size and begin to fall.

The ice-crystal theory of rain led to the first scientific and reasonably effective method of rainmaking: the artificial seeding of supercooled clouds with solid carbon dioxide ("dry ice"). In one of the most famous experiments in the history of meteorology, Vincent J. Schaefer of the General Electric Research Laboratory dropped six pounds of dry ice into a cloud over New England on November 13, 1946, and caused snow flurries over four miles.

Schaefer, research assistant to G.E.'s Nobel Prize laureate chemist, Irving Langmuir, had been involved in wartime in an attempt to create artificial fog to hide troop movements. In the course of this work he learned of the Bergeron-Findeisen theory, and of Findeisen's suggestion that introducing ice crystals into a supercooled cloud might cause precipitation. Actually, a Dutch experimenter named August Veraart had dropped dry ice into clouds from an airplane as early as 1930, with showers following, but he had lacked the financial resources to continue his research. Schaefer and Langmuir had the enormous wealth of General Electric behind them as they carried out laboratory work with dry ice and a deep-freeze unit, and then tested their ideas in the atmosphere.

While Langmuir watched from the ground, Schaefer dumped the dry ice into a carefully selected supercooled cloud. The dry ice, at a temperature more than 100° below zero, cut through the cloud, creating long tunnels of great cold, along which the cloud vapor was instantly converted to ice crystals. Snowflakes swiftly formed and went fluttering to the ground in the wake of the plane.

Shortly another G.E. researcher, Bernard Vonnegut, found a second material that could be used for cloud-seeding: silver-iodide particles, which are similar in structure to ice crystals and can act as nuclei in supercooled clouds. Silver iodide did not have to be dropped from a plane; cloud-seeding could be accomplished from the ground by burning silver iodide at high temperatures and allowing the particles to escape into the atmosphere.

The initial reaction to these cloud-seeding projects was a general overrating of their effectiveness. Hundreds of free-lance rain-makers went into business, and found enthusiastic buyers for their services among farmers and ranchers. Suddenly the air was full of dry ice and silver iodide as rainmaking work began over millions of acres. Schaefer himself declared, "I think we know enough that eventually we can do anything we want to with the weather," and Vonnegut said, "I feel with almost 100 percent certainty that cloud seeding can be of enormous value to our country."

Early reports seemed to confirm these high hopes. News of greatly increased precipitation in seeded areas came from Colorado, Arizona, and Oregon. The rainmakers were unable to handle all the assignments offered them.

This early rush of optimism was accomplished by fears of the effects of too-successful rainmaking. If cloud-seeding caused rain to fall over Iowa that would otherwise have landed on the fields of Illinois, did Illinois have a valid grievance? Senator

Clinton Anderson of New Mexico declared, "We are going to need policemen in the skies to see that some state doesn't steal another's weather." In New York State, lawsuits asking total damages of $2,138,000 were filed against New York City after that city had made cloud-seeding experiments in an attempt to end its 1950 drought. Cities near New York objected that the metropolis was obtaining more than its fair share of the region's water through such practices, while the owner of a summer resort in the Catskills argued that the artificially induced rain was hurting his business. The claim was denied as Justice Ferdinand Pecora ruled that "the remote possibility of inconvenience to plaintiff's resort and its guests must be balanced against the problem of maintaining and supplying the inhabitants of the city of New York and surrounding areas, with a population of about ten million, with an adequate supply of pure and wholesome water. The relief which plaintiff asks is opposed to the general welfare and the public good; and the dangers which plaintiff apprehends are purely speculative. . . ." But in Texas a court granted an injunction against farmers who are trying to suppress hail by silver-iodide seeding, in favor of neighboring ranchers who wanted precipitation in any form, including hail. (It was thought that overseeding a cloud would *prevent* precipitation, particularly in the form of hail.)

Nearly two dozen states have enacted weather-control legislation as a result of these and other disputes. The first of these laws was passed by Wyoming in February, 1951; Colorado, Arizona, Utah, and California followed within a few months, and others later. Most of the weather-control laws required cloud-seeders to be licensed, and some require proof of financial responsibility in the event damage claims arise.

However, out of the welter of optimistic claims and angry accusations that marked the beginning of cloud-seeding there developed the disquieting awareness that the new rainmaking process was not the miracle-worker it was thought to be. The Weather Bureau, the Air Force, and the National Advisory Committee for Aeronautics inaugurated a lengthy series of cloud-seeding experiments in various parts of the United States, and after 170 tests concluded that when the method was applied to certain types of clouds, "dissipation rather than new development was the general rule. There is no indication that seeding will initiate self-propagating storms, and therefore the only precipitation that can be extracted from a cloud is that contained within the cloud itself. The methods are certainly not promising for the relief of drought."

This turned out to be somewhat too pessimistic a verdict. Later research under the auspices of the National Academy of Sciences showed, according to a report released in 1964, that there was "some evidence for precipitation increases of as much as 10 or even 20 per cent over areas as large as 1,000 square miles from weeks to years" as a result of cloud-seeding. Nevertheless, the NAS panel noted, cloud-seeding was effective only under particularly favorable conditions; and in the worst droughts, where no clouds are available for seeding, artificial rainmaking methods are useless at present.

Studies are continuing, both in the United States and in a number of other countries, into the value of cloud-seeding with silver iodide or dry ice. Techniques have been developed with varying degrees of success for increasing or diminishing rainfall in a given region, for suppressing hail, and for dissipating fog. A great deal has been accomplished, but even the most partisan supporter of weather modification work admits that we are still in the earliest stages of our ability to adjust our climate to our needs.

Far more ambitious programs of weather modification, at present purely in the realm of science fiction, have been proposed by some far-seeing scientists. Many of these ideas deal with thawing out the Arctic, which would create ice-free northern harbors, shorten the sea journey between Atlantic and Pacific ports by thousands of miles, and give New York, London, and Moscow a much balmier climate. Dr. Harry Wexler of the United States Weather Bureau has suggested doing this by setting off ten ten-megaton hydrogen bombs beneath the surface of the Arctic Ocean. The resulting blast would throw a cloud of steam high into the atmosphere; the cloud would condense into ice crystals, and a blanket of icy fog would form, preventing the escape of heat from the Arctic by infrared radiation. A similar scheme, offered by the American meteorologist J. O. Fletcher, involves detonating twenty-five evenly spaced one-megaton H-bombs around the perimeter of the Arctic ice pack in the spring. The great waves thus created would break up the ice, induce melting, and set in motion a chain of events leading to the disappearance of the entire polar icecap.

Altering the albedo, or reflectivity, of that icecap is another method sometimes suggested for improving the Arctic climate. At present the polar ice has an albedo of almost 100 percent, so that virtually all the solar energy reaching it is reflected back to space. By laying down a thin coating of soot, carbon-black, or black plastic sheeting, the capacity of the Arctic to absorb this energy would be greatly enhanced. Certain practical problems stand in the way of doing this, though: to lay a .004-inch-thick coating of carbon-black over the area extending from the North Pole to 65°N. would take 1.5 billion tons of carbon dust. If C-124 Globemaster transports with a carrying capacity of ten tons were used for the job, they would have to fly 150 million sorties. "This," one scientist notes, "would take considerable time."

In 1959 the Soviet scientist P. M. Borisov proposed building a dam across the 56-mile-wide Bering Strait. Nuclear power would be used to pump cold Arctic Ocean water through the dam into the Pacific, while warm Atlantic water would be admitted to temper the harsh climate of the Far North. A year later, another Russian scientist pointed out that even a slight warming of the Arctic would drastically alter precipitation patterns and turn most of the Soviet Union into a desert. And according to the Ewing-Donn theory of glaciation, it was precisely such a thawing of the Arctic by warm Atlantic water that brought on the ice ages; an ice-free Arctic Ocean would moisten the air and cause a great increase in precipitation, which would come down on land as snow and build up into glaciers.

Other grandiose climate-modification plans have the same flaw: the difficulty of predicting, on the basis of our present imperfect meteorological theories, what the actual effect of a large-scale alteration of the environment might be. Tampering with the delicate balance of climate could have unforeseen results thousands of miles away. Projects for diverting ocean currents, for rearranging the path of the winds, for moderating tropical storms by coating large areas of the ocean with an evaporation-reducing sealant, have all aroused fears of unknown side effects. Measures taken to reduce drought in the Dakotas might bring floods to Louisiana; the Sahara might be made to bloom at the cost of turning Italy and France into deserts; meddling with the polar icecaps could drown thousands of miles of coastal land, bring on a new ice age, or rob temperate-zone areas of their normal rainfall. Undoubtedly attempts will be made in the future to seize control of the climate in some fashion deemed fantastic today, but those attempts are best postponed until we are more certain of the consequences of our acts.

We may already be altering our climate unintentionally, irreversibly, and perhaps dangerously by our own unchecked industrial expansion. The peril lies in the "greenhouse effect" of atmospheric carbon dioxide, which admits solar heat and traps it by blocking the outward radiation of long-wave infrared. The amount of CO_2 in the atmosphere is minute: only .003 percent. But it is growing rapidly. Some ten thousand times that quantity of CO_2 was locked up long ago in the "fossil fuels"—coal, oil, natural gas—that were created by the decay of organic matter. We are now busily unlocking that treasurehouse of energy, and our rate of consumption is rising from year to year, with the liberation of CO_2 rising in proportion.

Between 1860 and 1959, the combustion of coal and other fossil fuels released an amount of CO_2 equal to 14 percent of the total already in the atmosphere. Some of this was absorbed by the oceans; the rest remained in the air. By 1960, the quantity of atmospheric CO_2 was about 7 percent greater than it had been in the middle of the nineteenth century. This is only an approximate figure, for nineteenth-century estimates of the composition of the atmosphere were not as accurate as those that can be made today; but with the aid of new measuring devices, some highly precise and disquieting figures for recent years have come forth. Between 1958 and 1962, the CO_2 content of the atmosphere grew by 1.15 percent. During those five years, 53 billion tons of CO_2 were liberated through the combustion of coal, petroleum, natural gas, and other fuels, and about 26 billion tons remained in the atmosphere. Today some 6 billion tons of CO_2 are being added yearly to the atmosphere, according to one estimate; another figure places the amount at well over 7 billion. This does not include the 650 million tons a year of CO_2 given off by human breathing alone.

The human population is increasing steadily, and energy consumption is rising at a much faster rate. We will shortly be liberating some 12 billion tons of CO_2 a year. Even allowing for the rapid growth of thermonuclear electric generation, which does not produce CO_2, it has been estimated by the Harvard oceanographer Roger Revelle that by A.D. 2000 there will be 25 percent more CO_2 in the atmosphere than in the nineteenth century. Revelle believes that this will increase global mean temperatures by 1.2° F. Gilbert Plass of Johns Hopkins University has calculated that if CO_2 production continues at the present accelerating rate of increase, the world's temperature will rise by about 2° F. each hundred years.

In not very many centuries, this would be sufficient to melt the polar icecaps, raise sea level by as much as two hundred feet, and swamp all low-lying land. Our entire planet would return to the steamy, tropical conditions of Carboniferous times. Long before then, however, profound climatic effects would have been felt, such as shifts in the rainfall belts or oceanic currents, or other consequences impossible to predict. Revelle suggests that countermeasures may be necessary to prevent major upheavals of civilized life. As an example he offers raising the earth's albedo, which could be brought about, he says, "by spreading very small reflecting particles over large oceanic areas. The particles should be sufficiently buoyant so that they will remain close to the sea surface, and they should have high reflectivity, so that even a partial covering of the surface would be adequate to produce a marked change in the amount of reflected sunlight. A fine powder of latex or of a light-colored opaque plastic, dispersed by a machine something like the smoke generators used in World War II, might do the job very well. Rough estimates indicate that enough particles to cover a square mile effectively could be produced for perhaps $100. A 1 per cent change in reflectivity might be brought about for about $500 million a year. . . ."

Another way in which man is inadvertently modifying his climate is through the growth of cities. Paved streets and compactly arrayed houses absorb energy and store it, so that cities are warmer than their surrounding suburbs. Cities generate tremendous quantities of heat both in winter and in summer, when air conditioners pump hot air from houses as they cool the interior. Cities get less sunlight than the country, because of the pall of dust and smoke and other pollutants hovering over them; but they receive more rain, since those pollutants act as condensation nuclei. Helmut E. Landsberg of the University of Maryland has calculated that cities in the middle latitudes receive 15 percent less sunshine on horizontal surfaces than in surrounding rural areas, 5 percent less ultraviolet radiation in summer, and 30 percent less in the winter. The city has a 6 percent lower annual mean relative humidity than the country, 10 percent more precipitation, 10 percent more cloudiness, 25 percent lower mean annual wind speed, and 30 percent more fog in summer, 100 percent more in winter. As urbanization spreads, these statistics will take on more meaning; and when unbroken strips of urbanized areas stretch for hundreds of miles, as will be the case in another few decades, sweeping changes in patterns of temperature and precipitation may result. It is a measure of the difficulty in predicting climatic trends that there is no agreement on the nature of these changes. Some climatologists hold that increasing urbanization will reinforce the effects of increasing atmospheric carbon dioxide and hasten the tropicalization of the world. Others point to the dust clouds hovering over our cities and say that air pollution will bring lower temperatures by blocking sunlight, while a third group maintains that the two effects will cancel one another out and leave the world's climate much as it is now.

Throughout his history, man has been at the mercy of his environment, and that is nearly as true today as in the years when glaciers forced our remote ancestors to flee from Europe. Our formidable technological skill has to some degree freed us from the challenge of climate; we can heat our homes in winter, cool them in summer, dam mighty rivers to ensure a reliable water supply, and even bring rain down from the sky. Yet we still must beware of flood, drought, storm; our mighty cities can be paralyzed by a few inches of snow; we have no assurance that sweeping and fundamental changes in local climate will not render whole regions unviable, as has happened in the past.

We have been shaped in many ways by climate, and we have by no means established our independence from those shaping forces yet. A century from now, we may be the shapers, and climate will serve our whims. As we move outward into the inhospitable worlds of the universe, we may transform planet after planet into Eden. Yet the possibility also exists that in tampering with our environment we may bring calamity down upon ourselves, and find ourselves faced with so drastic a reorganization of that environment that our proud civilization will be destroyed.

A third alternative exists: that we will abolish climate altogether, and live apart from its fluctuations. The visionary engineer R. Buckminster Fuller is the prophet of that new age, with his ambitious schemes for domed cities, insulated against the outer world's weather. "The domes over our cities," Fuller wrote in 1967, "will be so high and their structural members so delicate as to be nearly invisible. They will bring shadow when shadow is desirable and sun when sun is desirable, always keeping out rain, snow and storms as well as exterior industrial fumes, while collecting rain water in reservoirs. The temperature inside the domes will be so stabilized that a semitropical atmosphere will exist. Inasmuch as there will be no rain or snow, people will live in garden-terrace skyscrapers, with screening only for privacy."

Perhaps that dream will be transmuted into reality sooner than we expect. I think, though, that something vital and integral will go out of human existence if we free ourselves to that extent from the vagaries of our environment. From the first fur cloak to the latest thing in heat pumps, man has bent much of his ingenuity toward the task of meeting environmental challenges, and on the whole the results have been impressive. But who can foresee the effects if that shaping force were to be removed entirely? It was not while he dwelled in Eden, but after his expulsion from paradise, that man's climb to greatness began.

Bibliography

Author's Note: As I was nearing the completion of this book most of my notes and source materials were destroyed by fire. I have tried to reconstruct the bibliography as completely as possible, but I ask the reader's indulgence for any omissions that may exist.

BACON, EDWARD, ED., *Vanished Civilizations.* New York, McGraw-Hill, Inc., 1963.

BALK, ALFRED, "When the Wind Blew Black Blizzards." *New York Times Magazine* (November 10, 1963).

BATES, MARSTON, *Where Winter Never Comes.* New York, Charles Scribner's Sons, 1963.

BIBBY, GEOFFREY, *The Testimony of the Spade.* New York, Alfred A. Knopf, Inc., 1956.

BRAIDWOOD, ROBERT, "The Agricultural Revolution." *Scientific American,* Vol. 203, No. 3 (September, 1960).

BROECKER, WALLACE S., "Absolute Dating and the Astronomical Theory of Glaciation." *Science,* Vol. 151, No. 3708 (January 21, 1966).

BROOKS, C. E. P., *Climate Through the Ages.* New York, McGraw-Hill, Inc., 1949.

——— *The Evolution of Climate.* New York, R. V. Coleman, 1922.

BROTHWELL, DON, AND HIGGS, ERIC, EDS. *Science in Archaeology.* New York, Basic Books, 1963.

BRYSON, REID A., "Is Man Changing the Climate of Earth?" *Saturday Review* (April 1, 1967).

BULLARD, FRED M., *Volcanoes.* Austin, Texas, University of Texas Press, 1962.

BUTZER, KARL W., *Environment and Archaeology.* London, Methuen & Co., Ltd., 1965.

CARRINGTON, RICHARD, *A Biography of the Sea.* New York, Basic Books, 1960.

CARSON, RACHEL, *The Sea Around Us.* New York, Oxford University Press, 1950.

CHANG, JEN-HU, "The Indian Summer Monsoon." *The Geographical Review,* Vol. 57, No. 3 (July, 1967).

CHILDE, V. GORDON, *Man Makes Himself.* New York, New American Library, 1951.

——— *New Light on the Most Ancient East; The Oriental Prelude to European Prehistory.* New York, Appleton-Century, 1934.

——— *What Happened in History.* Harmondsworth, England, Penguin Books, 1942.

CLARK, J. D., "The Later Pleistocene Cultures of Africa." *Science,* Vol. 150, No. 3698 (November 12, 1965).

COON, CARLETON S., "Climate and Race," in Harlow Shapley, ed., *Climatic Change.* Cambridge, Harvard University Press, 1954.

——— *The Origin of Races.* New York, Alfred A. Knopf, Inc., 1962.

COWEN, ROBERT C., *Frontiers of the Sea.* Garden City, New York, Doubleday & Company, Inc., 1960.

CURRY, J.C., "Climate and Migrations." Washington, D. C., Smithsonian Institution Annual Report, 1929.

DABBS, JACK A., *History of the Discovery and Exploration of Chinese Turkestan.* The Hague, Netherlands, Mouton, 1963.

DALES, GEORGE F., "The Decline of the Harappans." *Scientific American,* Vol. 214, No. 5 (May, 1966).

DARLING, FRASER, AND MILTON, JOHN P., EDS., *Future Environ-*

ments of North America. New York, Natural History Press, 1966.

DEEVEY, EDWARD S., JR., "Bogs." *Scientific American,* Vol. 199, No. 4 (October, 1958).

DUNBAR, CARL O., *The Earth.* Cleveland and New York, The World Publishing Company, 1966.

DYSON, JAMES L., *The World of Ice.* New York, Alfred A. Knopf, Inc., 1962.

EMERY, K. O., "Sea Levels 7,000 to 20,000 Years Ago." *Science,* Vol. 157, No. 3789 (August 11, 1967).

EMERY, W. B., *Archaic Egypt.* Harmondsworth, England, Penguin Books, 1961.

EMILIANI, CESARE, "Ancient Temperatures." *Scientific American,* Vol. 198, No. 2 (February, 1958).

ERICSON, DAVID B., AND WOLLIN, GOESTA, *The Deep and the Past.* New York, Alfred A. Knopf, Inc., 1964.

EVENARI, MICHAEL, AND KELLER, DOV, "Ancient Masters of the Desert," *Scientific American,* Vol. 194, No. 4 (April, 1956).

FAIRSERVIS, WALTER A., *The Ancient Kingdoms of the Nile.* New York, Thomas Y. Crowell, 1962.

FINNELL, H. H., "The Dust Storms of 1948." *Scientific American,* Vol. 179, No. 2 (August, 1948).

——— "The Dust Storms of 1954." *Scientific American,* Vol. 191, No. 1 (July, 1954).

FITCH, JAMES M., AND BRANCH, DANIEL P., "Primitive Architecture." *Scientific American,* Vol. 203, No. 6 (December, 1960).

FREEMAN, T. W., *A Hundred Years of Geography.* Chicago, Aldine Publishing Company, 1961.

FULLER, R. BUCKMINSTER, "City of the Future." *Playboy,* Vol. 15, No. 1 (January, 1968).

GLUECK, NELSON, *Deities and Dolphins.* New York, Farrar, Straus, and Giroux, 1965.

——— *Rivers in the Desert.* New York, Farrar, Straus, and Cudahy, 1959.

HARRINGTON, MARK W., "Weather Making, Ancient and Modern." *National Geographic Magazine,* Vol. VI (April 25, 1894), pp. 35–62.

HARRIS, DAVID R., "New Light on Plant Domestication and the

Origins of Agriculture." *Geographical Review*, Vol. 57, No. 1 (January, 1967).

HAWKES, JACQUETTA, AND WOOLLEY, SIR LEONARD, *Prehistory and the Beginnings of Civilization.* New York and Evanston, Harper & Row, 1962.

HEDIN, SVEN, *My Life as an Explorer.* New York, Garden City Publishing Company, 1925.

HOLAND, HJALMAR R., *Explorations in America Before Columbus.* New York, Twayne Publishers, Inc., 1956.

HUNTINGTON, ELLSWORTH, *Civilization and Climate.* New Haven, Yale University Press, 1915.

——— *Mainsprings of Civilization.* New York, John Wiley, 1945.

——— *The Pulse of Asia.* Boston, Houghton Mifflin Company, 1907.

KELLEY, JAMES B., "Heat, Cold, and Clothing." *Scientific American,* Vol. 194, No. 2 (February, 1956).

KRICK, IRVING P., AND FLEMING, ROSCOE, *Sun, Sea, and Sky.* Philadelphia and New York, J. B. Lippincott Company, 1954.

LAMB, H. H., *The Changing Climate.* London, Methuen & Co., Ltd., 1966.

LHOTE, HENRI, *The Search for the Tassili Frescoes.* New York, E. P. Dutton & Co., Inc., 1959.

LONGSTRETH, T. MORRIS, *Understanding the Weather.* New York, Macmillan and Co., Ltd., 1953.

LOWDERMILK, W. C., "The Reclamation of a Man-Made Desert." *Scientific American,* Vol. 202, No. 3 (March, 1960).

LOWRY, WILLIAM P., "The Climate of Cities." *Scientific American,* Vol. 217, No. 2 (August, 1967).

MCDONALD, JAMES E., "The Coriolis Effect." *Scientific American,* Vol. 186, No. 5 (May, 1952).

MELLAART, JAMES, "A Neolithic City in Turkey." *Scientific American,* Vol. 210, No. 4 (April, 1964).

MIRSKY, JEANNETTE, *To the Arctic!* New York, Alfred A. Knopf, Inc., 1948.

NANSEN, FRIDTJOF, *In Northern Mists.* New York, Stokes, 1911.

ÖPIK, E. J., "Climate and the Changing Sun." *Scientific American,* Vol. 198, No. 6 (June, 1958).

OSBORNE, DOUGLAS, ED., *Contributions of the Wetherill Mesa Archeological Project.* Washington, D. C., Society for American Archaeology, 1965.

OXENSTIERNA, ERIC, *The Norsemen.* Greenwich, Connecticut, New York Graphic Society, 1965.

PALMER, WAYNE C., *Meteorological Drought.* Washington, D. C., Government Printing Office, 1965.

PARR, PETER J., "The Capital of the Nabataeans." *Scientific American,* Vol. 209, No. 4 (October, 1963).

PIGGOTT, STUART, *Ancient Europe.* Chicago, Aldine Publishing Company, 1965.

——— ed., *The Dawn of Civilization.* New York, McGraw-Hill, Inc., 1961.

PLASS, GILBERT N., "Carbon Dioxide and Climate." *Scientific American,* Vol. 201, No. 1 (July, 1959).

RAIKES, ROBERT, *Water, Weather, and Prehistory.* London, John Baker, 1967.

REVELLE, ROGER, "The Role of the Oceans." *Saturday Review* (May 7, 1966).

RUSSELL, J. C., "Late Ancient and Medieval Population." *Transactions of the American Philosophical Society,* Vol. 48, Part 3 (June, 1958).

SCHUCHERT, CHARLES, "Climates of Geologic Time." Washington, D. C., Smithsonian Institution Annual Report, 1914.

SILVERBERG, ROBERT, *Empires in the Dust.* Philadelphia, Chilton Book Company, 1963.

——— *Frontiers in Archaeology.* Philadelphia, Chilton Book Company, 1966.

——— *The Great Wall of China.* Philadelphia, Chilton, Book Company, 1965.

——— *Home of the Red Man.* Greenwich, Connecticut, New York Graphic Society, 1963.

——— *Lost Cities and Vanished Civilizations.* Philadelphia, Chilton Book Company, 1962.

——— *Man Before Adam.* Philadelphia, Macrae Smith Co., 1964.

——— *The Morning of Mankind: Prehistoric Man in Europe.* Greenwich, Connecticut, New York Graphic Society, 1967.

——— *The Old Ones: Indians of the American Southwest.* Greenwich, Connecticut, New York Graphic Society, 1965.

STEIN, AUREL, *On Central-Asian Tracks.* London, Macmillan and Co., Ltd., 1933.

——— *Ruins of Desert Cathay.* London, Macmillan and Co., Ltd., 1912.

STOMMEL, HENRY, "The Circulation of the Abyss." *Scientific American,* Vol. 199, No. 1 (July, 1958).

SUTCLIFF, R. C., *Weather and Climate.* New York, W. W. Norton & Company, Inc., 1966.

SUTTON, ANN AND MYRON, *Nature on the Rampage.* Philadelphia and New York, J. B. Lippincott Company, 1962.

TAYLOR, GEORGE C., "Water, History, and the Indus Plain." *Natural History,* Vol. 74, No. 5 (May, 1965).

THOMAS, HAROLD E., "Reality of Drought Is Always with Us." *Natural History,* Vol. 74, No. 9 (November, 1965).

Weather Modification: Sixth Annual Report. National Science Foundation. Washington, D. C., Government Printing Office, 1964.

WEGENER, ALFRED, *The Origin of Continents and Oceans.* New York, Dover Publications, 1966.

WELLARD, JAMES, *The Great Sahara.* New York, E. P. Dutton & Co., Inc., 1965.

WHEELER, MORTIMER, *The Indus Civilization.* New York, Cambridge University Press, 1960.

WILSON, J. T., "Continental Drift." *Scientific American,* Vol. 208, No. 4 (April, 1963).

ZEUNER, FREDERICK E., *Dating the Past.* London, Methuen & Co., Ltd., 1958.

Index

Index

Abbevillean culture, 94–95, 105, 117, 149–150
Achaeans, 194–197, 217
Acheulian culture, 95–96, 97, 102–103, 105, 117, 154, 155, 249–250
Africa, 15, 16, 17, 23, 154–156
Agassiz, Louis, 44–45
Agriculture, 1–4, 142–151, 162–173, 211, 213, 260, 261, 279; beginning of, 3–4; corn cultivation, 257, 258; desert, 160–162, 206–207, 210; dessication theory of, 148–150
Air: expansion of, 28; pollution, 299–300
Aïr highlands, 156–157
Alaska, 248, 250–251
Albedo, 25
Aldred, Cyril, 167, 169
Aleutian Current, 38
Alexander VI, Pope, 2, 242
Alexander the Great, 216
Alexandria, Egypt, 200
Alfred the Great, 233
Algeria, 159
Allen, J.A., 98–99
Alleröd period, 123–124, 149
Alps, 45, 53, 58
American Indians, 139–140, 285–288; *see also* individual tribes
Anasazi culture, 263–265
Anau (Neolithic site), 146–147
Ancylus Lake, 127
Anderson, Clinton, 293–294
Andes Mountains, 40, 54, 58
Antarctica, 35, 57, 58
Anthropithecus erectus, 87
Anticyclones, 32–33
Antigua Island, 24
Antioch in Merv, 219
Apennines Mountains, 53
Apes, 80, 81, 82

Appalachian Mountains, 39
Aqueducts, 208
Arabian Desert, 34
Arabs, 162, 216–217
Archaeozoic Era, 12, 13
Arctic Ocean, 70–72, 75
Arctic Sea, 245, 248
Argentina, 17
Aristotle, 28
Arizona desert, 261
Arkell, W. J., 165
Armenia stone houses, 1–2
Armenta Camacho, Juan, 254
Aryans, 180, 183–185, 189, 194, 216
Asia, 193–194, 210–231
Assyria, 178, 179
Aterian Neanderthals, 155, 157
Atlanthropus, 88, 95, 97–98
Atlantic Ocean, 71
Atlantic period, 127
Atmosphere, 26–35; carbon dioxide in, 63–64, 298; composition of, 26–27; pressure of, 27
Aurignacian culture, 112, 113, 116, 117, 190
Australia, 6, 15, 17, 54
Australopithecines, 81–86, 87, 250
Australopithecus africanus, 81–82
Austria, 190
Avdat (city), 204
Axes, 90–93, 105, 117, 125
Azilian culture, 119
Aztec pueblo, 272

Babylon, 140, 178–179
Baffin Island, 238, 239
Bain, G.W., 76
Ball, Sir Robert, 56–57
Baltic Ice Lake, 123, 126
Banerji, R.D., 181
Banks, Joseph, 247
Bede, Venerable, 232–233
Bedouins, 4, 137
Beersheba, 199, 203
Bergeron, Tor, 290–292
Bergeron-Findeisen Theory of Condensation, 290–292
Bergmann, Carl, 98–99
Bering Strait, 70, 250–251, 296
Bern Historical Museum, 191
Bible, 174, 175, 176
Biskupin site, 194–195
Blue Nile, 164, 167–168
Bölling period, 123, 149
Bonnegut, Bernard, 293
Boreal period, 124–126
Borisov, P.M., 296
Braidwood, Robert J., 146, 149, 150
Brain, C.K., 83
Brazil, 15, 77
Bronze Age, 193
Brooks, C.E.P., 12, 19, 59–60, 65, 66, 192–193, 208, 233

Brückner, Eduard, 46–47
Bryson, Reid A., 185–186
Buffon, Georges, 43
Bulbalus antiquus, 158
Bulgaria, 150–151, 190
Butler, H.C., 199
Butzer, Karl W., 85, 168, 169
Byzantine period, 202, 209

Caesar, Julius, 232
Cairo, Egypt, 200
California, 217, 254; rainfall in, 200–201
California Current, 38
Caloric equator, 153
Cambrian Period, 13, 14, 15, 16, 46, 73
Canada, 15, 18, 21, 53
Caravan routes, 207–208, 218, 219–220, 223, 224
Carbon dioxide, 297–299; changes in level of, 63–64, 298; in glaciers, 63–64; in oceans, 63, 64
Carbon-14 dating, 20–21, 47–48, 144, 159, 239, 253, 256, 257, 259–260
Carboniferous period, 16–17, 64
Carpathian Mountains, 53
Cascade Mountains, 40
Caspian lake basin, 215
Caspian Sea, 3, 216
Catal Hüyük (Neolithic site), 150
Cave paintings, 114–115, 116–117
Celts, 235
Cenozoic Era, 12, 13, 14, 18, 51–52, 64, 80
Central Asia, 210–231
Chaco Canyon pueblos, 269–274
Chadota (city), 226–227
Charpentier, Jean de, 44
Chatelperronian culture, 113
Chellean axes, 91, 92, 105
Childe, V. Gordon, 147–149, 151
Chimpanzees, 80
Ch'in Shih Huang Ti, Emperor, 212–213
China, 11, 86, 88, 89, 98, 140, 211–231
Chou Dynasty, 212
Christian era, 200, 204, 209, 215, 232
Christy, Henry, 105, 115
Chuckchi Sea, 251
Cimmerian nomads, 216
Cities, 131–197; oldest known, 143–145; buried, 221–231; *see also* names of cities
Clactonian culture, 93–95, 98, 102–103, 105, 106, 108, 249–250
Clark, Wilfred E. Le Gros, 82
Cliffs, 55

Climate, 131–142, 192–193, 249–295; body type and, 98; changes, 1–9; cycles related to, 134–135; in the future, 285–301; ideal, 4; the making of, 23–41; of the past, 9–22; modification programs for, 295–301; shift to cold, 232–248
Climatic optimum period, 127–130, 189–192
Clovis points, 253
Cochise people, 257–258, 260
Continental climate, 192–193
Continental-drift hypothesis, 73–78
Coon, Carleton S., 98, 99, 109
Coral reefs, 14, 16, 18
Coriolis, G.G. de, 29
Coriolis effect, 29–32
Corn, 258–260
Cretaceous period, 13, 58
Crete, 194
Croll, James, 56–57, 72
Cro-Magnon man, 112, 113
Cropp, Richard, 275
Ctesiphon (city), 220
Cuneiform writing, 173
Cyclones, 32–33, 54
Cyclonic storms, 136, 163, 179, 196, 245
Cyrus, King, 179
Czechoslovakia, 115, 190
Dahomey, 77
Dales, George F., 184, 188, 189
Dandan-uilik (city), 225–226, 230
Danubian farming cultures, 190
Dart, Raymond A., 81, 82
Darwin, Charles, 132
Darwin, Sir George, 72
Day, length of, 26
Dead Sea, 55, 199
Death Valley, 39
Dendrochronology, 265
Denmark, 21, 123
Deserts, 34–35, 39, 55, 160–162, 206–207, 210
Devonian Period, 13
Domesday Book, 1, 233
Domestication, 145, 146, 150
Dominica Island, 24
Donn, William L., 70–73, 75, 78
Dorians, 196–197, 216, 217
Douglas, Andrew E., 65, 265–269
Drift ice, 240, 241, 242, 248
Droughts, 193–194, 217, 241, 266–267, 272–284
Dryas periods, 122–124
Du Toit, Alex. L., 74–75
Dubois, Eugène, 87
Dust bowl, 274–278, 279
Dust storms, 274–280
Dyrenforth, R.G., 289–290

Earth, 11, 25–35, 59–60
East Greenland Current, 38
Ecbatana (city), 220
Egypt, 9, 140, 162–171, 183, 189, 194, 197, 200, 203
Eiseiba, 204
Emiliani, Cesare, 49–50, 57–59
Endere River, 226, 229
Energy, solar, 24–26, 58
England, 1, 3, 8, 22, 123, 151, 192–193, 232–235, 239, 241; past climate of, 9–10, 18, 21, 22
Environmental determinism, 4–5, 131–142, 146–149
Eocene Period, 13, 51
Equator, 27, 28, 30, 33, 53, 65
Ericson, David B., 20, 50–51, 52, 60, 62, 69–70, 89, 102, 103
Erik of Norway, King, 241
Erik the Red, 237–238, 241
Eriksson, Leif, 238–239
Ertebølle culture, 128–130
Eskimos, 4, 99, 101, 137, 243–244
Esmark, Jens, 44, 55–56
Espy, James Pollard, 288–289
Ethiopia, 9
Euphrates River, 171–173, 198
Europe, 8, 149, 154, 155–156, 189–197, 233
Evolution, 18, 19; of culture, 3–5; of man, 19, 79–111
Ewing, Maurice, 70–71, 72–73, 75, 78
Ewing-Donn theory, 296
Ezion-geber, 198–199

Fairbridge, Rhodes W., 50
Farming, 131–197; beginning of, 142–143
Ferghana (city), 211, 218–219
Figgins, J.D., 252–253
Findeisen, Walter, 291–292
Finland, 21
Finnell, H.H., 277–280
Fire, 86
Fishing, 125, 129
Fletcher, J.O., 296
Flint, Richard Foster, 65–66
Floods, 172, 174–177, 187–189, 205–206, 211–212, 241
Folsom points, 252–257
Foraminifera, 50–51, 70
Fossil(s), 2–3, 10, 12, 14, 15, 42, 45, 80–81, 96, 107–108; oldest known of man, 97; rivers, 153–154
France, 10, 11, 21, 118–119, 123, 190
Franklin, Benjamin, 10, 61
Frederik of Norway and Denmark, King, 243

Frode, Are, 235
Fronts, 31–32
Frost, John, 285–286
Fuller, R. Buckminister, 300-301

Galileo, 10
Gathman, Louis, 290
Geer, Baron Gerhard de, 120–121, 126, 127
Genghis Khan, 211, 214, 217
Geological eras, 12–14
Germany, 11, 18, 21, 123, 190, 193
Ghana, 77
Gilgamesh epic, 174–177
Glaciers, 7, 12, 14–15, 17, 19–21, 63–64, 113–127, 255; theories of, 43–111, 296
Grasshopper plague of 1892, 275
Globigerina pachyderma, 50–51
Glueck, Nelson, 202–205, 209
Grasses, domestication of wild, 150
Gravettian culture, 113-115
Great Salt Lake, 54–55
Great Victoria Desert, 34
Great Wall of China, 212–213, 218–221, 227–228
Greece, 150–151, 190, 196
Greenhouse effect, 27
Greenland, 2, 7, 15, 16, 18, 25, 53, 54, 57, 58, 233, 237–245, 246, 248
Gobi Desert, 211, 218
Gondwanaland, 73–74, 75
Goths, 216
Gulf Stream, 37–39
Günz Age, 45, 47, 50, 249
Guyana, Republic of, 77
Gyoljuk lake basin, 215, 216
Gypsum Cave points, 253

Hacilar (Neolithic site), 150
Hamy, E.T., 104
Han Dynasty, 218–219, 220–221, 224, 226, 227, 228, 230
Hannibal of Carthage, 159
Harald Fairhari, King, 236
Harald Hardraade, King, 241
Harappa (city), 181, 182–183, 189
Harappa, *see* Indus Valley
Hawaii, 36
Hawkes, Jacquetta, 168, 169
Heat-loss problem, 98–99
Hecatompylos (city), 220
Hedin, Sven, 221–224, 225
Heidelberg man, 91–92, 101
Halbaek, Hans, 149, 150
Henri-Martin, Germaine, 107
Herjulfsnes (Norse settlement), 244–245
Herjulfsson, Bjarne, 238
Herodotus, 3, 160
Hibben, Frank C., 255–256

Himalaya Mountains, 40, 58
Hohokam culture, 260–262, 263, 264, 284
Holland, 21, 193
Holocene Era, 13, 14
Homer, 196
Homo erectus, 88–90, 92–96, 101
Homo habilis, 83
Homo heidelbergensis, 92
Homo neanderthalensis, 106
Homo sapiens, see Man
Homo sapiens neanderthalensis, 106
Homo sapiens sapiens, 106
Hooke, Robert, 10
Hopi Indians, 266, 267, 268, 273, 286–287
Houses, first constructed, 114–115
Hrdlicka, Ales, 251–252
Hsien-pi tribe, 211
Hsiung-nu tribe, 211, 213, 214, 216, 217, 218, 220
Hsüan-tsang, 226
Huerzeler, Johannes, 81
Humboldt Current, 38
Humphreys, W.J., 61–62
Hungary, 190
Huns, 214, 216
Hunting, 114–115, 118, 119–120, 125, 128–129
Huntington, Ellsworth, 4, 5, 132–142, 146, 171, 178–179, 196, 197, 198–199, 204, 208, 210, 217, 239; on buried cities, 228–229, 231; on rainfall, 200–201; central Asian explorations, 214–216; on climatic cycles, 134–135; on climatic oscillation, 200–201, 202; on climatic pulsations, 226; on Negroes, 137–138; pulsatory hypothesis of, 140–141, 200, 218
Hutton, James, 45–46
Hypervitaminosis D, 99–100
Hypsithermal period, 127–130

Ice Age, 42–127
Iceland, 7, 195, 233, 235–240, 246–247
Illinoian Age, 45, 50, 249
India, 5, 17, 23, 36–37, 140, 180, 183–185, 189, 194, 216
Indian corn, 258–259
Indian Ocean, 73
Indus Valley, 180, 182, 183–185, 187–189, 194, 216; Harappa region, 180–189; writing, 183
Insolation, 25–26; of equator, 28
Ionians, 196–197
Iowan (glacial stage), 249
Ionium, 50
Iraq, 145–146, 217

Ireland, 193, 200, 201–202, 235
Irrigation, 161, 170–173, 211–212, 261–262; floodwater, 261
Israel, 198–199, 200, 202, 209–210
Italy, 36, 151
Ivory Coast, 77

Japan Current, 38
Jarmo (city), 145–146, 163, 167, 171
Java, 86, 87, 88, 98
Javan ape-man, 79
Jefferson, Thomas, 11
Jerash (city), 199
Jericho, 143–145, 150, 163, 167
Jews, 137
Jordan, 198, 199
Judaean kingdom, 198–199
Jung tribe, 211, 212, 213, 216
Jurassic Period, 13
Jurchen tribe, 211, 214

Kalahari Desert, 34, 55
Kanjera man, 96–97
Kansan Age, 45, 50, 249
Kansu (city), 228
Kansu panhandle, 220
Kapalilua, 36
Kara Kum, 211
Karim Shahirian culture, 145, 167, 171
Kariz (water system), 208
Kashgar (city), 211, 221
Kashmir lake basin, 215
Kattegat strait, 240–241
Kenya, 96
Kenyapithecus, 80–81
Kenyon, Kathleen, 143
Keratin, 100, 102
Khirokitia (Neolithic site), 150
Khitan tribe, 211, 214
Khotan (city), 211, 221–222
Kilimanjaro, 53
Kin Kletso pueblo, 271–272
Kish (city), 177
Kitchen middens, 128–130
Koenigswald, G.H.R. von, 87
Krakatoa Island, 60–61
Kublai Khan, 211
Kunlun Mountains, 226
Kurnub (city), 204
Kuroshio Current, 38
Kyzyl Kum, 211

Labrador, 53, 239
Labrador Current, 38
Lake Chad, 153
Lake Cochise, 258
Lake Dwellers, 191–192
Lake Ragunda, 121
Lake Zurich, 191
Lakes, pluvial, 54–55
Lamb, H.H., 156
Lamont Geological Observatory, 49

Land bridges, 95
Landnámabók (saga), 237
Landsberg, Helmut E., 299
Langmuir, Irving, 292, 293
Lartet, Edouard, 115
Lattimore, Owen, 217
Law of Uniformitarianism, 45–46
Leakey, Louis S.B., 81, 83, 91, 96–97
Levalloisian culture, 103, 105, 155, 166
Lhote, Henri, 147–148, 153, 162
Libby, Willard F., 48
Litorina Sea, 127
Livingstone, D.A., 72
Loomis, W. Farnsworth, 100–101, 102, 106
Lop desert, 225
Lop Nor (lake), 215, 219, 227
Loulan (city), 223–224, 227
Lowdermilk, Walter C., 204

Mackay, Ernest, 181, 183–184, 185
MacNeish, Richard S., 259
Magdalenian culture, 116–128, 190
Mangelsdorf, Paul C., 259
Magle Mose, 125
Malta, 151
Man: arrival in North America, 250–256; early, 1–5; evolution of, 19, 79–111; body type and climate, 98; body weight of, 99; oldest known fossils of, 97
Manchurian steppe, 212
Mandan Indians, 285–286
Markham, S.F., 4
Maritime Alps, 39
Mars, 57
Marshall, Sir John, 181, 184
Marston, A. Theophilus, 97
Mathias, Bishop, 242
Mauritanians, 162
Medes tribe, 216
Mediterranean Sea, 140, 164
Mela, Pomponius, 201
Melanin, 100, 102
Menes, Pharaoh, 170
Mesa Verde pueblo, 264, 265, 266–268, 272, 273
Mesopotamia, 140, 163, 171–179, 194, 203, 216
Mesozoic Era, 12, 13, 18, 51, 58, 64, 80
Mexico, 259–260
Microliths, 119
Middle Ages, 232–233, 235–245
Migrations, 86–87, 95–96, 101–103, 110, 115, 117, 128, 216–217; Achaeans, 196–197; to Alaska, 250–251; of Dorians, 196–197; Eskimo, 243–244; Homeric Greek,

196–197; Hopi, 268; Ionian, 196–197; Neolithic, 149–152, 189–192; to North America, 256–257
Milankovitch, Milutin, 47, 57, 58, 89, 153
Mindel Age, 45, 47, 50, 249
Ming Dynasty, 214
Minoans, 194
Miocene period, 13, 51–52, 80
Mississippian period, 13, 16
Mogollon, Juan de, 260
Mogollon culture, 260–261, 264
Mohammed, 216
Mohenjo-daro, 181, 182–185, 187–189
Mongolia, 18, 211, 216, 219
Mongoloids, 100
Mongols tribe, 214, 217
Monkeys, 80, 82
Monsoons, 37
Mont Pelée, 61
Moraines, 15, 17, 20, 43, 45
Morocco, 159
Mortillet, Louis de, 105, 112
Mount Hekla, 61
Mount Katmai, 61
Mountains, 39–40, 51, 54, 59; formation of, 51–52
Mousterian culture, 103–105, 106–108, 155, 249–250
Müller-Beck, Hansjürgen, 191–192
Nabataean culture, 204–207, 208–210, 284
Nansen, Fridjtof, 234–235, 243
National Academy of Sciences, 295
National Advisory Committee for Aeronautics, 294–295
National Geographic Society, 267
Natufian culture, 144–145, 148, 167, 168, 203
Natural selection, 101
Nea Nikomedeia (Neolithic site), 150
Neanderthal man, 79, 94, 98, 104–111, 155, 157, 250; appearance of, 106; emigration to Africa, 155–156
Nebraskan Age, 45, 50, 249
Nebuchadnezzar, King, 179
Negev desert region, 198–210
Negroes, 99, 100, 137–138, 157
Neolithic period, 129, 145–152, 167–172, 189–192; agricultural revolution, 142–151
New York City, 282–284
New York Indians, 139–140
New Zealand, 54
Newfoundland, 239
Nicholas V, Pope, 243–244

Nigeria, 77, 217
Nile River, 134, 162–171
Niya River, 226, 227, 229
Nomads, 144–145, 198–231, 254–255; *see also* names of tribes
Norlünd, Poul, 244
North America, 217, 233, 238–239, 247, 250–258, 260–262, 263–284; climatic shifts, 249–284
North Equatorial Current, 37
North Pole, 71–72, 74–75
Norway, 7, 15, 193, 248

Oceanic climate, 192
Ocean(s), 35–39, 63, 64, 69–78; currents, 37–39
Olaf Trygvasson, King, 238
Old Silk Road, 218, 219–220, 223, 224
Older Dryas period, 122–123
Oligocene period, 51
Opik, Ernst J., 66–68
Ordovician Period, 13
Oreopithecus, 81
Österbygden (Norse settlement), 243–244

Pacific Ocean, 71
Pakistan, 5
Paleocene period, 13, 51
Paleo-Indian culture, 254–255, 256, 257
Paleozoic Era, 12–17
Palestine, 86, 200–204, 209; climatic shifts, 200–203, 204
Palmyrans, 207–209
Papyrus swamps, 168
Peat deposits, 122
Pecora, Ferdinand, 294
Penck, Walter, 46–47
Pennsylvanian period, 13, 16
Permian period, 13, 17–18, 46, 54, 64, 74–77
Peru, 23
Peru Current, 38
Petra, 199, 204, 207, 209
Pettersson, Otto, 245–246
Piggott, Stuart, 182
Pima Indians, 260
Pithecanthropoids, 87, 250
Pithecanthropus erectus, 87–88
Pithecanthropus pekinensis, 88
Plass, F. Gilgert, 298
Plass, Gilbert N., 63–64
Pleistocene period, 13, 14, 19–20, 50–51, 52–54, 57, 59, 60, 69, 71, 78, 86–90, 94, 96, 119, 127, 152, 154–156, 164, 165–167, 249–250
Pliny, 234
Pliocene period, 13, 18–19, 51–52, 164
Plow, invention of, 173
Pluvial lakes, 54–55
Pluvial periods, 156, 164

Points (archaeology), 252, 253–254
Poland, 21, 123, 190, 194–195
Pollen: counts, 20, 122–123; zones, 122
Ponente, 36
Population, 254, 270, 298
Post, Lennart von, 122–123
Postglacial thermal maximum period, 127–130
Powers, Edward, 289
Pre-Cambrian Era, 13
Preboreal period, 124, 125, 126
Precipitation, 23–24, 33, 36–37, 39–40, 152, 156, 195, 198, 200, 205, 261, 280–284, 295; changes in, 83; during the glacial epochs, 54–55; effect of mountains on, 39; fluctuations in, 6–7; patterns of, 33–35
Probus, Emperor, 232
Proconsul, 80
Prosimians, 80
Proterozoic Era, 12, 13, 14, 15
Ptolemy of Alexandria, 9, 163, 200
Pueblo Bonito, 264, 266–267, 270
Pueblo Indian(s), 255; dwellings, 263–274
Pulsatory hypothesis theory, 140–141, 200, 218
Pumpelly, Raphael, 146–147, 214
Pyrenees Mountains, 53
Pytheas, 233–235, 246

Qanat (water system), 208
Quaternary Era, 13, 14

Radiation, solar, 27, 58
Radioactive time indicators, 46, 47–50
Radiocarbon dating, 47–50
Rai Bahadur Daya Ram Sahni, 180
Raikes, Robert L., 187–188
Rainfall, *see* Precipitation
Rainmaking, 285–295; cloud-seeding for, 293–295
Rajputana desert, 185–186
Red Sea, 198
Reed, Charles, 148
Reusch, Hans Henrik, 15
Revelle, Roger, 298
Riss Age, 45, 47, 50, 249
Robinson, J.T., 84–85
Rock paintings, 157–159, 160, 162
Rocks, 77; magnetism, 75–76
Rocky Mountains, 39, 58
Roman Empire, 159, 160–162 207–208
Roosevelt, Franklin D., 277
Rubidium, 46
Russia, 7, 53, 115, 193

Sahara Desert, 3, 34, 55, 151–162, 203
Sahni, M.R., 187
Sailboat, invention of, 173
Salt deposits, 17
Samarkand, 211, 219
Sandia Cave, 255
Sandia points, 253, 256
Sanford, K.S., 165
Santa Rosa Island, 254
Sargon II, King, 178, 179, 208
Scandinavia, 15, 123, 190, 193, 248
Schaefer, Vincent J., 292–293
Scythians, 216
Sebilian hunters, 166–167
Sediments (deep-sea), 48–51, 69–70
Seistan lake basin, 215
Seleucia, 220
Semple, Ellen Churchill, 132
Sennacherib, King, 175
Sequoia trees, 200–201, 266
Shang Dynasty, 212
Sheep, domestication of, 145, 146
Shih Huang Ti, 218
Shivta, 204
Shurppak, 177
Siberia, 7, 53, 115
Sicily, 151
Sierra Nevada Mountains, 39–40
Silk trade, 218, 219–220, 223, 224
Silurian period, 13, 14
Silver iodide, 293, 295
Simpson, Sir George, 68–69, 78
Sinai desert, 205
Sinanthropus pekinensis, 88, 89
Skaggerrak strait, 241
Skin color, 99–102
Smith, George, 175
Smith, Philip E.L., 116
Smithsonian Institution, 65
Socrates, 196
Solinus, Gaius Julius, 201
Solomon, King, 198–199
Sonora Desert, 34
Soultrean culture, 115–116, 117
South Equatorial Current, 37
South Pole, 71–72, 74–75
Spain, 118–119, 125, 151, 190
Sparta, 197
Spitaler, R., 57
Ssu-ma Ch'ien, 218–219
Stefansson, Vilhjalmur, 235
Stein, Mark Aurel, 224–231
Stone Age, 154, 166, 202
Stone hoe, invention of, 265
Strabo (geographer), 160, 216, 234
Sturluson, Snorri, 195
Subarctic Current, 38
Sub-Atlantic period, 194–197, 201
Sub-boreal weather, 192–193

Suess, Eduard, 73
Sumer, 173–178, 182, 189; writing, 183
Sun, 24–27, 58, 65–69
Sung Dynasty, 214
Sunspots, 64–65
Suntanning, 101–102
Swamps, 168, 169–170
Swanscombe man, 97, 107
Sweden, 10, 21, 120–122
Swedish Deep-Sea Expedition (1947–48), 49
Switzerland, 190–192
Syria, 217
Syrian desert, 199

Tacitus, Cornelius, 232
Taklamakan Desert, 218, 221, 225, 226
T'ang Dynasty, 214, 221, 225, 226, 229, 230
Tardenoisian culture, 119
Tarim Basin, 219, 228–231; abandoned cities in, 221–231
Tashkent (city), 211
Tassili paintings, 157–159, 160, 162
Tayacian culture, 103, 107
Temperature, 7–9, 21–22, 24, 60–65, 70, 152, 182, 190, 233; determining ancient, 48–49; at the equator, 65; of oceans, 35; orbital variations in, 57
Ténéré region, 153–154
Teosinte, 259
Tepe Sarab, 146, 171
Tethys Sea, 73
Thebes, 140
Thermometer, invention of, 10
Thorium, 46
Thorolf, 236
Ti tribe, 211
Tibet, 218, 219
Tibetan plateau, 212
Tides, 245–246
T'ien Shan Mountains, 211, 219
Tigris River, 171–173, 177
T'o-pa tribe, 211
Tools, 82–83, 90–93, 94, 95–96, 105, 113, 117, 119, 125, 129
Tornadoes, 33
Torricelli, Evangelista, 10
Toynbee, Arnold, 142, 148, 214, 216–217
Trade winds, 31
Trajan, Emperor, 207
Tree-ring dating, 21, 265
Triassic period, 13
Tripsacum, 259
Troy, 194
Tsaidam Plateau, 219
Tuareg tribe, 160, 162
Tun-huang, 219, 221, 229
Turfan lake basin, 215
Tyndall, John, 63

Ubaidan culture, 172–173, 176, 177; irrigation, 172–173
United States, 7, 12, 14–15, 18, 21, 22, 136–137, 294
United States Air Force, 294–295
United States Weather Bureau, 275-277, 288, 294–295
University of Pennsylvania, 181, 187
Ur, 173, 176, 177
Uranium, 46
Urey, Dr. Harold C., 48–49
Uruk people, 173
Ussher, James, 42

Van Hilten, D., 76
Varve counting, 20, 120–122, 126
Vedic hymns, 180
Venetz, Ignaz, 44
Veraart, August, 292–293
Vikings, 233–245
Vilgerdsson, Floke, 236
Vinland, 239, 243
Vineyards, 1, 22, 232–233
Vitamin D, 99–102, 106
Volcanoes, 60–63

Wagon wheel, invention of, 173
Walchendorf, Archbishop Erik, 243
Water conservation, 280–284
Weapons, 118, 119, 125
Weather: factors governing, 23-41; first observations of, 10
Weekly Weather and Crop Bulletin, 275-277
Wegener, Alfred, 73–74
Westerlies, 31-32, 54
Wexler, Harry, 295
Wheeler, Sir Mortimer, 181 182, 184, 185
White Nile, 164
William of Malmesbury, 1
Willian I, King, 1, 233
Winds, 27–29, 30–32, 35-36, 39, 59
Wisconsian Age, 45, 48, 50, 249, 250, 251
Wolbach, John, 72, 75
Wollin, Goesta, 20, 50–51, 52, 60, 62, 69–70, 89, 102, 103
Woolley, Sir Leonard, 176, 177
World War II, 279, 299
Writing: Cuneform, 173; earliest known paper, 223; Egyptian, 183; Indus Valley, 183; Sumer, 183
Wu Ti, Emperor, 218–219
Würm Age, 45, 47, 48, 50, 115, 154, 155–156, 190, 249

Xerxes, King, 179

Yoldia Sea, 126–127
Younger Dryas period, 124
Yuëh-chih tribe, 214
Yuma points, 253

Zea mays, 258–259
Zealand Island, 125
Zenobia, Queen, 208–209
Zero varves, 121
Zeuner, Frederick E., 47, 89
Zionist movement, 209–210